A Century of Research at Petrified Forest National Park:

Geology and Paleontology

Edited by William G. Parker, Sidney R. Ash, and Randall B. Irmis

MUSEUM OF NORTHERN ARIZONA
Bulletin No. 62
Flagstaff, 2006

MUSEUM OF NORTHERN ARIZONA

Original Printing of the Museum of
Northern Arizona Bulletin 62
ISBN 0-89734-120-1

Museum of Northern Arizona
3101 N. Fort Valley Road
Flagstaff, Arizona 86001

Executive Editor: David D. Gillette, Ph.D.

Cover design by T. Scott Williams
Cover photos: top, skull of the phytosaur *Pseudopalatus* from Petrified Forest National Park; bottom, petrified wood in
exposures of the Sonsela Member (Chinle Formation) at Petrified Forest National Park.

Printed by the Petrified Forest Museum Association ©2006

TABLE OF CONTENTS

ARTICLES

Geology and Stratigraphy

Paleobotany

Vertebrate Paleontology

SHORT PAPERS

FIELD TRIP GUIDE

FORWARD

SEVERAL YEARS ago during congressional visits regarding the potential boundary expansion of Petrified Forest National Park (now a reality), we discussed, along with Sid Ash, the possibility of producing a research volume to commemorate the 100th anniversary of the park in 2006. The idea was hardly original as a similar volume had been produced for the 75th anniversary in 1981 (although the volume did not print until 1985); however, recent years have seen an increase in paleontological and geological research in the park, including a stratigraphic revision of the Chinle Formation and the discovery of many new fossil plants and animals. We felt that presenting these new findings would be a great way to commorate the centennial year. The articles in this volume represent a sample of those new discoveries and are dedicated in honor of all of the geologists and paleontologists who have conducted research in the park since its inception in 1906.

It is a great pleasure to dedicate this volume (unbeknownst to him…surprise!) to Dr. Sidney Ash who has conducted work in the park for five decades and published numerous descriptions of the fossil plants of the park and their paleoecological significance. We would also like to thank the following park staff without whom this volume would not be possible, Superintendent Lee Baiza, Chief of Resource Management Karen Dorn, T. Scott Williams, Pat Thompson, Lyn Carranza, Marge Post, Hallie Larsen, and Barbara Bean. We would also like to thank the contributors of invited articles, including Rodney Savidge, Brian Axsmith, Joan Watson, Timothy Jones, and Bill Mueller. Finally, we would like to thank all of the authors who contributed short papers and all of our reviewers who are too numerous to list here.

We would like to acknowledge our co-editor Sid Ash who put in copious amounts of time staring at proofs and providing many contributions of his own. This project would not have been possible without the generous support of the Petrified Forest Museum Association, especially Paul DoBell and the members of the board. Finally, we would like to thank Dr. Robert Breunig, the Director of the Museum of Northern Arizona, and the MNA Board of Trustees for permitting this volume to be published as part of the bulletin series of that institution, continuing a decades old partnership between the museum and the park.

William G. Parker, David D. Gillette, and Randall B. Irmis, March 9, 2006

Main: John Muir examining a fossil log in 1906. Inset: phytosaur excavation in 2005.

DEDICATION

WITH ONLY slight exaggeration, friends of Sidney Roy Ash would all agree that he has explored every square meter of the Chinle Formation in Petrified Forest National Park. And with no exaggeration, we all agree that our friend "Sid" has been a mentor, leader, colleague, and coach in the world of Triassic paleontology in a career that has spanned five decades.

The vision of Sid on an outcrop, rock hammer in one hand and a newly recovered fossil plant in the other, is an indelible image of the hearty geologist on a quest for discovery and revelation. To hear Sid shout, "Hey, look at this!" always quickens our hearts, knowing that he has found something new or interesting. Although his professional goals of exploring for fossil plants dominate his search plans in the field, he just as often finds other fossils: fish, amphibians, reptiles, clams, snails, microscopic fossils, and tracks and traces.

With his geologist's rock pick, Sid has split tons of shale throughout the Southwest. The bounty of fossils exposed and collected by this indefatigable paleontologist has shaped our understanding of the Triassic landscape in North America more than any other researcher. His work is reflected in probably every artist's interpretation of the Petrified Forest habitat in the Late Triassic, when dinosaurs were just beginning to become important predators. Artist Margaret Colbert relied on Sid's interpretations of the Triassic forests in three important murals completed in the 1980s, at the Petrified Forest National Park, New Mexico Museum of Natural History and Science, and at Ghost Ranch, New Mexico. Those interpretations reflected Sid's comprehensive understanding of the plants in that landscape, a profound contribution to science education and outreach. Most recently, Sid has provided detailed descriptions of the three trees that made up the majority of these Triassic forests, *Araucarioxylon*, *Woodworthia*, and *Schilderia*, resulting from decades of careful research.

Sid's research perspective is global. He has conducted important research investigations in the American Southwest, the Pacific Northwest, Australia, South Africa, and the Canadian arctic. He began his academic career at Midland Lutheran College, Fremont, Nebraska where he graduated with a B.A. Degree in History in 1951. Following three years of service in the U. S. Navy, he returned to school at the University of New Mexico where he earned a second B.A. Degree in geology, and a M.S. Degree also in geology. In 1966 he earned his Ph.D. in paleobotany from The University of Reading, England. Armed with this distinguished background, he found employment with the U. S. Geological Survey for six years. Sid began his career in the academic world in 1970 at Weber State University in Ogden, Utah where he taught geology and conducted his paleobotanical research for the next twenty-seven years. With his retirement in 1997, Sid intensified his research and field studies, especially in Petrified Forest National Park. Over the years Sid has become an icon in the park, persistently improving our knowledge of the life and landscape 225 million years ago, along the way coaxing all of us as a mentor and friend.

Sid's first publication was in 1959 with the title "The Indians of west-central New Mexico" for a geology field trip guidebook. Fossil plants dominated his subsequent publications, but he also published important works on conodonts, hydrology, stratigraphy, plate tectonics, paleogeography, general geology, Native Americans, and history. As of the release of this volume, Sid's publication list includes 129 technical papers, editorships for four volumes, and 39 abstracts for professional talks and we all look forward to seeing that list continue to grow.

The dedication of this centennial volume to Sidney Roy Ash is a fitting tribute to a man whose remarkable career has spanned half a century, and has concentrated on the paleontology of the park and surrounding areas.

David D. Gillette and William G. Parker
May, 2006

BIBLIOGRAPHY OF SIDNEY ROY ASH, PH.D., THROUGH MAY, 2006

Published Articles

1. 1959. The Indians of west-central New Mexico. New Mexico Geological Society Guidebook, 10:154-156.
2. 1960. The Jicarilla Apache Indians of northern New Mexico. New Mexico Geological Society Guidebook, 11:128-129.
3. ____. (jr. author with E.H. Baltz and G.M. Lamb) Road log from Lumberton to El Vado. New Mexico Geological Society Guidebook, 11:27-32.
4. ____. (jr. author with E.H. Baltz) Road log from Gallinas to vicinity of Cuba and alternate road log from Gallina to Upper San Jose drainage divide. New Mexico Geological Society Guidebook, 11:40-44.
5. 1961. Bibliography and index of conodonts, 1949-1958. Micropaleontology, 7:213-244.
6. ____. (sr. author with Alfred Clebsch, Jr.) Cretaceous rocks in Lea County, New Mexico. U.S. Geological Survey Professional Paper, 424D:D139-D142.
7. ____. (jr. author with C.B. Read) Stratigraphic significance of the Cretaceous fern *Tempskya* in the western conterminous United States. U.S. Geological Survey Professional Paper, 424D:D250-254.
8. ____. Indians, ancient and modern, in the Albuquerque area. New Mexico Geological Society Guidebook, 12:75-81.
9. 1962. (jr. author with E.H. Baltz and S.W. West) Potential yield of deep water wells in the southern part of the Jicarilla Apache Indian Reservation and vicinity, San Juan Basin, New Mexico. U.S. Geological Survey Professional Paper, 450D:D173-D175.
10. 1963. Ground-water conditions in northern Lea County, New Mexico. U.S. Geological Survey Hydrological Inventory Atlas HA-62, 2 sheets.
11. 1964. Bibliography and index of conodonts, 1959-1961. Brigham Young University Geological Studies, 10:3-50.
12. ____. Bibliography of New Mexico Geological Society Guidebooks. New Mexico Geological Society Special Pubublication, 1:1-31.
13. 1966. (jr. author with E. H. Baltz and R. Y. Anderson) History of nomenclature and stratigraphy of rocks adjacent to the Cretaceous-Tertiary boundary, western San Juan Basin, New Mexico. U.S. Geological Survey Professional Paper, 524D:D1-D23.
14. 1967. The Chinle (Upper Triassic) megaflora, Zuni Mountains, New Mexico. New Mexico Geological Society Guidebook, 18:125-31.
15. 1968. A new species of *Williamsonia* from the Upper Triassic Chinle Formation of New Mexico. Linnean Society (London), Journal (Botany), 61:113-120. Reprinted in Alvin, K. L. and P. D. W. Barnard, (eds.), 1968, Studies on fossil plants. London, Academic Press, p. 113-120.
16. 1969. (sr. author with D. D. May) Petrified Forest—the story behind the scenery. Petrified Forest Museum Association, Holbrook, Arizona, 32 p., 23 photographs.
17. ____. (jr. author with W. J. Breed) New fossil plants from the Chinle Formation. Plateau, 42:34-36.
18. 1970. Ferns from the Chinle Formation (Upper Triassic) in the Fort Wingate area, New Mexico. U.S. Geological Survey Professional Paper 613D:1-40.

19. ____. *Pagiophyllum simpsonii*, a new conifer from the Chinle Formation (Upper Triassic) of Arizona. Journal of Paleontology, 44:945-952.

20. ____. *Dinophyton*, a problematical new plant from the Upper Triassic of the southwestern United States. Palaeontology, 13:646-664.

21. 1972. *Piazopteris branneri* from the Lower Jurassic, Egypt. Review of Palaeobotany and Palynology, 13:147-154.

22. ____. Plant megafossils of the Chinle Formation, p. 23-43. *In* Breed, W. J. and C. S. Breed, (eds.), Investigations in the Triassic Chinle Formation. Museum of Northern Arizona Bulletin 47.

23. ____. The search for plant fossils in the Chinle Formation, p. 45-58. *In* Breed, W. J. and C. S. Breed, (eds.), Investigations in the Triassic Chinle Formation. Museum of Northern Arizona Bulletin 47.

24. ____. Upper Triassic Dockum flora of eastern New Mexico and Texas. New Mexico Geological Society Guidebook, 23:124-128.

25. ____. *Marcouia* gen. nov., a problematical plant from the Late Triassic of the southwestern U. S. A. Palaeontology, 15:423-429.

26. ____. Late Triassic plants from the Chinle Formation in northeastern Arizona. Palaeontology, 15:598-618.

27. 1973. Two new Late Triassic plants from the Petrified Forest of Arizona. Journal of Paleontology, 47:46-53.

28. ____. (with D. L. Baars, and others) Road log from Farmington, New Mexico to Kayenta, Arizona. New Mexico Geological Society Guidebook, 24:1-24.

29. ____. (with D. L. Baars, and others) Road log from Kayenta, Arizona, to Black Mesa and Navajo National Monument. New Mexico Geological Society Guidebook, 24:26-36.

30. ____. (with D. L. Baars and H. L. James) Road log of Monument Valley-Navajo Tribal Park. New Mexico Geological Society Guidebook, 24:37-45.

31. ____ (with D. L. Baars and others) Road log from Kayenta, Arizona to Gallup, New Mexico. New Mexico .Geological Society Guidebook, 24:46-60.

32. 1974. (sr. author with R. H. Hevly) Road log [from Tempe, Arizona to Petrified Forest National Park and St. Johns and return]. Paleobot. Sec. Botanical Society America Guidebook, Devonian, Permian, and Triassic plant localities, east-central Arizona, p. 1-25.

33. ____. Notes on the Chinle Formation (Upper Triassic) in east-central Arizona. Paleobot. Sec. Botanical Society America Guidebook, Devonian, Permian, and Triassic plant localities, east-central Arizona, p. 40-42.

34. ____ The Upper Triassic Chinle flora of Petrified Forest National Park Arizona. Paleobot. Sec. Botanical Society America Guidebook, Devonian, Permian, and Triassic plant localities, east-central Arizona, p. 43-48.

35. ____. Upper Triassic plants of Canon del Cobre, New Mexico. New Mexico Geological Guidebook, 25:179-184.

36. 1975. *Zamites powelli* and its distribution in the Upper Triassic of North America. Palaeontographica, Pt. B, 149:139-152.

37. ____. The Chinle (Upper Triassic) flora of southeastern Utah. Four Corners Geological Society Guidebook 8, 143-147.

38. 1976. (sr. author with C. B. Read) North American species of *Tempskya* and their stratigraphic significance, *with a section on* Stratigraphy and age of the *Tempskya*-bearing rocks of southern Hildalgo County, New Mexico, by R. A. Zeller, Jr. U.S. Geological Survey Professional Paper, 874:1-40.

39. ____. (sr. author with W. D. Tidwell) Upper Cretaceous and Paleocene floras of the Raton Basin, Colorado and New Mexico. New Mexico Geological Society Guidebook, 27:197-203.

40. ____. Occurrence of the controversial plant fossil *Sanmiguelia* in the Upper Triassic of Texas. Journal of Paleontology, 50:799-804.

41. ____. The systematic position of *Eoginkgoites*. America Journal Botanical, 63:l327-1331.

42. 1977. An unusual bennettitalean leaf from the Upper Triassic of the southwestern United States. Palaeontology, 20:641-659.

43. 1978. (jr. author with R.W. Moyle) Road log from Echo Canyon Junction to Salt Lake City, Utah. Rocky Mountain Association of Geologists, Symposium on geology of the cordilleran hingeline, p. 393-406.

44. ____. Preface, p. v. *In* Ash, S. R., (ed.), Geology, paleontology and paleoecology of a Late Triassic Lake, western New Mexico. Brigham Young Univ. Geology Studies, 25, pt. 2.

45. ____. Stratigraphy of the Ciniza Lake Beds and related strata, p. 1-14. *In* Ash, S. R., (ed.), Geology, paleontology and paleoecology of a Late Triassic Lake, western New Mexico. Brigham Young Univ. Geology Studies, 25, pt. 2.

46. ____. Summary of the fossils in the Ciniza Lake Beds, p. 21-22. *In* Ash, S. R., (ed.), Geology, paleontology and paleoecology of a Late Triassic Lake, western New Mexico. Brigham Young Univ. Geology Studies, 25, pt. 2.

47. ____. Plant megafossils, p. 23-42. *In* Ash, S. R., (ed.), Geology, paleontology and paleoecology of a Late Triassic Lake, western New Mexico. Brigham Young Univ. Geology Studies, 25, pt. 2.

48. ____. Fish scales, p. 67-68. *In* Ash, S. R., (ed.), Geology, paleontology and paleoecology of a Late Triassic Lake, western New Mexico. Brigham Young Univ. Geology Studies, 25, pt. 2.

49. ____. Coprolites, p. 69-73. *In* Ash, S. R., (ed.), Geology, paleontology and paleoecology of a Late Triassic Lake, western New Mexico. Brigham Young Univ. Geology Studies, 25, pt. 2.

50. ____. (sr. author with Dean, W. E. and others) Paleoecology of Lake Ciniza, p. 89-95. *In* Ash, S. R., (ed.), Geology, paleontology and paleoecology of a Late Triassic Lake, western New Mexico. Brigham Young Univ. Geology Studies, 25, pt. 2.

51. 1979. *Skilliostrobus* gen. nov., a new lycopsid cone from the Early Triassic of Australia. Alcheringa, 3:73-89.

52. ____. (jr. author with W. B. K. Holmes) An Early Triassic megafossil flora from the Lorne Basin, N.S.W. New South Wales Linnean Society, Proceedings, 103:47-70.

53. ____. Ancient plants of the Petrified Forest. Plateau, 51:6-11.

54. 1980. Upper Triassic floral zones of North America, p. 153-270. *In* Dilcher, D. L. and T. M. Taylor (eds.), Biostratigraphy of fossil plants. Stroudsburg, Dowden, Hutchinson and Ross, Inc.

55. 1981. (jr. author with W. D. Tidwell and L. R. Parker) Cretaceous and Tertiary floras of the San Juan Basin, p. 307-332. *In* Lucas, S.G. and others, (eds.), Advances in San Juan Basin paleontology. University of New Mexico Press, Albuquerque.

56. ____. Tectonic features, p. 22-23. *In* D. C. Greer and W. L.Wahlquist, (eds.), Atlas of Utah. Weber State College and Brigham Young University Press.

57. 1982. Glossopterid leaves from the early Mesozoic of northern Mexico and Honduras. Paleobotany, 28/29:201-206.

58. ____. (sr. author with Ronald Litwin and Alfred Traverse) The Upper Triassic fern *Phlebopteris smithii* (Daugherty) Arnold and its spores. Palynology, 6:203-219.

59. ____. Occurrence of the controversial plant fossil *Sanmiguelia* in the Upper Triassic of Utah. Journal of Paleontology, 56:751-754.

60. ____. (sr. author with W. D. Tidwell) Notes on the Upper Paleozoic plants of central New Mexico. New Mexico Geological Society Guidebook, 33:245-248.

61. 1985. A short thick cycad stem from the Upper Triassic of Petrified Forest National Park, Arizona, and vicinity. Museum of Northern Arizona Bulletin, 54:17-32.

62. 1986. First record of the Gondwana plant *Schizoneura* (Equisetales) in the Upper Triassic of North America, p. 59-65. *In* Weber, R., (ed.), 3d Congresso Latinoamericano Paleontologia, Simposio sobre flores del Triasico Tardio su fitogeografia y paleoecologia: Univ. Nat. Auton. Mexico, Inst. Geologia, Memoria.

63. ____. (with D.D. Gillette and R.A. Long) Paleontology of the Petrified   Forest National Park, Arizona, p. 59-71. *In* Nations, J.D., Conway, C.M., and G. A. Swann, (eds.), Geology of central and northern Arizona: Geological Society America, Rocky Mountain Section, Field Trip Guidebook.

64. ____. Petrified Forest–the story behind the scenery. Petrified Forest Museum Association, Holbrook, Arizona, 48 p.

65. ____. The early Mesozoic land flora of the Northern hemisphere, p. 143-161. *In* Broadhead, T. W., (ed.), Land plants, notes for a short course organized by R. A. Gastaldo (Prepared for the short course on land plants sponsored by the Paleontological Society held at San Antonio, Texas, November 9, 1986). University of Tennessee, Department of Geological Science, Studies in Geology, 15.

66. ____. (sr. author with W.D. Tidwell) *Arnoldia kuesii,* a new juvenile fernlike plant from the Lower Permian of New Mexico. Botanical Gazette, 147:236-242.

67. ____. Fossil plants and the Triassic-Jurassic boundary, p. 21-30. *In* Padian, K. (ed.), The beginning of the age of dinosaurs. Cambridge University Press, New York.

68. 1987. Growth habit and systematics of the Upper Triassic plant *Pelourdea poleoensis,* southwestern U. S. A. Review of Palaeobotany and Palynology, 51: 37-49.

69. ____. (sr. author with W. D. Tidwell) *Arnophyton,* a new name for *Arnoldia* Ash and Tidwell, 1986. Phytologia, 63:64.

70. ____. Petrified Forest National Park, Arizona, p. 405-410. *In* Beus, S. S., ed., Centennial Field Guide, Volume 2, Rocky Mountain Section of the Geological Society of America, Geological Society of America.

71. ____. The Upper Triassic red bed flora of the Colorado Plateau, western United States. Journal of the Arizona-Nevada Academy of Sciences, 22:95-105.

72. 1988. Chapter C - Fossil plants from the Mudstone Member of the Santa Rosa Formation at the principal reference section,p. 19-25. *In* Finch, W. I., (ed.), Principal reference section for the Santa Rosa Formation of Middle and Late Triassic age, Guadalupe County, New Mexico. U.S. Geological Survey Bulletin, 1804.

73. ____. (jr. author with Gary Miller) The oldest freshwater decapod from the Triassic of Arizona. Palaeontology, 31:273-279.

74. ____. (jr. author with V. A. Krassilov) On *Dinophyton* - protognetalean Mesozoic plant. Palaeontographica, Pt. B, 208:33-38.

75. 1989. A catalog of Upper Triassic plant megafossils of the western United States through 1988, p. 189-222. *In* Lucas, S. G. and A. P. Hunt, (eds.), Dawn of the Age of Dinosaurs in the American Southwest. New Mexico Museum of Natural History, Albuquerque.

76. ____. The Upper Triassic Chinle flora of the Zuni Mountains, New Mexico. New Mexico Geological Society Guidebook, 40:225-230.

77. 1990. (jr. author with William D. Tidwell). On *Hermanophyton* Arnold and its species. Palaeontographica. Pt. B, 208:77-92.

78. ____ (jr. author with Geoffrey Creber). A widespread fungal epidemic on Upper Triassic trees in the southwestern United States. Review of Palaeobotany and Palynology, 63:189-195.

79. 1991. A new Jurassic flora from the Wallowa Terrane in the Snake River Canyon, Oregon and Idaho. Oregon Geology, 53:27-33, 45.

80. ____. (jr. author with Ronald J. Litwin). First early Mesozoic amber from the Western Hemisphere. Geology, 19:273-276.

81. ____. A new Jurassic *Phlebopteris* (Plantae, Filicales) from the Wallowa Terrane in the Snake River Canyon, Oregon and Idaho. Journal of Paleontology, 65:322-329.

82. ____. A new pinnate cycad leaf from the Upper Triassic Chinle Formation of Arizona. Botanical Gazette, 152:123-131.

83. ____. (jr. author with R. J. Litwin and A. Traverse). Preliminary palynological zonation of the Chinle Formation, southwestern U. S. A., and its correlation with the Newark Supergroup (eastern U. S. A.). Review of Palynology and Palaeobotany, 68:269-287.

84. ____. (sr. author with K. B. Pigg). A new Jurassic *Isoetites* (Isoetales) from the Wallowa terrane in Hells Canyon, Oregon and Idaho. American Journal of Botany, 78:1636-1642.

85. ____. (sr. author with J. H. Basinger). A high latitude Upper Triassic flora from the Heiberg Formation, Sverdrup Basin, Arctic Archipelago. Geological Survey of Canada Bulletin, 412:101-131.

86. 1992. The Black Forest Bed, a distinctive rock unit in the Upper Triassic Chinle Formation, northeastern Arizona. Bulletin of the Arizona-Nevada Academy of Sciences, 24/25:59-73.

87. ____. (jr. author with J. D. L. White, D. L. White, T. Vallier, and G. D. Stanley, Jr.). Middle Jurassic strata link Wallowa, Olds Ferry, and Izee terranes in the accreted Blue Mountains island arc, northeastern Oregon. Geology, 20:729-732.

88. ____. (sr. author with G. Creber). Palaeoclimatic interpretation of the wood structures of the trees in the Chinle Formation (Upper Triassic) in the area of Petrified Forest National Park, Arizona, U.S.A. Palaeogeography, Paleoclimatology, Paleoecology, 96:299-317.

89. 1993. (jr. author with R. J. Litwin). Revision of the biostratigraphy of the Chatham Group (Upper Triassic), Deep River basin, North Carolina, USA. Review of Palaeobotany and Palynology, 77:75-95.

90. ____. (sr. author with M. Morales). Anisian plants from Arizona: the oldest Mesozoic megaflora in North America. New Mexico Museum of Natural History and Science Bulletin, 3:27-29.

91. ____. (jr. author with M. Morales). The last phytosaurs? New Mexico Museum of Natural History and Science Bulletin, 3:357-358.

92. ____. (jr. author with Pigg, K., Davis, W. C.). A new permineralized Upper Triassic flora from Petrified Forest National Park, Arizona: A preliminary report. New Mexico Museum of Natural History and Science Bulletin, 3: 411-413.

93. ____. (jr. author with Dubiel, R., and Hasiotis, S. T.) Syndepositional deformation in the Monitor Butte Member of the Chinle Formation at Fort Wingate, NM and St. Johns, AZ. New Mexico Museum of Natural History and Science Bulletin, 3:G27-G29.

94. 1994. First occurrence of *Czekanowskia* (Gymnospermae, Czekanowskiales) in the United States: Review of Palaeobotany and Palynology, 81:129-140.

95. ____. (jr. author with A. T. Traverse) Well-preserved fungal spores from the Jurassic rocks of Hells Canyon on the Idaho-Oregon border. Journal of Paleontology, 68:664-668.

96. ____. (jr. author with P. S. Herendeen and P. R. Crane) Vegetation of the dinosaur world, p. 347-364. *In* Rosenberg, G. D., and D. L. Wolberg, (eds.), Dino Fest: The Paleontological Society Special Publication, 7.

97. ____. *Donwelliacaulis chlouberii* gen. et sp. nov. (Guaireaceae, Osmundales) one of the oldest Mesozoic plant megafossils in North America. Palaeontographica, pt. B, 234:1-17.

98. 1995. (jr. author with Tidwell, W. D.) A review of selected Triassic to Early Cretaceous ferns. Journal of Plant Research, 107:417-442.

99. ____. (jr. author with Mamay, S. H., and Lyons, P. C.) Charles Brian Read (1907-1979): American paleobotanist and geologist, p. 225-236. *In* Lyons, P. C., Morey, E. D., and R. H. Wagner, (eds.), Historical perspective of twentieth century Carboniferous paleobotany in North America (W. C. Darrah volume). Geological Society of America Memoir, 185.

100. 1996. (sr. author with Litwin, R. J.) Two new species of the pinnate microsporophyll *Pramelreuthia* from the Upper Triassic of the southwestern United States. American Journal of Botany, 83:1091-1099.

101. 1997. Evidence of arthropod-plant interactions in the Upper Triassic of the southwestern United States. Lethaia, 29:237-248.

102. 1998. (sr. author with W.D. Tidwell) Plant megafossils from the Brushy Basin Member of the Morrison Formation near Montezuma Creek Trading Post, southeastern Utah, p. 321-339. *In* Carpenter, K., Chure, D. J., and J. I. Kirkland, (eds.), The Upper Jurassic Morrison Formation: An interdisciplinary study. Modern Geology, 22.

103. ——. (jr. author with W.D. Tidwell and Brooks B. Britt) Preliminary floral analysis of the Mygatt-Moore Quarry in the Upper Jurassic Morrison Formation, west-central Colorado, p. 341-378. *In* Carpenter, K., Chure, D. J., and Kirkland, J. I. (eds.). The Upper Jurassic Morrison Formation: An interdisciplinary study. Modern Geology, 22.

104. 1999. An Upper Triassic *Sphenopteris* showing evidence of insect predation from Petrified Forest National Park, Arizona. International Journal of Plant Science, 160:208-215.

105. ——. An Upper Triassic upland flora from north-central New Mexico, U.S.A. Review of Palaeobotany and Palynology, 105:183-199.

106. ——. (jr. author with A. T. Traverse) Preliminary assesssment of the age of the palynoflora of the Red Tanks Member, Madera Formation, Carrizo Arroyo, New Mexico. New Mexico Geological Society Guidebook, 50:293-296.

107. ——. (jr. author with W. D. Tidwell, B. S. Kues, K. K. Kietzke, and S. G. Lucas) Early Permian plant megafossils from Carrizo Arroyo, Central New Mexico. New Mexico Geological Society Guidebook, 50:297-304.

108. ——. (jr. author with , L. Grauvogel-Stamm) *Lycostrobus chinleana*, an equisetalean cone from the Upper Triassic of the Southwestern United States and its phylogenetic implications. American Journal of Botany, 86:1391-1405.

109. 2000. (sr. author with Creber, G.) The Late Triassic *Araucarioxylon arizonicum* trees of the Petrified Forest National Park, Arizona, USA. Palaeontology, 43:15-28.

110. ____. Evidence of oribatid mite herbivory in the stem of a Late Triassic tree fern from Arizona. Journal of Paleontology, 74:1065-1071.

111. 2001. New cycadophytes from the Upper Triassic Chinle Formation in the southwestern United States. PaleoBios, 21:15-28.

112. ____. Plant-animal interactions: herbivory, p. 424-426. *In*: Briggs, D. E. G., and P. R. Crowther, (eds.), Palaeobiology II. Blackwell Science Ltd., Oxford.

113. ____. The fossil ferns of Petrified Forest National Park, Arizona, and their paleoecological implications, p. 3-10. *In*: Santucci, V. L., and L. McClelland, (eds.), Proceedings of the 6th Fossil Resource Conference, National Park Service.

114. 2002. (second author with Jones, T. P., and Figueiral, I.) Late Triassic charcoal from Petrified Forest National Park, Arizona, USA. Palaeogeography, Palaeoclimatology, Palaeoecology, 188:127-139.

115. 2003. (jr. author with Tidwell, W. D.), Revision and description of two new species of *Charliea* from the Pennsylvanian of Utah and New Mexico. Review of Palaeobotany and Palynology, 124:297-306.

116. ____. The Wolverine Petrified Forest. Survey Notes, 35: 3-6

117. ____. (second author with Riggs, N. R., Barth, A. P., Gehrels, G. E., and Wooden, J. L.) Isotopic age of the Black Forest Bed, Petrified Forest Member, Chinle Formation, Arizona, an example of dating a continental sandstone bed. Geological Society of America Bulletin, 115:1315-1323.

118. 2004. (jr. author with G. Creber) The Late Triassic *Schilderia adamanica* and *Woodworthia arizonica* trees of the Petrified Forest National Park, Arizona, USA. Palaeontology, 47:21-38.

119. ____. (jr. authorwith W. D. Tidwell) Synopsis of the flora in the Red Tanks Formation in Carrizo Arroyo [New Mexico], p. 97-103. *In* Lucas, S. G., and K. Zeigler, (eds). Carboniferous-Permian transition at Carrizo Arroyo, central New Mexico, New Mexico Museum of Natural History and Science Bulletin, 25.

120. ____. (sr. author with Savidge, Rodney A.) The bark of the Late Triassic *Araucarioxylon arizonicum* tree from Petrified Forest National Park, Arizona. International Association of Wood Anatomists Journal, 25:349-368.

121. 2005. A new Upper Triassic flora and associated invertebrate fossils from the basal beds of the Chinle Formation, near Cameron, Arizona. PaleoBios, 25:17-34.

122. ____. Petrified Forest: A story in stone. Petrified Forest Museum Association. 48 p.

123. ____. (jr. author with L. Grauvogel-Stamm). Recovery of the Triassic land flora from the end-Permian life crisis. Comptes Rendus Palevol, 4:525-540.

124. ____. Synopsis of the Upper Triassic Flora of Petrified Forest National Park and vicinity, p. 59-70. *In* Nesbitt, S. J., Parker, W. G., and R. B. Irmis (eds.), Guidebook to the Triassic Formations of the Colorado Plateau in northern Arizona: Geology, Paleontology, and History. Mesa Southwest Museum Bulletin, 6.

126. 2006. *Chilbinia* gen. nov., an archaic seed fern in the Late Triassic Chinle Formation of Arizona, USA. Palaeontology, 49:237-245.

127. ____. (jr. author with R. A. Savidge) *Arboramosa semicircumtrachea*, an unusual Late Triassic tree in Petrified Forest National Park, Arizona, USA. Museum of Northern Arizona Bulletin, 62:65-81.

128. ____. (jr. author with B. J. Axsmith) Two rare fossil cones from the Upper Triassic Chinle Formation in Petrified Forest National Park, Arizona, and New Mexico. Museum of Northern Arizona Bulletin, 62:82-94.

129. ____. (jr. author with J. Watson) A rare bipinnate microsporophyll attributable to the cycadales from the Late Triassic Chinle Formation, Petrified Forest National Park, Arizona. Museum of Northern Arizona Bulletin, 62:95-105.

130. ____. (jr. author with T. P. Jones) Late Triassic charcoal and charcoal-like plant fossils from Petrified Forest National Park, Arizona. Museum of Northern Arizona Bulletin, 62:106-116.

131. ____. (second author with W. G. Parker and D. G. Gillette) Roadlog through Petrified Forest National Park. Museum of Northern Arizona Bulletin, 62:177-187.

Editorships

1. 1964. (sr. editor with L. V. Davis) Guidebook of the Ruidoso County: New Mexico Geology Society, 15th Annual Field Conference, 195 p.

2. 1974. Guidebook to Devonian, Permian, and Triassic Plant localities, east-central Arizona: Paleobotany Section of the Botanical Society America 25th Annual AIBS Meeting, Arizona State University, Tempe, Arizona, 63 p., 6 pls., 10 figs.

3. 1978. Geology, paleontology and paleoecology of a Late Triassic lake, western New Mexico: Brigham Young University Geology Studies, 25, pt. 2, 95 p.

4. 2006. (second editor with W. G. Parker and R. B. Irmis) A century of research at Petrified Forest National Park: Geology and Paleontology. Museum of Northern Arizona Bulletin, 62, 187p.

Abstracts

1. 1961. (with C.B. Read) The stratigraphic significance of the fossil fern *Tempskya* in the western states. New Mexico Geological Society Guidebook, 12:198.

2. 1962. The conodonts—a neglected stratigraphic tool in New Mexico: New Mexico Geological Society Guidebook, 13:173.

3. 1964. Upper Triassic Plants of New Mexico and Arizona: New Mexico Geological Society Guidebook, 15:185.

4. 1967. Preliminary results of a reinvestigation of the Chinle megaflora New Mexico and Arizona: Geological Society of America, Rocky Mountain Section, 20th Annual Meeting, Program, p. 20.

5. 1971. Observations on a Late Triassic lake deposit in western New Mexico: Utah Academy of Sciences, Art, and Letters, Proceedings, 48:94.

6. 1975. Upper Triassic floras of western North America: 12th International Botanical Congress, Abstracts, 1:109.

7. ____. Paleoecology of an Upper Triassic lake in western New Mexico: Geological Society of American, Abstracts and Programs, 7:981-982.

8. 1976. Preliminary report on the floral zones in the Upper Triassic Chinle Formation, southwestern United States: Geological Society America Abstracts and Programs, Rocky Mountain Section, 29th Annual Meeting, 8:562-563.

9. 1978. Plant megafossils of the Upper Triassic Dockum Group of Texas: Botanical Society America Program and Abstracts, 1978 Annual Meeting. Miscellaneous Series, Publication, 156:59.

10. 1979. Cycads of the Chinle Formation (Upper Triassic), southwestern United States - a summary: Botanical Society America Program and Abstracts, 1979 Annual Meeting. Miscellaneous Series, Publications, 157:30.

11. 1980. Early Mesozoic floras of the United States of America: IV Coloquio sobre paleobotanica y palinologia, Resumen de Trabajos, p. 11-12.

12. 1980. (jr. author with W. D. Tidwell) Preliminary report on a flora in the Red Tanks Member of the Madera Formation, central New Mexico: Geological Society of America Abstracts with Programs, 12:305.

13. 1983. Contrasting floras of the Upper Triassic bentonitic and redbed lithogenetic sequences of the Colorado Plateau: America Journal Botany, 70:67.

14. 1984. The Waterfall locality revisited: International Organization of Paleobotany 2nd Conference, Abstracts, p. 2.

15. ____. Biostratigraphic distribution of Upper Triassic plant fossils in Petrified Forest National Park, Arizona: Abstracts, Symposium on SW. Geology and Paleontology, Museum of Northern Arizona, p. 2.

16. 1986. (sr. author with R. J. Litwin and Long, R. A.) Bio-stratigraphic correlation of the Chinle Fm. (Late Triassic) on the Colorado Plateau, A progress report: Geological Society America Abstracts and Programs, 18:338-339.

17. ____. (sr. author with R. A. Long) Preliminary investigations of an enigmatic plant in the Chinle Formation (Upper Triassic), Petrified Forest National Park Arizona: America Journal Botany (Programs with Abstracts), 73:695.

18. 1987. (jr. author with T. L. Vallier, D. L. White, G. D. Stanley, and D. Jones) Jurassic rocks in Hells Canyon, Oregon and Idaho: volcanism, extension, and sedimentation in the Blue Mountains Island Arc: Geological Society America Abstracts and Programs, 19:339-340.

19. 1989. Was there a local source for some of the volcanic detritus in the upper part of the Chinle Formation in east-central Arizona?. Abstracts of the Symposium on southwestern geology and paleontology, 1989: Museum of Northern Arizona, Flagstaff, Arizona, p. 2.

20. 1990. (jr. author with Geoffrey Creber) Paleoclimatic interpretation of the wood structure of the trees in Petrified Forest National Park, Arizona: A progress report: Geological Society America Abstracts and Programs, 22:4.

21. ____. A new Jurassic flora from the exotic terranes of western North America and its climatic implications: American Journal of Botany, 77:81.

22. 1991. (sr. author with R. J. Litwin) On the widespread occurrence of amber in the Upper Triassic of the Southwest: Geological Society America Abstracts and Programs, 23(4):3.

23. 1992. North American Triassic megaplant genera. International Organization of Palaeobotany 4th Conference, Paris, Abstracts, p. 8.

24. ____. (sr. author with W.D. Tidwell, J. H. Madsen, and W. L. Stokes). The last supper of a Jurassic dinosaur: Geological Society of America Abstracts and Programs, 24(6):1.

25. 1993. (jr. author with E. A. Johnson, R. F. Dubiel, R. J. Litwin, and E, M. Brouwers). Triassic and Jurassic rocks at Currie, Nevada? Preliminary paleontologic evidence. Geological Society America Abstracts and Programs, 25(5):57-58.

26. 1994. (jr. author with K. B. Pigg and W. C. Davis) Anatomically preserved plant reproductive structures from the Upper Triassic Chinle Formation in Petrified Forest National Park, Arizona. Geological Society America Abstracts and Programs, 26(6):59.

27. ____. (jr. author with N. R. Riggs and J. M. Mattinson) Isotopic dating of a non-volcanic continental sequence, Chinle Formation, Arizona. Geological Society America Abstracts and Programs, 26(6):61.

28. ____. (sr. author with W. D. Tidwell) Plant megafossils from the Brushy Basin Member near the Montezuma Creek Trading Post, southeastern Arizona. Presented to a Symposium on the Upper Jurassic Morrison Formation, Denver, Colorado, May 26-28, 1994.

29. ____. (jr. author with W. D. Tidwell and B. Britt) Preliminary floral analysis of Mygatt-Moore Quarry in the Upper Jurassic Morrison Formation, west-central Colorado. Presented to a Symposium on the Upper Jurassic Morrison Formation, Denver, Colorado, May 26-28, 1994.

30. ____. (sr. author with R. J. Litwin) The use of plant fossils for interpretation of paleoclimates: Petrified Forest National Park, AZ. Partners in Paleontology. Fourth Conference on Fossil Resources, Colorado Springs, CO., October 31 - November 4, 1994.

31. ____. (jr. author with Hasiotis, S. T.,Demko, T. F., Riggs, N. R., May, C. L., Litwin, R. J. A composite measured section, Upper Triassic Chinle Formation, Petrified Forest National Park, Arizona, p. 6-7. *In* Santucci, V. L., (ed.), Petrified Forest National Park, Research Abstracts, 3.

32. ____. (jr. author with Riggs, N.R., Demko, T.M., Dubiel, R.F., Hasiotis, S.T.,and May, C.L., 1994, Distal effects of volcanism on fluvial sedimentation, Upper Triassic Chinle Formation, Arizona: GSA Abstracts with Programs, 26(7):68.

33. 1995. (jr. author with Demko, T. F., Hasiotis, S. T., Riggs, N. R., May, C. L., Litwin, R. J.) Triassic paleoecosystem reconstruction via fossil, ichnofossil, isotopic, and sedimentologic evidence integrated into a complete measured section, Chinle Formation, Petrified Forest National Park, AZ. Geological Society America Abstracts and Programs, 27(4):9.

34. 1998. (jr. author with G. T. Creber). A reconstruction of the Upper Triassic *Araucarioxylon arizonicum* tree in Petrified Forest National Park, AZ Geological Society America Abstracts and Programs, 30(6).

35. ____. (jr. author with S. T. Hasiotis). Late Triassic arthropod-plant interactions in the American Southwest. Geological Society America Abstracts and Programs, 30(6):10.

36. 1999. (jr. author with P. T. Kay) Triassic ambers from the Chinle USA help provide preliminary biochemical links to the identity of contributor plants. Geological Society America Abstracts and Programs, 31(7):A467. .

37. ____. The paleoclimatic implications of the Late Triassic ferns and fern allies of Petrified Forest National Park, Arizona. Fifth Biennial Conference of Research on the Colorado Plateau. Programs and Abstracts of presented papers and posters. p. 26.

38. 2002. Paleobotanical resources of the Grand Staircase-Escalante Natonal Monument, Utah. Geological Society America Abstracts and Programs, 34(4):2.

39. ____ (sr. author with R. J. Litwin) Creation and burial of a major Mesozoic landform: new microfossil evidence bearing on the age of the J-2 unconformity (Grand Staircase-Escalante National Monument). Geological Society America Abstracts and Programs, 34(4):2.

Parker, W. G., Ash, S. R., and Irmis, R. B., eds., 2006.
A Century of Research at Petrified Forest National Park: Geology and Paleontology.
Museum of Northern Arizona Bulletin No. 62.

ON THE SHOULDERS OF GIANTS: INFLUENTIAL GEOLOGISTS AND PALEONTOLOGISTS AT PETRIFIED FOREST NATIONAL PARK

WILLIAM G. PARKER

Division of Resource Management, Petrified Forest National Park, Box 2217, Petrified Forest, AZ. <William_Parker@nps.gov>

INTRODUCTION

The papers in this volume present some of the latest findings that are the result of a large amount of paleontological and geological research that has taken place in the park during the last decade; however, these findings are heavily based on a large pool of literature based on research that has taken place in the park since the 1920s. As is typical in science, current researchers as well as the staff and visitors to Petrified Forest National Park in general are indebted to these past researchers who have established such a strong literature base. Past researchers are listed in order of their contributions and the main dates of their contributions to the park are listed after thier names.

CHARLES L. CAMP (1921-1927)

In 1906 the naturalist John Muir was staying at the Forest Hotel in Adamana, Arizona adjacent to what was to become Petrified Forest National Monument later that year. Muir was enamored by the vast petrified wood deposits and scenic badlands of the area and in the Second (Crystal) and North (Black) Forests made a small collection of vertebrate material that he subsequently turned over to his friend John C. Merriam, of the University of California at Berkeley (Irmis, 2005). This small collection caught the attention of Annie Alexander, a prolific explorer and heiress who had established the Vertebrate Zoology (MVZ) and Paleontology (UCMP) museums at the Berkeley campus. Moreover, in 1919 another UCMP researcher, Ynez Mexia, had collected a partial phytosaur skull from the Blue Forest area, east of Adamana. In April 1921, Alexander made a brief reconnaissance to the Blue Forest, and encouraged by what she had seen, returned in May with her close friend and field partner Louise Kellogg (Stein, 2001). The two women immediately discovered a large amount of good fossil material including phytosaur and metoposaur skulls from the Blue Forest and Devils Playground areas. Alexander quickly wired Charles L. Camp, who fresh from completing his Ph. D. at Columbia University had recently accepted a position at the UCMP. Camp soon joined the women and proceeded to collect numerous fossil vertebrates. Whereas Alexander had made many of these initial discoveries, she did not conduct any further fieldwork in the

region; however, Camp continued working near Adamana four four additional summers and in 1930 published a seminal monograph on the Late Triassic phytosaurs of the southwestern United States based almost entirely on this work (Camp, 1930). Camp continued to visit the Petrified Forest sporadically over the next three decades; however he never initiated further fieldwork in the park, instead focusing on Chinle Formation deposits near St. Johns, Arizona and Ghost Ranch, New Mexico, as well as intensive work in the Middle Triassic Moenkopi Formation of Arizona.

MYRL V. WALKER (1933-1938)

Walker was the first permanent naturalist at Petrified Forest National Park. Trained in paleontology, Walker was friends with Charles Gilmore of the Smithsonian Institution as well as the Sternberg family. In 1932, during road construction through the Tepees area of the monument, workers stumbled upon a large deposit of fossil leaves. When he arrived shortly afterwards, Walker recognized the significance of this deposit and preserved many of the specimens. Walker discovered numerous fossil localities throughout the park and made the first collections of invertebrates, plants, and trace fossils. He also collected several phytosaur skulls, one of which is still on display at the Smithsonian. In 1936, Walker excavated a stand-

Figure 1. Park naturalist Myrl V. Walker examining a petrified log from the park in 1934.

Figure *2*. Park naturalist Howard R. Stagner with preserved roots in Rainbow Forest.

ing stump in the Flattops area of the monument and was the first to argue that not all of the logs had been transported from outside of the area of the park. Walker (1938) also published a paper documenting insect traces in petrified wood and also arranged for Lyman Daugherty (see discussion below) to study the fossil plant material from the Tepees.

HOWARD R. STAGNER (1939-1941)

Stagner was the second park naturalist, replacing Walker who left in 1939 for an appointment at Zion National Park. Stagner extensively explored the Tepees area discovering and documenting many more plant localities. Stagner was also the first to attempt to relocate and mark many of the known paleontological sites. The stakes that he set at these sites are still visible today. Stagner also wrote the first general stratigraphic description of the Chinle Formation near the Tepees and was the first to use the term "newspaper rock sandstone" (Stagner, 1941).

LYMAN H. DAUGHERTY (1941-1963)

Daugherty was a paleobotanist from San Jose State College who provided the first descriptions of fossil leaves and pollen from the park. Daugherty's (1941) monograph is the foundation for paleobotanical research in the park. Subsequently Daugherty published several more descriptions of material from the park (Daugherty, 1960, 1963). This work is significant because it essentially represented the first new work on Triassic plants in North America since 1883 and demonstrated that there was a well-preserved Late Triassic flora from the western United States. Daugherty also did pioneering work on Late Triassic pollen and spores and many of the taxa erected by Daugherty are still considered valid. This is even more amazing considering that Daugherty made palyno-

Figure *3*. Park naturalist Phillip Vancleave circa 1950.

logical preparations under very primitive conditions in his kitchen at home (S. R. Ash, pers. commun., 2006).

EDWIN H. COLBERT (1941-2001)

Edwin "Ned" Colbert was the curator of fossil reptiles at the American Museum of Natural History in New York. In 1945, Colbert traveled to northeastern Arizona with Charles Camp to examine Camp's old Chinle localities. In 1946, Colbert collected several phytosaur skulls from the Devils Playground and Billings Gap areas (Colbert, 1946; Long and Murry, 1995). Colbert was set to return in 1947; however, the discovery of the *Coelophysis* Quarry at Ghost Ranch, New Mexico while enroute to the park derailed those plans. Colbert never conducted paleontological excavations in the park; however, several events that occurred during the 1946 field season directed Colbert towards a more geomorphological study in the park. In the summer of 1946, Colbert had discovered some well-preserved metoposaur material in the Blue Forest area of the park, which he marked and planned on returning to excavate. Unfortunately, a subsequent heavy rainstorm destroyed the material before it could be collected (Colbert, 1946, 1981). A similar event happened concerning a phytosaur skull in the

Devils Playground. Colbert (1981:279) described what happened as follows, "we...located a beautiful phytosaur skull, in situ in the side of a little badland hill along a wash. So we spent the morning exposing it, and then in the early afternoon we encased it, ...in a plaster jacket. At about this point in our work the skies became dark and threatening. It looked like trouble, so we covered our fossil with a cavas tapaulin, weighted down by rock, drove our jeep to high ground, and waited for things to happen. There was thunder and lightning crashing all around us, and then for about twenty or thirty minutes a rainstorm of the utmost violence, during which the wind came up and ripped the canvas cover away from our fossil. Just as the rain slackened off, there was a roar and a wall of water came down the wash, carrying everything before it and completely inundating our beautiful fossil in its cast. There was nothing to do but wait until the water had subsided, at which time we waded through the mud to where the fossil had been. Wonder of wonders and joy supreme! The flood had neatly undercut our specimen and turned it over. All we had to do was load it on the jeep, go down the wash and rescue our tarpulin, and drive back to headquarters."

These two events led Colbert to set three series of wooden stakes at several locations in the Chinle Formation (two are in PEFO) to try to determine erosional rates for these exposures. Colbert (1956, 1966) estimated that 5.7 mm of sediment were removed each year through erosion.

Colbert was a frequent visitor to the park and was on the park's scientific advisory committee until his passing in 2001. His wife, Margaret, painted a mural that is on display at the Rainbow Forest Museum.

PHILLIP F. VANCLEAVE (1956-1963)

Phillip Vancleave is another park naturalist that had a profound impact on paleontological and geological research in the park. Vancleave collected several paleobotanical specimens from the park including a tree-fern that now bears his name (*Itopsidema vancleavei*) (Daugherty, 1960). In the early 1960s Vancleave collected the partial skeleton of a small reptile in the Blue Forest, which Long and Murry (1995) described as a new taxon (*Vancleavea campi*). Vancleave also showed S. R. Ash around the park in 1962 and encouraged Ash to return the following year to conduct research (see discussion below).

MAURICE E. ("SPADE") COOLEY (1953-1965)

Cooley's (1957) unpublished masters thesis on the Chinle Formation focused mainly on Petrified Forest National Park and provided the first stratigraphic scheme for the park, including first usage of the name Rainbow Forest for a stratigraphic unit (Rainbow Forest sandstone). Cooley was also the first to specifically mention the "tuff" bed now formally known as the Black Forest Bed. Cooley's later work in the park concentrated on source areas for extrabasinal clasts from the "Sonsela Sandstone Bed" and as a part-time scientific advisor for various projects.

SIDNEY R. ASH (1962-present)

Sid Ash has published over 80 papers on the geology flora of the Chinle Formation of Petrified Forest National Park. This includes reconstructions of the three dominant fossil woods from the park (Ash and Creber, 2000; Creber and Ash, 2004); leaf, cone, and shoot descriptions (e. g., Ash, 1970a, b, Ash, 1972, Ash, 1973, Ash, 1985, Ash, 1991); descriptions of stratigraphic units (Ash, 1992); as well as discussions of insect-plant interactions (Ash, 1997, 1999, 2000). He also coauthored papers on the first crayfish, amber, and charcoal found in the park and was the first to correlate the major plant fossil localities and forests in the park (Miller and Ash, 1988; Litwin and Ash, 1991; Jones et al., 2002; Creber and Ash, 2002). He is also the author of two popular books about the park (Ash, 1986, 2005). Sid Ash has also served as a frequent scientific advisor to the park and his contributions continue to the present (4 co-authored papers in this volume).

GEORGE H. BILLINGSLEY (1979-1985)

In 1979 George Billingsley was part of a research group from the Museum of Northern Arizona who conducted the first paleontological inventory of the park (Cifelli et al., 1979) and created the first geological map of the park (Billingsley et al., 1985). This preliminary map and subsequent report (Billingsley, 1985) have been the basis for all subsequent geological work done in the park until the recent work of Heckert and Lucas (2002) and Woody (2003).

ROBERT A. LONG (1981-1997)

Robert Long was a researcher at the University of California Paleontological Museum in the early 1980s. Along with Samual Welles and Kevin Padian, he led a project to relocate Charles Camp's old localities and to reinitiate UCMP paleontological research in the park This work continued in 1982-87 and as recently as 1997. Long and colleagues not only relocated almost all of Camp's localities but also discovered numerous new localites and important specimens including the holotypes of *Pseudopalatus mccauleyi* (Phytosauria) and *Chindesaurus bryansmalli* (Saurischia). In 1995, Long published a monograph with Phillip Murry, which is possibly the most cited paper in Late Triassic vertebrate paleontology and is the cornerstone for current research in the southwestern United States. Furthermore, Long and Ballew (1985) was a pivotal paper in Late Triassic vertebrate paleontology that clarified aspects of phytosaur and aetosaur taxonomy and biochronology, and was based mainly upon research in the park.

RONALD J. LITWIN (1983-1991)

Litwin trained under Al Traverse at Penn State, where he received his PhD in 1986, and was the first to provide a detailed palynostratigraphy for the Chinle Formation and was the first to recognize and document the Carnian-Norian bound-

ary in the park and elsewhere in the southwestern United States based on palynomorphs (Litwin et al., 1991). Litwin also was the first to discover amber in the Chinle Formation (Litwin and Ash, 1991).

ACKNOWLEDGMENTS

This paper is dedicated to the staff and board of the Petrified Forest Museum Association who has funded paleontological and geological research in the park since the 1960s, including most of the studies mentioned in this paper. Comments by Sid Ash improved the manuscript.

REFERENCES

Ash, S. R. 1970a. *Pagiophyllum simpsoni*, a new conifer from the Chinle Formation (Upper Triassic) of Arizona. Journal of Paleontology 44:945-952.

Ash, S.R. 1970b. *Dinophyton*, a problematical new plant genus from the Upper Triassic of southwestern United States. Palaeontology, 13:646-663.

Ash, S. R. 1972. *Marcouia* gen. nov., a problematical plant from the Late Triassic of the Southwestern United States. Palaeontology, 15:423-429.

Ash, S. R. 1973. Two new plants from the Petrified Forest of Arizona. Journal of Paleontology, 47:46-53.

Ash, S.R. 1985. A short thick cycad stem from the Upper Triassic of Petrified Forest National Park, Arizona and vicinity. Museum Northern Arizona Bulletin, 54:17-32.

Ash, S. R. 1986. Petrified Forest; the story behind the scenery. Petrified Forest Museum Association, 48 p.

Ash, S. R. 1991. A new pinnate cycad leaf from the Upper Triassic Chinle Formation of Arizona: Botanical Gazette, 152:123-131.

Ash, S. R. 1992. The Black Forest Bed, a distinctive unit in the Upper Triassic Chinle Formation, northeastern Arizona. Journal of the Arizona-Nevada Academy of Science, 24/25:59-73.

Ash, S.R. 1997. Evidence of arthropod-plant interactions in the Upper Triassic of the southwestern United States. Lethaia, 29:237-248.

Ash, S.R. 1999. An Upper Triassic *Sphenopteris* showing evidence of insect predation from Petrified Forest National Park, Arizona. International Journal of Plant Science, 160:208-215.

Ash, S. R. 2000. Evidence of oribatid mite herbivory in the stem of a Late Triassic tree fern from Arizona. Journal of Paleontology, 74:1065-1071.

Ash, S. R. 2005. Petrified Forest: a story in stone. Petrified Forest Museum Association, Petrified Forest, 48 p.

Ash, S.R. and G. Creber. 2000. The Late Triassic *Araucarioxylon arizonicum* trees of the Petrified Forest National Park, Arizona, USA. Palaeontology, 43:15-28.

Billingsley, G. H.1985. General stratigraphy of the Petrified Forest National Park, Arizona. Museum of Northern Arizona Bulletin, 54:3-8.

Billingsley, G. H., W. J. Breed, and S. R. Ash. 1981. Geologic map of the Petrified Forest National Park. Museum of Northern Arizona, scale 1:48000, unpublished.

Camp, C. L. 1930. A study of the phytosaurs with description of new material from western North America. Memoirs of the University of California, 10:1-174.

Cifelli, R. L., G. H. Billingsley, and W. J. Breed 1979. The paleontological resources of the Petrified Forest: a report to the Petrified Forest Museum Association (unpubl.), pp. 1-9, with 2 appendices.

Colbert, E. H. 1946. Paleontological field work of the American

Museum of Natural History in the Petrified Forest National Monument area, 1946. Unpublished report.

Colbert, E. H., 1956. Rates of erosion in the Chinle Formation. Plateau, 28:73-76.

Colbert, E. H., 1966. Rates of erosion in the Chinle Formation – ten years later. Plateau, 38:68-74.

Cooley, M. E. 1957. Geology of the Chinle Formation in the upper Little Colorado Drainage area, Arizona and New Mexico. Unpublished M. S. Thesis, University of Arizona, Tucson, 314 p.

Creber, G. T., and S. R. Ash. 1992. Palaeoclimatic interpretation of the wood structures of the trees in the Chinle Formation (Upper Triassic) in the area of Petrified Forest National Park, Arizona, USA. Palaeogeography, Palaeoclimatology, and Palaeoecology 96:299-317.

Creber, G. T., and S. R. Ash. 2004. The Late Triassic *Schilderia adamanica* and *Woodworthia arizonica* trees of the Petrified Forest National Park, Arizona, U. S. A. Palaeontology, 47:21-38.

Daugherty, L. H. 1941. Upper Triassic flora of Arizona. Carnegie Institute of Washington Publication, 526:1-108.

Daugherty, L. H. 1960. *Itopsidema*, a new genus of the Osmundaceae from the Triassic of Arizona. American Journal of Botany, 47:771-777.

Daugherty, L. H. 1963. Triassic roots from the Petrified Forest National Park, American Journal of Botany, 50:802-805.

Heckert, A.B., and S.G. Lucas. 2002. Revised Upper Triassic stratigraphy of the Petrified Forest National Park. New Mexico Museum of Natural History and Science Bulletin, 21:1-36.

Jones, T. P., Ash, S. R., and I. Figueiral. 2002. Late Triassic charcoal from Petrified Forest National Park, Arizona, USA. Palaeogeography, Palaeoclimatology, and Palaeoecology 188:127-139.

Litwin, R. J., and S. R. Ash. 1991. First early Mesozoic amber from the Western Hemisphere. Geology, 19:273-276.

Litwin, R. J., Traverse, A., and S. R. Ash. 1991. Preliminary palynological zonation of the Chinle Formation, southwestern USA., and its correlation with the Newark Supergroup (eastern USA). Review of Palynology and Palaeobotany 68:269-287.

Long R. A. and K. L. Ballew. 1985. Aetosaur dermal armor from the late Triassic of southwestern North America, with special reference to material from the Chinle Formation of Petrified Forest National Park. Museum of Northern Arizona Bulletin 54:45-68.

Long, R. A., and P. A. Murry 1995. Late Triassic (Carnian and Norian) tetrapods from the southwestern United States. New Mexico Museum of Natural History and Science Bulletin, 4:1-254.

Miller, G., and S. R. Ash. 1988. The oldest freshwater decapod from the Triassic of Arizona. Palaeontology, 31:273-279.

Stagner, H.R. 1941. Geology of the fossil leaf beds of the Petrified

Forest National Monument [Ariz.]. Carnegie Institute of Washington Publication, 526:9-17.

Stein, B. R. 2001. On her own terms: Annie Montegue Alexander and the Rise of Science in the American West. University of California Press, Berkeley. 380 p.

Walker, M. V. 1938. Evidence of Triassic insects in the Petrified Forest National Monument, Arizona. U. S. National Museum Proceedings 85:137-141.

Woody, D. T., 2003. Revised geological assessment of the Sonsela Member, Chinle Formation, Petrified Forest National Park, Arizona. Unpublished M. S. Thesis, Northern Arizona University, Flagstaff.

ARTICLES

GEOLOGY AND STRATIGRAPHY

Parker, W. G., Ash, S. R., and Irmis, R. B., eds., 2006.
A Century of Research at Petrified Forest National Park: Geology and Paleontology.
Museum of Northern Arizona Bulletin No. 62.

REVISED STRATIGRAPHY OF THE LOWER CHINLE FORMATION (UPPER TRIASSIC) OF PETRIFIED FOREST NATIONAL PARK, ARIZONA

DANIEL T. WOODY*

Department of Geology, Northern Arizona University, Flagstaff, AZ 86011-4099
* current address: Department of Geological Sciences, University of Colorado at Boulder, Boulder CO 80309 <Daniel.Woody@colorado.edu>

ABSTRACT— The Sonsela Sandstone bed in Petrified Forest National Park is here revised with specific lithologic criteria. It is raised in rank to Member status because of distinct lithologies that differ from other members of the Chinle Formation and regional distribution. Informal stratigraphic nomenclature of a tripartite subdivision of the Sonsela Member is proposed that closely mimics past accepted nomenclature to preserve utility of terms and usage. The lowermost subdivision is the Rainbow Forest beds, which comprise a sequence of closely spaced, laterally continuous, multistoried sandstone and conglomerate lenses and minor mudstone lenses. The Jim Camp Wash beds overlie the Rainbow Forest beds with a gradational and locally intertonguing contact. The Jim Camp Wash beds are recognized by their roughly equal percentages of sandstone and mudstone, variable mudstone features, and abundance of small (<3 m) and large (>3 m) ribbon and thin (<2 m) sheet sandstone bodies. The Jim Camp Wash beds grade into the overlying Flattops One bed composed of multistoried sandstone and conglomerate lenses forming a broad, sheet-like body with prevalent internal scours. The term "lower" Petrified Forest Member is abandoned in the vicinity of PEFO in favor of the term Blue Mesa Member to reflect the distinct lithologies found below the Sonsela Member in a north-south outcrop belt from westernmost New Mexico and northeastern Arizona to just north of the Arizona-Utah border. The Petrified Forest Member is here restricted in the vicinity of PEFO to the red mudstone-dominated sequence found between the Sonsela Member and the Owl Rock Member.

Keywords: Triassic, Petrified Forest, Chinle Formation, stratigraphy, Sonsela, Blue Mesa

INTRODUCTION

PETRIFIED FOREST National Park (PEFO) is a focal point for studies of Upper Triassic terrestrial strata in the American Southwest. Despite numerous studies of plant and vertebrate remains, stratigraphic assessment of the Chinle Formation has lagged behind. Previous biostratigraphic study has indicated a change in the fauna and flora in the middle of the PEFO section, surrounding the level of the Sonsela Sandstone (Long and Padian, 1986; Litwin et al., 1991; Lucas and Hunt, 1993; Long and Murry, 1995; Murry and Kirby, 2002). However, detailed lithostratigraphic studies have not concentrated on this important interval, despite their importance for any biostratigraphic framework.

Lithostratigraphic study of the PEFO region, south of the Navajo and Hopi Reservations, began in earnest with Cooley (1957; 1958; 1959) and Akers et al. (1958). Stewart et al. (1972a) produced an overview of the regional lithostratigraphy, but did not focus on the PEFO section. Billingsley et al. (1985) produced the first full geologic map of PEFO at a 1:50,000 scale and Billingsley (1985) published a companion explanation of PEFO stratigraphy. Billingsley's (1985) and Billingsley et al.'s (1985) work largely followed the nomenclature of previous workers, and was the standard for the stratigraphy of PEFO that was followed by most workers for the next 15-20 years with only local additions and revision (Ash, 1987; Ash, 1992; Therrien and Fastovsky, 2000; Hasiotis et al., 2001).

During the 1990s views regarding the stratigraphy of the Chinle Formation, and thus PEFO, split into two main phi-

losophies. One philosophy continued along the lines of Stewart et al. (1972b) and Billingsley, Breed, and Ash (Billingsley, 1985; Billingsley et al., 1985) maintaining informal regional lithologic unit designations, and emphasizing regional correlations between units (e.g., Dubiel, 1994; Lehman, 1994; Dubiel et al., 1999). The other philosophy was initiated by Lucas and colleagues (e.g., Lucas and Hayden, 1989; Lucas and Hunt, 1989; Lucas, 1991; Lucas, 1993; Lucas et al., 1997; Lucas et al., 1999) who incorporated all Upper Triassic terrestrial strata of western North America into the Chinle Group and either formalized existing local nomenclature into broad members, abandoned existing stratigraphic nomenclature or changed the stratigraphic rank of units.

Recently, Heckert and Lucas (2002b) expanded the Sonsela Member (=Sonsela Sandstone bed) within PEFO by introducing a tripartite subdivision. The new revision is similar to what is observed at the type section of the Sonsela (Akers et al., 1958) and incorporates some observations seen by previous workers that indicated that the Sonsela within PEFO consists of several sandstone beds (Cooley, 1957; Roadifer, 1966). However, the stratigraphy as proposed by Heckert and Lucas (2002b) includes correlations of subunits contradictory to mapping and does not provide a sound foundation for the recognition of units on a regional level. Regional recognition of the Sonsela has been complicated in the past by subjective interpretation of isolated sandstone bodies that may or may not be restricted to the Sonsela interval throughout the region.

The present study was initiated independently of Heckert and Lucas (2002b) and aims to provide a consistent framework for the Sonsela interval on which to base other studies. Lithologic criteria are given to recognize the Sonsela and its three subunits, and justify the status of the Sonsela as a member of the Chinle Formation. The lithostratigraphic framework presented here provides a background for recognition of the Sonsela on a regional level, as well as locally within the PEFO area.

BACKGROUND

Geologic setting.—The Chinle Formation is a collection of fluvial, lacustrine and floodplain rocks that were deposited in a back-arc basin formed inland of a Late Triassic magmatic arc associated with the subduction zone off the west coast of North America (Dickinson, 1981; Dickinson et al., 1983; Fig. 1). Local subsidence was controlled by tectonic events associated either with a dynamic forebulge of the island-arc portion of the magmatic arc (Lawton, 1994) or local uplifts, such as the Mogollon Highlands along the continental portion of the magmatic arc (Harshbarger et al., 1957; Stewart et al., 1972b; Dickinson, 1981) and the ancestral Front Range and Uncompahgre uplifts (Stewart et al., 1972b; Dubiel, 1991; Dubiel, 1994; Lucas et al., 1997). Dubiel (1992) and DeLuca and Eriksson (1989) documented movement on the Ancestral Rockies uplifts near the time of Sonsela deposition. Local salt tectonism during the Late Triassic has been documented by several workers (Blakey and Gubitosa, 1983, 1984; Hazel, 1991; Dubiel, 1994).

The climate during Chinle deposition has been described as humid or subhumid to semiarid. Dubiel et al. (1991, p. 364) interpreted the "lower" Petrified Forest interval as representing an "unusual[ly] wet episode". Vertebrate faunas are typically dominated by aquatic to amphibious forms such as metopsaurid amphibians and crocodile-like phytosaurs attesting to prevalent lakes and streams, although certain 'upland' elements, such as dinosaurs, rauisuchians, dicynodonts and aetosaurs are locally pervasive, particularly in strata above the Sonsela interval (Colbert, 1972; Long and Murry, 1995). Ash has interpreted the flora of PEFO as indicative of a humid environment (1972; 1986; 1992). Gottesfeld (1972) interpreted distinct upland, lowland and riparian floras in an overall arid to semiarid environment with through flowing streams dominating the paleohydrology of the riparian and lowland floras. Demko (1995a; 1995b) arrived at a conclusion similar to Gottesfeld (1972) during a study of the taphonomy of plant localities. Paleosols below and at the base of the Sonsela interval were compared to modern subhumid forest soils by Retallack (1997). Jones (2000) interpreted a shift towards drier climates near the base of the Sonsela. Other studies have indicated a semiarid climate marked by episodes of heavy precipitation (Blodgett, 1988; Dubiel et al., 1991; Dubiel, 1994; Therrien, 1999; Therrien and Fastovsky, 2000).

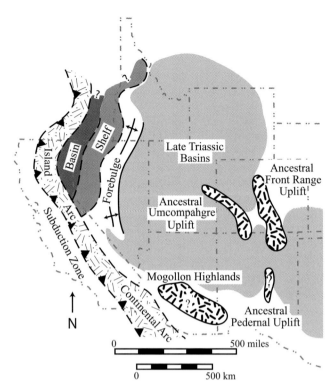

Figure *1*. Geologic setting for the Late Triassic of western North America. The Chinle basin extends from the west side of the ancestral Rocky Mountain uplifts of the ancestral Uncompahgre and Front Range uplifts in Colorado and northern New Mexico to the magmatic arcs and forebulge in Nevada and western Arizona. The western edge of the Dockum basin is shown to the east of the ancestral Front Range and possible Pedernal uplifts. The extent and timing of the ancestral Pedernal Uplift and Mogollon Highlands are debated. Modified from Lawton (1994).

Stratigraphic nomenclature.—The name Chinle Formation was first proposed by Gregory (1917) for Upper Triassic terrestrial rocks on the Navajo Reservation of northern Arizona. Gregory subdivided the Chinle into four units, A though D, in descending order (Fig. 2.1). Division A included the upper part of the Chinle that is dominated by red mudstones and siltstones. Division A has been variously assigned to the Ochre, Orange siltstone, Church Rock or Rock Point members depending on location and predominant lithology (Stewart et al., 1972a, 1972b; Lucas et al., 1997). Division B consisted of the laterally persistent limestone bearing part of the Chinle below division A and was subsequently formalized as the Owl Rock Member (Stewart, 1957; Witkind and Thaden, 1963). Division C, the dominantly variegated middle portion, was later formally named the Petrified Forest Member by Gregory in 1950. The Petrified Forest Member was named for the exposures in and around PEFO, but the type section is near Zion National Park (Gregory, 1950). Division D represents the basal portion of the Chinle Formation of Gregory and is characterized by relatively inconsistent lithologies, typically with relatively high sandstone/mudstone ratios, although still mostly mudstone. Division D has been assigned to the siltstone and sandstone member (= Cameron Member of Lucas, 1993), Monitor Butte Mem-

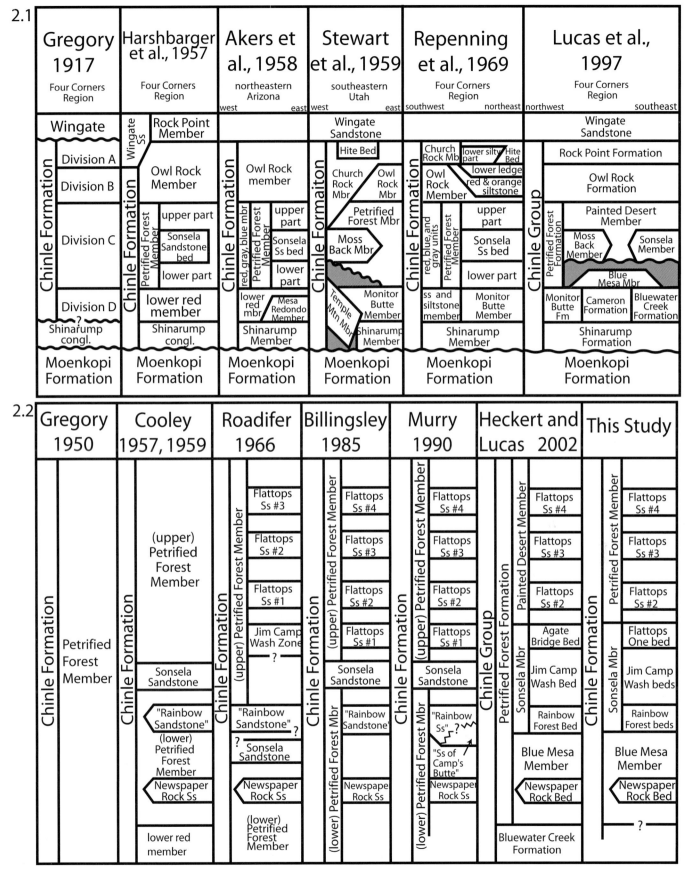

Figure 2. Stratigraphic correlation chart for the Chinle Formation. 2.1. Stratigraphic correlation chart for the Four Corners region of Arizona, Colorado, New Mexico, Utah; 2.2. Stratigraphic correlation chart for the PEFO region. Note the variable relative positions and nomenclature of the units assigned to the Sonsela Member.

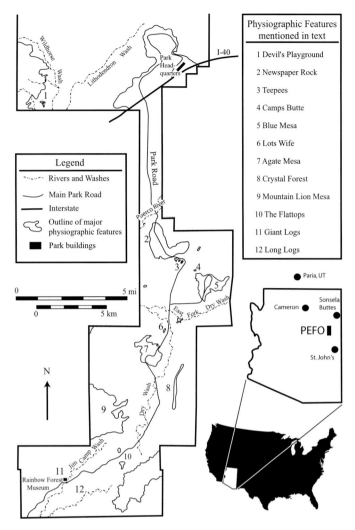

Figure 3. Study area of the southern portion of PEFO. Major physiographic features discussed in text are listed. Inset shows position of PEFO relative to the type area of Sonsela Buttes, and towns in Arizona and Utah mentioned in text regarding outcrop distributions.

ber, Mesa Redondo Member, or lower red member (=Bluewater Creek Member of Lucas and Hayden, 1989), depending on the dominant facies (Cooley, 1958; Witkind and Thaden, 1963; Stewart et al., 1972a, 1972b; Lucas et al., 1997).

Akers et al. (1958) named a distinctive ledge-forming sandstone unit near the middle of the Petrified Forest Member, the Sonsela Sandstone bed. The type section is 3½ miles from the western-most Sonsela Butte near the Arizona-New Mexico border (Fig. 3). At its type section, the Sonsela consists of a lower sandstone, medial mudstone, and upper sandstone subdivisions. In other areas, the unit was recognized as a single sandstone bed or as an interval of several sandstone lenses (Cooley, 1957, 1959; Repenning et al., 1969). The recognition of the Sonsela led to division of the Petrified Forest Member into informal "lower" and "upper" members based upon both the relative position to the Sonsela interval and the lithologic and color changes that were locally observed (Akers et al., 1958; Repenning et al., 1969).

Various sandstone beds within PEFO have been informally described and associated with the Sonsela Sandstone bed (Fig. 2.2). Cooley (1957) informally named the Rainbow Forest sandstone for the log-bearing sandstone and conglomerate at the Giant Logs and Long Logs "forests" near the southern end of PEFO. He commented on its lithologic similarity to the more widely recognized Sonsela Sandstone bed of PEFO and postulated that the Rainbow Forest sandstone was possibly a lower tongue of the Sonsela. Cooley (1957) commented on the existence of several other unnamed tongues of the Sonsela within PEFO. Roadifer (1966, p. 19) believed that the Rainbow Forest sandstone was located 20 ft (~6 m) stratigraphically above the Sonsela. The Jim Camp Wash zone was named by Roadifer (1966) for an interval of interbedded sandstone and mudstone stratigraphically above the Rainbow Forest sandstone along Jim Camp Wash north of Giant Logs. Roadifer postulated that this interval may also represent an upper tongue of the Sonsela, similar to his assessment of the Rainbow Forest sandstone. In the same report Roadifer also named the Flattops sandstones, numbered 1 to 3, in ascending order, for laterally persistent sandbodies above the Sonsela Sandstone bed within the upper part of the Petrified Forest Member.

Billingsley et al.'s (1985) geologic map and Billingsley's (1985) stratigraphic description of PEFO only recognized the Sonsela Sandstone as a single sandstone bed. Billingsley et al. agreed with Cooley that the Rainbow Forest sandstone was stratigraphically below the Sonsela but did not associate the two. Whereas Billingsley et al. did not recognize the Jim Camp Wash zone of Roadifer (1966), they did recognize the Flattops sandstones. However, Flattops sandstones 1, 2 and 3 of Roadifer became Flattops sandstones 2, 3 and 4, respectively, of Billingsley et al.. Billingsley (1985) reassigned the name Flattops sandstone #1 for laterally persistent sandstone between the Rainbow Forest sandstone and Flattops sandstone #2 that is probably equivalent to Roadifer's Jim Camp Wash zone (see Heckert and Lucas, 2002b). Deacon (1990, pg. 7) agreed with Roadifer that the Rainbow Forest sandstone represents an upper tongue of the Sonsela Sandstone bed and was "part of the same fluvial system". Ash (1987) and Creber and Ash (1990) recognized the Rainbow Forest sandstone as a separate unit below the Sonsela. Murry (1990) described an informal sandstone on Camp Butte northeast of Blue Mesa and interpreted it as a possible lateral equivalent to the Rainbow Forest sandstone. Both Murry (1990) and Demko (1994; 1995a; 1995b) associated the Rainbow Forest sandstone and Sonsela Sandstone bed and cited them as the "Rainbow-Sonsela Complex" without discussion of the stratigraphic relationship between the two sand bodies.

Lucas (1993) raised the Petrified Forest Member to formational rank. He also raised the rank of the Sonsela Sandstone bed to member status, and named the Blue Mesa and

Painted Desert members of the Petrified Forest Formation for what was previously considered the lower and upper portions of the Petrified Forest Member, respectively. Heckert and Lucas (1998b) directly correlated the Rainbow Forest sandstone and the traditional Sonsela Sandstone bed (*sensu* Akers et al., 1958) in their description of the stratigraphic distribution of petrified wood within PEFO. Later, Heckert and Lucas (2002b) proposed a tripartite subdivision of their Sonsela Member, which will be further discussed below.

METHODS

This study was conducted using standard stratigraphic section measuring techniques. Nineteen sections were measured and correlated in the southern portion of PEFO. Section locations were chosen based on obtaining representative lateral variability, representative facies, and access to a known stratigraphic level for the base and top of the section. Where possible, the entire Sonsela Member was measured, as well as a portion of the underlying and/or overlying strata (i.e., Camp Butte and Blue Mesa 1 sections). Stratigraphic relations were observed along outcrop in various portions of PEFO, including the southern part of the park and the Devil's Playground area (Fig. 3) north of I-40. A preliminary 1:24,000 scale map was produced by standard geologic mapping practices. Representative hand samples and thin sections were collected and examined to enhance lithologic description and to compare to previous studies (e.g., Espegren, 1985; Deacon, 1990).

DESCRIPTION OF SEDIMENTARY FACIES

The present study recognizes eight sedimentary facies assemblages (A-H) in the medial portion of the Upper Triassic section in PEFO from the measured sections and outcrop descriptions. The term "facies assemblages" is used in a modified form, similar to that of Parsons et al. (2003). Facies assemblages in this study designate lithologies or groups of lithologies that are connected by similarities in characteristic features and architecture between facies associations that are recognizable in outcrop. Characteristic features include relationships between facies associations, sandstone composition, sandstone/mudstone ratios, architectural relationships, and paleosol characteristics. The assemblages form the basis of the stratigraphy described below.

Facies Assemblage A.—Facies assemblage A is present at the base of the study section. This assemblage is dominated by dusky-blue, blue-gray and gray claystone and mudstone with locally common purple and local green, yellow, and red mudstone. Most non-gray mudstone has diffuse gray, blue-gray or green-gray mottling. Red and/or purple mottles may be present in gray and blue-gray beds. The traceability of individual mudstone units is variable, although most are only traceable for

distances between 50 and 500 m, where topography permits. Contacts between beds are typically gradational. Small rhizoliths preserved as carbonate or silica are locally common. Moderate to large slickensides are common in several horizons, but are not consistently present. Carbonate nodules are common in particular horizons and only locally follow slickenside and/or root traces (Demko, 1995b; Therrien and Fastovsky, 2000). Paleosol profiles are typically composite (cf., Marriott and Wright, 1993) resulting in thick profiles, often thicker than several meters (Fastovsky et al., 2000).

Sandstone is uncommon in facies assemblage A. Where present, sandstone bodies typically have sheet-like geometries with width/thickness ratios (W/T) >50-100. Locally sandstone bodies have W/T ratios of about 15-25 and fill shallow scours. True ribbons (cf., Friend et al., 1979) are rare. Sandstone beds are typically <0.5 m thick, and rarely over 1 to 3 m thick. Sandstone is typically greenish-gray, but can range from light- to pinkish-gray on fresh surfaces. Sandstone is usually texturally and compositionally immature with large percentages of matrix and pseudomatrix from the alteration of volcanic clasts (Roadifer, 1966). Sandstone is typically lithic wackes. Most sandstone is poorly indurated and preserved sedimentary structures are rare.

Facies assemblage A is interpreted here as predominantly floodplain deposits. Pedogenic features indicate moist conditions with some seasonal variation in drainage (Vepraskas, 1994; PiPujol and Buurman, 1997; Retallack, 1997). The predominance of diffuse mottles indicates that groundwater was the predominant means of saturation (Duchaufour, 1982; PiPujol and Buurman, 1994). The predominance of composite paleosol profiles suggests stable landforms (Kraus and Aslan, 1993; Marriott and Wright, 1993; Kraus, 1997), although slight variations in floodbasin-scale base level are interpreted from the lack of lateral continuity of beds and scour surfaces. Sandstone bodies are interpreted as ephemeral tributary or crevasse channels extending out onto the floodplain, or as rare sheetflood deposits.

Facies Assemblage B.—Facies assemblage B consists of medium-grained, locally fine- to coarse-grained, sandstone and local conglomerate. The sandstone is typically gray to pinkish-gray or pale tan on fresh surfaces. Sandstone is generally compositionally mature to submature and texturally mature (Woody, 2003). The unit is multi-storied and forms a sheet that can be traced for several kilometers in the vicinity of Blue Mesa. Individual stories are typically 10-60 cm thick. Thickness of the assemblage ranges from 0 m at its pinchout at Lots Wife, to ~16 m at Blue Mesa. Moderate- and large-scale crossbedding (5-15 cm and >15 cm, respectively) is common. The base of the assemblage is generally a shallow scour with local relief typically less than 1 m. The assemblage typically weathers to low ridges due to poor induration, but locally caps small buttes, such as Camp Butte, where it is well-indurated.

Granules of chert or mudstone rip-up clasts commonly define crossbedding. Lag deposits of moderately to very weakly rounded vertebrate remains are locally present. Volcanic and yellow, white, or orange chert pebbles form local lenses within the unit, particularly where the unit is thicker and coarser grained. Quartzite forms a minority of clasts in lenses with volcanic and chert clasts. Sandstone is lithic arenites to lithic wackes. Petrified wood occurs locally as trunk fragments up to 1 m in diameter, but typically less than 30 cm. Fragments longer than 1 m are rare. Most observed *in situ* wood fragments are oblique to perpendicular to paleoflow.

The multi-storied nature, predominance of large-scaled crossbedding and lack of mudstone indicates that facies assemblage B was deposited by a low-sinuosity, bedload stream system (Miall, 1977; Blodgett and Stanley, 1980; Miall, 1985).

Facies Assemblage C.—Facies assemblage C is composed of medium-to coarse-grained, locally fine-grained, sandstone. Sandstone is typically light (light gray to pinkish-gray), but locally is maroon or medium gray. Texturally it is typically mature to submature. In the upper part of the assemblage and near the edges of lenses textural maturity can be immature to very immature. The assemblage weathers to irregular ridges and flats where texturally immature and moderately- to poorly-indurated, and forms resistant, low ridges where texturally mature and well-indurated. Large-scale crossbedding is the most abundant sedimentary structure. Lateral accretion sets (cf., Allen, 1965) are locally seen in the upper portion of assemblage C.

Compositional maturity is highly variable but is typically submature (Woody, 2003). Pebble- to cobble-sized gravel clasts comprise 0 to ~70% of the unit, typically concentrated along bedding surfaces or as massive "lag" deposits. Gravel consists of extrabasinal volcanic, quartzite and chert clasts and intrabasinal mudstone rip-ups, rounded vertebrate remains, and rare carbonate nodules. Chert clasts are typically white, yellow, orange, or less commonly brown. Sandstone is lithic wackes to lithic arenites. Petrified wood is typically abundant as brightly colored logs (Ash and Creber, 1992; Heckert and Lucas, 1998b; Ash and Creber, 2000).

Mudstone is typically rare but increases in abundance near the top of the unit. Lenses of mudstone are relatively common at the top of the assemblage where it interfingers with assemblages D and E. Mudstone ranges from dusky-blue to gray. Dusky-blue mudstone typically possesses common large to small gray mottles, although they are locally absent. Other pedogenic features are generally absent, although large-scale slickensides do occur locally. Small, but very abundant carbonate nodules locally accompany the slickensides and are often aligned with the slickenside surfaces. Carbonate rhizocretions and rhizoliths are typically also observed in these areas.

The base of facies assemblage C is not well exposed but appears to be very similar to facies assemblage B. The sheet-like morphology and internal scours between stories is also similar to assemblage B. The main differences are the more abundant gravel and lenses of mudstone and sandstone in the upper portion of assemblage C.

The predominance of gravel clasts, morphology, and prevalence of large-scale crossbedding suggest that facies assemblage C was also deposited by a low-sinuosity stream system (e.g., Jackson, 1978; Brierley, 1996). Increasing sinuosity and/or increased avulsion frequency is indicated by mudstone lenses and lateral accretion sets in the upper portion of the unit (Allen, 1965; Jackson, 1978; Ethridge et al., 1999). The lack of, or small and subdued nature of pedogenic features in most exposures suggest little time for pedogenesis before burial (Marriott and Wright, 1993; Kraus, 1997). The nature of these pedogenic features is consistent with weak groundwater gleying (Duchaufour, 1982; Vepraskas, 1994). Where pedogenic features are more pronounced they suggest a predominance of surface water gley during seasonally poor drainage conditions (PiPujol and Buurman, 1994, 1997; Vepraskas, 1992).

Facies Assemblage D.—Facies assemblage D consists of a complex of sandstone sheets and ribbons (cf., Friend et al., 1979), and mudstone. Sandstone/mudstone ratios are generally ~2.5-1. Sandstone is typically fine-grained and poorly sorted. Sandstone is typically a shade of gray or tan on fresh surfaces, but weathers into a wide variety of colors. Sandstone textural and compositional maturity is generally immature, but is locally submature (Woody, 2003). Ribbons vary from <1 m to ~3 m thick, but all have W/T ratios <10. Ribbons at the top of the assemblage can reach ~5 m in thickness. Sheets are usually <0.5 m in thickness and usually traceable throughout the outcrop (up to 1-2 km). In a few locations sheets can be traced to where they connect several ribbon sandstones (Fig. 4.1), similar to the "tiers" of Kraus and Gwinn (1997). Granule- to pebble-sized gravel within ribbons is rare, but where observed it is typically intraformational in nature. In a few locations dark chert (mostly black and brown) and volcanic clasts were observed in lenses of texturally very immature conglomerate to sandy conglomerate. Sandstone is typically lithic wackes. Petrified wood is relatively rare, with most being in sandstone ribbons in the upper part of the facies assemblage.

Mudstone ranges in color from dusky-purple to red to dusky-blue to gray, in decreasing order of abundance. Individual beds typically are less than 1 m and can be traced for ~1 km, before they are lost due to erosional truncation. Bed contacts are often sharp. Most mudstone exhibits gray mottling, particularly prevalent along slickensides and root traces. Slickensides are variable in development but are rarely larger than 0.3 m in height. Carbonate nodules are often present, but rarely in high abundances. A thin (<10 cm), orange to red siliceous horizon is seen in the lower third of the assemblage at several

Figure 4. Sandstone 'tiers' low in facies assemblages D and E (Jim Camp Wash beds). 4.1. Sandstone "tiers" on the east face of Blue Mesa; 4.2. Sandstone "tier" connecting three small ribbons immediately below the siliceous horizon near Mountain Lion Mesa. Note the relatively lower W/ T and deeper basal scour of the ribbons relative to those in 4.1. The presence of several ribbon sandstone bodies connected with a thin sheet sandstone body is one of the criteria for recognizing avulsion deposits listed in Kraus and Wells (1999). These types of deposits are relatively common throughout facies assemblages D and E (Jim Camp Wash beds).

locations in the Blue Mesa area. This siliceous horizon typically exhibits a coarse dendritic pattern on the upper surface.

Facies assemblage D is interpreted as a floodplain deposit in the outer part of the avulsion belt. The ribbon and sheet sandstones as well as common intervals of thinly interbedded sandstone and mudstone (heterolithic deposits) closely resemble the characteristics cited by Kraus and Wells (1999), among others, as indicative of avulsion processes. The lack of thick ribbon and sheet sandstones suggest a more distal position to the site of avulsion and crevasse-splay deposition. The larger ribbons at the top of the assemblage may indicate environments closer to the trunk channel.

The pedogenic features of the mudstone indicates that they are moderately- to poorly-drained paleosols predominantly affected by surface water gleying (PiPujol and Buurman, 1994; Vepraskas, 1994). The moderately- to poorly-drained paleosols are also suggestive of a relatively medial floodplain deposition. More proximal positions are subjected to the influence of frequent, relatively coarse-grained deposition that would promote

better drainage (Bown and Kraus, 1987; Pizzuto, 1987; Marriott, 1996; Kraus, 1997) . The coarse dendritic morphology of the siliceous material suggests preservation of plant debris. The siliceous horizon may also locally represent root mats (Klappa, 1980).

Facies Assemblage E.—Facies Assemblage E is similar to assemblage D, except for more variability in coloration, relationship between ribbon and sheet sand bodies, paleosol characteristics and size of ribbon sand bodies. In general, sandstone is more abundant. Sandstone/mudstone ratios are generally 1.5-2.5, but can be as high as 3.5 or as low as 0.5. Sandstone sheets are typically less continuous laterally, although they do locally connect ribbons into tiers as in assemblage D (Fig. 4.2). Sandstone sheets are generally <1 m, although they are as much as 3 m thick, and can be traced for only several 10s of meters before they are lost due to erosional truncation. In a few locations sheet sandstones can be traced for ~1 km. Ribbons can be divided into small ribbons (<3 m) and large ribbons, locally as much as 18 m in thickness (Fig. 5). Small

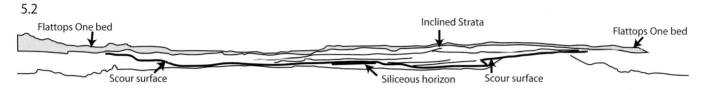

Figure 5. Large sandstone with basal scour within facies assemblage E (Jim Camp Wash beds). Facies assemblage G (Flattops One bed) erosionally overlies the scour fill. Large-scaled inclined strata within the scour indicating probable lateral accretion are seen along the north (right) side of the sandstone body. *5.1.* photomosaic; *5.2.* line tracing.

ribbons have W/T <15, typically between 5 and 10. Large ribbons have W/T <20, typically 10-15. Granule- to cobble-sized gravel within ribbons is more common than in assemblage D, but is usually restricted to intraformational clasts, predominantly carbonate nodules. However, extraformational clasts are locally seen in high percentages, particularly within the large ribbons. Textural maturity is generally low, submature to immature, with large ribbons locally being mature (Woody, 2003). Sandstone is typically lithic wackes.

The sedimentary structures present are dependant upon the type of sandbody. Large ribbons possess the most variability in sedimentary structures, including very large- (>1 m), large- (15-100 cm), moderate- (5-15 cm), and small-scale (<5 cm) crossbedding, lateral accretion sets (Fig. 5), and rare ripple and horizontal laminations. Sedimentary structures are relatively rare in small ribbon and sheet sandstone bodies, but small- to moderate-scale crossbedding, and ripple and horizontal laminations were locally observed. Lateral accretions sets are locally common in thicker sheet sandstones. Petrified wood is locally common within large ribbons, and rarely within small ribbons. Wood is typically observed as trunk fragments ranging in size from 15 to 60 cm in diameter and 30 to 90 cm in length. *In situ* fragments were most commonly observed with their long dimensions perpendicular to the slope of inclined heterolithic strata.

Mudstone has the most variability within this assemblage. Individual beds are typically traceable for a few meters to a few 100s of meters. The most common coloration is purple, although green-gray, gray, red and dusky-blue are also common. Locally, green to black mudstone fills moderate to large scour-like features, such as in section Dry Wash North (Appendix A).

Complete paleosol profiles are rarely preserved. Where preservation allows assessment, profiles range from simple to composite (Kraus and Aslan, 1993; Marriott and

Wright, 1993), with a majority being composite. Gray mottling is common, both along slickensides and root traces and less commonly within the matrix. Carbonate nodules are abundant in most localities (typically as *in situ* horizons) and commonly associated with slickensides and root traces. The presence of slickensides is variable with most locations having slickensides from 0.2-0.5 m in height, a few localities posses numerous slickensides >0.5 m. Ped structures are commonly poorly-developed, but are locally well-developed. Rhizoliths and rhizocretions, including carbonate and siliceous preservation, are common in certain horizons.

A discontinous horizon (0-30 cm thick) of siliceous material preserved in numerous depositional settings is seen 7-15 m above the top of facies assemblage C. Many exposures exhibit a dendritic pattern on the surfaces similar to that seen in the siliceous horizon found in assemblage D. Other locations exhibit increasing size and abundance of siliceous rhizoliths culminating in a nearly continuous horizon, similar to a silcrete horizon in morphology (Klappa, 1980; Wright and Tucker, 1991), or simply a horizon with a silcrete-like morphology. Creber and Ash (1990) also described silicified whole logs, branches and roots with a "rope-like" texture within this horizon.

Facies assemblage E is interpreted as floodplain, avulsion, and channel deposits. Large channels (>3m thick) commonly show evidence of high sinuosity by abundant and well-defined lateral accretion surfaces (Thomas et al., 1987; Brierley, 1996). Smaller channels exhibit almost no evidence of lateral migration (e.g., Bridge and Leeder, 1979; Friend et al., 1979). The poor sorting and channel geometry suggests that they were sinuous (Miall, 1985); however, Kraus and Gwinn (1997) described very similar channels that were relatively straight in planview, which is supported by the lack of evidence of lateral migration. The interpretation of avulsion deposits is supported by similarity in facies, geometry, and lateral and vertical associations to strata previously interpreted as representing avul-

Figure 6. Ridge-and-swale topography developed on the top surface of facies assemblage G (Flattops One bed) along the east rim of Jim Camp Wash.

sion deposits (Smith et al., 1989; Kraus and Wells, 1999; Slingerland and Smith, 2004).

A range in floodplain positions relative to the channel, from proximal to distal, is interpreted from lateral relationships and the high variability in pedogenic features, including slickenside abundance and size, matrix and mottling color and carbonate abundance, suggesting variation in both duration of pedogenesis and drainage conditions (e.g., Bown and Kraus, 1987; Kraus, 1987; Bown and Kraus, 1993; Aslan and Autin, 1998). The siliceous horizon was interpreted by Creber and Ash (1990) as an interval of increased silification due to increased pore space from a period of widespread fungal attack on plant material. These authors also commented on the potential regional stratigraphic utility this horizon.

Facies Assemblage F.—Medium- to coarse-grained sandstone and granule to cobble conglomerate and sandy conglomerate comprise facies assemblage F. Mudstone lenses are rare and make up less than 10% of any vertical section. Mudstone, where present, is generally dusky-blue or gray. Sandstone ranges from pale tan to moderate tan and light gray to yellowish gray on fresh surfaces and gray to brown on weathered surfaces. Sandstone is typically moderately- to well-sorted and texturally mature to submature, locally very mature (Woody, 2003). Conglomerate clasts range from granules (relatively rare) to cobbles. Chert clasts are the most widespread gravel-sized clasts and are typically white or orange, although brown and black clasts are locally present in small abundances. Quartzite clasts comprise a moderate percentage of clasts in most localities. Volcanic clasts are typically almost as abundant as chert clasts, and are often the largest in size within most given clast populations. Local sandstone clasts are also among the largest clasts present in a few areas. Intraformational clasts are rare and typically among the smallest gravel-sized clasts. Sandstones are lithic arenites to lithic wackes. Petrified wood is common in most locations as fragments of trunks ranging

from ~15 cm to 1 m in diameter and ~20 cm to over 1 m in length (Ash and Creber, 1992; Heckert and Lucas, 1998b; Ash and Creber, 2000). Orientations of petrified logs are variable (Demko, 1995b; Ash and Creber, 2000).

The most common sedimentary structures in facies assemblage F are moderate- to very large-scale, planar crossbedding. Other sedimentary structures include local, small- to large-scale, trough cross-bedding, horizontal laminations, pebble imbrication and soft sediment deformation (Deacon, 1990; Woody, 2003). Deacon (1990) described local inclined bedding surfaces and levee deposits in the vicinity of Blue Mesa, and herringbone cross-stratification in the vicinity of Crystal Forest.

Sandbodies are sheet-like and multistoried (cf., Friend et al., 1979). Individual stories are 0.3-5m thick (typically ~1m) and are commonly separated by well-defined scours. Complex lateral and slightly vertical amalgamation patterns are indicated by the individual stories (Deacon, 1990; Woody, 2003). The assemblage typically holds up mesas and buttes and is well-indurated at most localities.

Large- to very large-scale, crossbedding, abundant gravel and consistent paleocurrent directions within individual stories suggest deposition of assemblage F by a braided stream (Miall, 1977; Miall, 1985; Brierley, 1996). Deacon (1990) interpreted the traditional Sonsela Sandstone bed (mostly facies assemblage F) as a large braided stream complex with well-defined linguloid and transverse bars. Local lateral accretion surfaces and increasing paleocurrent variability indicate that sinuosity increased slightly in the upper portion of the assemblage. Mudstone, as lenses and interbeds, is also more common in the upper part further supporting increasing sinuosity (e.g., Jackson, 1978; Miall, 1985; Miall, 1987).

Facies Assemblage G.—Facies assemblage G is comprised of fine- to coarse-grained sandstone, sandy conglomerate, and minor mudstone lenses. Gravel is predominantly carbonate nodule intraformational clasts, but locally in lenses includes large percentages (up to 70%) of volcanic and chert extraformational clasts. Chert clasts are generally brown, black, or white in color, in order of decreasing abundance. Orange chert clasts are rare. Quartzite is only locally present. Gravel ranges in size from granule to cobble, but is typically granule to pebble. Sandstone is poorly- to locally well-sorted lithic wackes to lithic arenites. Sandstone ranges in color from pale tan to brown and light to moderate gray on fresh surfaces. Weathered surfaces are generally yellow-tan to brown. Sandstone is typically either massive or has well developed moderate- to large-scale (5-15 cm and >15cm, respectively) crossbedding. Small-scale (<5 cm) crossbedding and horizontal laminations are locally common, typically in the upper portion of the assemblage. Petrified wood is locally common as trunk fragments typically ranging from 10-75 cm (locally up to 2 m) in diameter and 20 cm to several meters in length. The orienta-

Figure 7. Complex internal architecture of facies assemblage G (Flattops One bed). 7.1. Sandstone and conglomerate of facies assemblage G (Flattops One bed) with irregular scouring between individual beds suggesting fluctuations in local base level and possible localized and small-scale (under 2°) tilting from salt tectonism. Mountain Lion Mesa; 7.2. Sandstone and conglomerate lenses within lower part of facies assemblage G (Flattops One bed) indicating rapid fluctuations in local base level. East rim of Jim Camp Wash.

tion of the petrified wood is variable but is typically perpendicular to paleocurrent direction. The upper part of the assemblage possesses common inclined bedding surfaces and local ridge-and-swale topography (cf., Nanson and Page, 1983; Fig. 6).

Sandbodies have sheet-like morphologies (cf., Friend et al., 1979) and are often multistoried. Individual stories are typically defined by shallow scour surfaces and range from 0.25-5 m thick (typically ~0.75 m). Thin mudstone lenses locally separate stories and even sandbodies in some instances. Locally complex architecture similar to that reported by Blakey and Gubitosa (1984) and Hazel (1991) in the Salt Anticline region of Utah is seen between stories or between thin sheets separated by mudstone (Fig. 7). Sandstone is generally moderately- to well-indurated and holds up mesas and buttes. However, in a few locations the assemblage is relatively incompetent and forms rounded ridges.

Mudstone lenses can comprise up to 40% of the vertical section. In these areas the assemblage appears as a series of sandstone lenses similar to those of assemblage E. The boundary between assemblages E and G are difficult to determine in these locations. However, the sandstone lenses included in facies assemblage G have W/T ratios greater than ~30, distinguishing them from those in assemblage E. Mudstone is variable, similar to facies assemblage E, although gray is the most common color in assemblage G, further distinguishing the two assemblages. Typical mudstone contents of the facies assemblage range from 5-25%.

Facies assemblage G is interpreted as the deposit of a low- to at least moderate-sinuosity bedload stream. Like assemblage F, sinuosity appears to increase upsection, although in this assemblage it reaches a level where ridge-and-swale topography developed. Paleocurrent variability (Espegren, 1985; Woody, 2003) also supports low to moderate sinuosity.

The stream system appears to be smaller than the one responsible for deposition of facies assemblage F as indicated by the finer average grain size, smaller largest and average gravel size, thinner stories, and smaller crossbedding. The more easterly flow direction and the smaller nature of the stream than the facies assemblage F stream system is interpreted as evidence that assemblage G was deposited by a tributary system to the large trunk channel belt of facies assemblage F. Deacon (1990) interpreted the confluence of a tributary system with the main trunk system of the traditional Sonsela (facies assemblage F) in the vicinity of Crystal Forest. Woody (2003) also described interfingering of facies assemblages F and G in the Crystal Forest area further supporting the interpretation of a trunk and tributary system, respectively.

Facies Assemblage H.—Facies assemblage H consists of predominantly mudstone with several laterally persistent sandstone bodies. Sandstone outside of the laterally persistent bodies is rare. The sandstone is fine- to medium-grained and poorly- to moderately-sorted. Sandstone is typically reddish gray on fresh surfaces, but is locally light gray. Weathered surfaces are generally brown or grayish-red. Gravel is rare and is almost exclusively intraformational carbonate nodule clasts. Small- to moderate-scale crossbedding is more common than large-scale crossbedding and lateral accretion sets are prevalent (e.g., Espegren, 1985).

Mudstone is predominantly deep purple or red with moderate to abundant gray mottling and large (>0.5 m) slickensides and vertically oriented columnar peds. Local clay-rich lenses are dusky blue to green and generally lack paleosol features, such as mottles and slickensides. Carbonate nodules are prevalent and well-developed. Paleosol profiles are typically thick and compound or composite with well-developed vertic features (Zuber, 1990; Marriott and Wright, 1993). Individual units can typically be traced for several kilometers, ex-

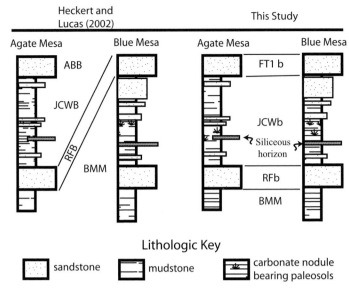

Figure 8. Schematic stratigraphic sections at Agate Mesa and Blue Mesa emphasizing the inconsistencies in correlation between this study and that of Heckert and Lucas (2002b). Both sections approximately are 40 m in thickness. Note the presence of the unique siliceous horizon in both sections and the similarity of facies and facies associations below the capping sandstones. BMM=Blue Mesa Member; RFB=Rainbow Forest Bed; RFb=Rainbow Forest beds; JCWB=Jim Camp Wash Bed; JCWb=Jim Camp Wash beds; ABB=Agate Bridge Bed; FT1b=Flattops One bed.

cept for where locally truncated by "gully systems" (Kraus and Middleton, 1987).

A well-drained landscape of well-developed floodplain paleosols is interpreted from the mudstone coloration, slickensides and carbonate nodules (e.g., Driese and Foreman, 1992; Kraus, 1999). The textural immaturity, abundance of lateral accretion sets, shallow-based geometry and dearth of gravel supports the interpretation of the sandstone bodies as being deposited by high-sinuosity streams laterally migrating across the well-drained floodplains (e.g., Brierley, 1996; Bristow, 1996).

STRATIGRAPHY

As shown in Figure 2.2, there is no consensus as to what units have been assigned to the Sonsela Sandstone bed or to the relationship of related units throughout PEFO, much less regionally. As outlined above, the Sonsela has typically been associated with large sandstone bodies, partially due to the nomenclatural terminology of the Sonsela being restricted to a sandstone "bed". Mudstone intervals that are clearly associated with the Sonsela are usually either disregarded or placed within the upper or lower part of the Petrified Forest Formation (Billingsley, 1985; Billingsley et al., 1985; Deacon, 1990; Long and Murry, 1995; Heckert and Lucas, 1998b), resulting in ambiguity in the placement of the upper and lower contacts of the Sonsela and difficulty in regional correlation.

Heckert and Lucas' (2002b) revision of the Sonsela solves some of these problems by addressing the relationship

between sandbodies and associated mudstone. Heckert and Lucas (2002b) noted the similarity of the PEFO section to that of the Sonsela type section with a medial mudstone unit separating lower and upper sandbodies; however, they did not provide a map detailing the geographic distribution of their units, in contradiction of the practices outlined by the NACSN (1983), and they did not provide robust descriptions of their subunits that would allow recognition outside of the immediate vicinity of PEFO. These two facts leave ambiguity in the identification of the Sonsela both regionally and within PEFO. Cooley (1957) and Roadifer (1966) commented on the presence of multiple beds assignable to the Sonsela in the region immediately adjacent to PEFO and the revisions of Heckert and Lucas (2002b) do not address how to recognize or interpret such beds as tongues, lenses, etc., or where they would fit within their nomenclature of a tripartite subdivision.

In fact, even within PEFO, the correlations of Heckert and Lucas (2002b) are not consistent, either stratigraphically or lithologically. For example, they cite their uppermost unit (Agate Bridge Bed) as the capping sandstone of Agate Mesa, but their lowest subunit (Rainbow Forest Bed) as the capping sandstone of Blue Mesa (Fig. 8). Mapping during this study (Fig. 9) shows that the capping sandstone of both of these mesas is laterally equivalent (Fig. 8), in agreement with numerous other workers (Cooley, 1957; Roadifer, 1966; Billingsley et al, 1985; Espegren, 1985; Murry, 1990; Long and Murry, 1995). Lithologic correlation of facies on the mesa faces and of the capping sandstones themselves also supports the correlation presented in this study (see below).

The following nomenclature is proposed to provide a regionally consistent framework upon which to base future studies, honor nomenclatural traditions of previous workers, and to conform to the guidelines of the North American Stratigraphic Code (NACSN, 1983). In agreement with numerous previous workers (Stewart et al., 1972a; Stewart et al., 1972b; Blakey and Gubitosa, 1983; Dubiel; Lehman, 1994; Demko, 1995b; Demko et al., 1998), the Chinle is retained as a formation in this study based on my interpretation that the bounds of the Chinle as a fundamental unit (formation) delimit the "surfaces of lithic change that give it the greatest practicable unity of constitution" (NACSN, 1983, Article 24 (a)). Retaining the name Chinle Formation does not negate recent advances in biostratigraphic, lithostratigraphic and chronostratigraphic correlation with other Upper Triassic units of the Western Interior (e.g., Long and Murry, 1995; Lucas et al., 1997; Lucas, 1998; Steiner and Lucas, 2000), contra Lucas and colleagues (e.g., Lucas et al., 1994; Lucas et al., 1997; Heckert and Lucas, 2002b). Concerns over the recognition of these recent advances should not outweigh the "distinctive lithic characteristics" for which lithostratigraphic units are named and utilized (NACSN, 1983, Article 24 (c)).

The assignment of facies assemblages to stratigraphic units adheres to the guidelines of the NACSN (1983), by describing specific lithologic characters that are the basis for the lithostratigraphy proposed herein. The facies assemblage descriptions are combined and discussed to delimit characteristic features and the lateral variability of those diagnostic features. It is my opinion that this method provides the most robust description of units and justification of inclusion, or exclusion, of subunits and lateral equivalents.

Blue Mesa Member

The Blue Mesa Member corresponds to facies assemblage A of this study. The term Blue Mesa Member is used in the capacity of Lucas (1993) to replace the term "lower" Petrified Forest Member; however, the Blue Mesa Member is here modified from its original definition (Lucas, 1993) to exclude units 16-20 of the type section, yielding a modified thickness of 57+ meters. There have been recent arguments about whether or not the base of the PEFO section contains strata below the Blue Mesa Member (Heckert and Lucas, 1997; Heckert and Lucas, 1998a; Dubiel et al., 1999; Therrien et al., 1999; Hasiotis et al., 2001), thus possibly further reducing the type section of the Blue Mesa Member. Complex interfingering of the Shinarump, Bluewater Creek, and Mesa Redondo Members would be expected in northeastern Arizona based upon the reports of Cooley (1957, 1958, 1959) and Stewart et al. (1972b). While preliminary examination did show lithologies similar to the upper two-thirds of the Mesa Redondo Member and the lower red member (=Bluewater Creek Member of Lucas and Hayden, 1989) as described by Cooley (1957, 1958), Lucas and Hayden (1989) and Heckert and Lucas (1998a, 2002a, 2002b), this study did not examine this lowest part of the stratigraphic section in enough detail to warrant its exclusion from, or inclusion within, the Blue Mesa Member at this time.

The Blue Mesa Member, as revised herein, is a sequence of blue-gray, dusky-blue, purple and locally green, yellow and red mudstone with local, relatively thin sandstone bodies that lies stratigraphically below the Sonsela Member. The typical outcrop expression is steep to rounded ridges and knolls of dusky-blue to purple bentonitic mudstone. Mudstone generally shows evidence of moderate to extensive pedogenesis by mottle and carbonate nodule development. The traceability of individual mudstone units is variable, although most are only traceable for distances between 50 and 500 m where topography permits. Many units seem to fill broad scours (e.g., Repenning et al., 1969).

Sandstone bodies are typically less than 0.5 m thick, and rarely over 1 to 3 m thick. Sandstone body geometries are typically sheet-like with width/thickness ratios (W/T) >50-100. Locally sandstone bodies have W/T ~15-25 and fill shallow scours. True ribbons (cf., Friend et al., 1979) are rare.

Discussion.— The nomenclature of the interval below the Sonsela Member within PEFO is somewhat ambiguous. The

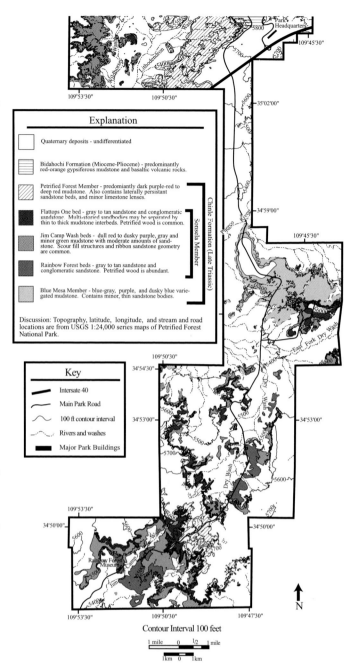

Figure 9. Preliminary geologic map of the southern part and the Devil's Playground region of PEFO. Mapping was completed at a scale of 1:24000 and reduced for display here. Full scale map is in Woody (2003).

term Blue Mesa Member is preferred over the term "lower" Petrified Forest Member due to its distinctive lithology and distribution, long recognized in the literature (Cooley, 1957; Akers et al., 1958; Stewart et al., 1972a, 1972b), warranting member status. The Blue Mesa has been equated, at least in part, to the Monitor Butte Member of southern Utah based upon molluscan fauna and some lithologic similarities (Good, 1993). The author does not agree with some recent assertions that the Monitor Butte should be extended to the PEFO area and up to the base of the Sonsela Member (e.g., Dubiel et al.,

1999; Hasiotis et al., 2001) for the following reasons: 1) The lithologies that are similar between the Monitor Butte and Blue Mesa Members are not a dominant portion of either member and most likely reflect ephemeral and/or local depositional environments as expected in a complex fluvial environment (Therrien, 1999). In fact, a complex interfingering relationship between the two members has been observed in other areas where the Blue Mesa Member (= "lower" Petrified Forest Member) overlies the Monitor Butte Member, such as in the southern Monument Valley (Repenning et al., 1969; Lucas et al., 1997). 2) The Monitor Butte in Utah has traditionally been associated with Gregory's original Division D, which is near the base of the formation (Stewart et al., 1972a, 1972b). Stratigraphic units at the base of the Chinle Formation or immediately above the Shinarump Conglomerate when it forms the base of the Chinle Formation, i.e., the lower red member (=Bluewater Creek of Lucas and Hayden, 1989), Mesa Redondo Member, and Monitor Butte Member, have historically been excluded from Gregory's original Division C (=Petrified Forest Member of Gregory 1950) due to either stratigraphic position or lithology. Division C (=Petrified Forest Member) is typically noted as being more mud dominated and variegated than units below (Gregory, 1950; Stewart et al., 1972a, 1972b), which is the case in the region surrounding PEFO. My opinion is that combining the nomenclature of divisions C and D, as currently understood, would add more confusion to analyses of the depositional history than it would clarify relationships. 3) The "lower" Petrified Forest Member (=Blue Mesa Member) interval has a long history of recognition as a distinct lithologic entity, both regionally and stratigraphically, in the literature (Cooley, 1957; Akers et al., 1958; Stewart et al., 1972b). In the outcrop belt described here, the "lower" Petrified Forest Member can be distinguished from the Monitor Butte Member based upon lithologic criteria, warranting separation under the NASC (NACSN, 1983). Additionally, the history of usage indicates that there is utility in distinguishing between the "lower" part of the Petrified Forest Member and the Monitor Butte. Continuity precludes dropping the separation where it is not necessary for clarity and consistency, which is accomplished by using the term Blue Mesa Member for the strata in PEFO and other areas.

The Blue Mesa lithology as described above is limited in outcrop distribution to a relatively narrow band running north-northwest from the Arizona-New Mexico border south of St. Johns, Arizona to the Cameron, Arizona area and north to the Utah-Arizona border. This distribution of the Blue Mesa Member either indicates a limited distribution of depositional environments responsible for the deposition of the Blue Mesa or defines the erosional extent of the Tr-4 unconformity as described by Heckert and Lucas (1996). The Tr-4 unconformity was proposed by Lucas (1993) to describe the erosional basal surface of the Sonsela Member and the local absence of the underlying strata, i.e. the Blue Mesa Member, in areas such as the Zuni Mountains and southeastern Utah as documented by previous workers (Stewart et al., 1972b; Blakey and Gubitosa, 1983; Lucas and Hayden, 1989; Dubiel, 1994). The unconformity was postulated to span a 1-2 Ma time span based upon faunal differences in strata above and below the surface. However, as has been discussed above, this study indicates that the basal surface of the Sonsela is related to the deposition of several individual sheet sandbodies, and even within the relatively small confines of PEFO is not as a single continuous erosional surface. Thus, the Tr-4 unconformity must either be limited in distribution to areas to the north and west of PEFO, or is not a regionally significant surface.

Sonsela Member

The Sonsela Sandstone bed and associated lithologic packages previously not recognized, warrants increase in rank to member status (Lucas, 1993) based upon its distinctive and recognizable lithologies and distribution (NACSN, 1983). Lucas (1993) originally raised the Sonsela to a member when he raised the rank of the Chinle Formation to the Chinle Group; however, no specifics of lithology or variation were noted to support the elevated rank. Heckert and Lucas (2002b) retained this nomenclature when they recently revised the stratigraphy of PEFO.

The unit, as redefined herein, can be distinguished by its moderate to high sandstone/mudstone ratios, cut-and-fill architecture, abundance of thin and thick (<3 m and >3 m, respectively) ribbon sandstone bodies, lateral extent of local sandstone bodies, conglomerate clast compositions (abundant volcanic clasts and to a lesser extent chert and quartzite clasts), variability in mudstone characteristics (where present), abundance of heterolithic deposits of alternating sandstone and mudstone within muddy intervals, and stratigraphic position. No other unit within the Chinle Formation in the vicinity of PEFO possess this complete list of features, although some of the features may be found in isolated sand bodies or as isolated lenses. Other coarse-grained units within the Chinle, such as the Shinarump Conglomerate and Moss Back Member, differ in having lower mudstone contents, less variability in mudstone characteristics (where it is present), different clast compositions, rare heterolithic deposits, a general lack of widespread cut-and-fill architecture on a small and large scale, and lack of association of several different horizons of lenticular sandstone. The Shinarump and Moss Back also appear to posses locally deep scours (locally several tens of meters) at their bases which are generally not present at the base of the Sonsela and its associated sandstones (Stewart et al., 1972b; Blakey and Gubitosa, 1984). Finer-grained units in the Chinle differ from the Sonsela Member in the low sandstone/mudstone ratios, general lack of thick, well-consolidated sandstones, particularly ones with large-scale crossbedding, general absence of sheet sandstone bodies, and a lack of variability in mudstone characteristics on short horizontal scales.

Facies assemblages B through G are included within the Sonsela Member. The Sonsela Member comprises all Upper Triassic strata geographically located in PEFO between Blue Mesa and The Flattops (Fig. 3; Fig. 9), and a majority of the Upper Triassic strata south of The Flattops (Woody, 2003; Fig. 9). Paleocurrents are predominantly to the north and northeast, and sometimes east, in contrast to other members of the Chinle Formation, which generally have a northwesterly transport direction (Akers et al., 1958; Stewart et al., 1972b; Espcgren, 1985; Deacon, 1990; Woody, 2003). Sections Blue Mesa 1 and Mountain Lion Mesa 1 are provided as reference sections for the Sonsela Member (Appendix A).

As recognized by Heckert and Lucas (2002b), the Sonsela Member within PEFO consists of a tripartite subdivision of a lower sandstone interval, a medial mudstone and sandstone interval, and an upper sandstone interval. This subdivision is similar to that found at the type section, as well as other regions of the Colorado Plateau (Akers et al., 1958; Heckert and Lucas, 2002a). Nomenclature for the individual subdivisions is proposed that differs from that proposed by Heckert and Lucas (2002b) because of differences in stratigraphic and lithologic correlation (Fig. 8) and the importance given to the maintenance of utility and tradition of past literature. Informal nomenclature is preferred here due to problems with regional recognition, which are attributable to local absences and rapid lateral facies changes (e.g., Cooley, 1957; Roadifer, 1966; Woody, 2003), and thus limiting regional utility. The lower sandstone interval is referred to as the Rainbow Forest beds, the medial mudstone and sandstone interval is referred to as the Jim Camp Wash beds, and the upper sandstone interval is referred to as the Flattops One bed.

Rainbow Forest beds.—The Rainbow Forest beds are the lowest subdivision of the Sonsela Member within PEFO. The unit includes Cooley's (1957) Rainbow Forest sandstone, which comprises most of the unit in the southern part of PEFO near the Giant Logs and Long Logs forests (facies assemblage C). The Camps Butte sandstone of Murry (1990) (more properly referred to as the Camp Butte sandstone) comprises the unit in more northerly parts of PEFO south of I-40 (facies assemblage B). The two sandstones were traced to a point of mutual pinchout at Lots Wife (north of Agate Mesa), with the pinchout of the Rainbow Forest sandstone of Cooley overlying the pinchout of the Camp Butte sandstone by approximately 30 cm (Woody, 2003; Fig. 10). The close stratigraphic proximity of the two sand bodies and similar details of geometry, architecture and lithology warrant inclusion within the same lithostratigraphic unit and support interpretation of a similar depositional history. The unit was either not observed in the Devil's Playground area or has a slightly different nature that eluded recognition, highlighting some of the difficulties in re-

gional correlation of individual subunits of the Sonsela Member (see Woody, 2003), and supporting their retention as informal units.

Facies assemblages B and C are here included within the Rainbow Forest beds. I feel that more utility is garnered by lumping the two facies assemblages and their respective informal nomenclature together, because they are very closely spaced stratigraphically and similar in lithology and sedimentary structure, indicating a similar genetic history. The Rainbow Forest beds are defined as the first large, laterally-persistent sandstone body or stratigraphically closely spaced series of sheetlike, multi-storied sandstone bodies possessing significant volcanic and/or chert extrabasinal clasts at the base of the Sonsela Member. Cooley's (1957) section is considered the type of the beds. Sections Lots Wife, Old 180 W, Blue Mesa 1 and Camp Butte are given as reference sections (Appendix A). Colors range from gray to maroon but are typically light (light gray to pale tan or pinkish gray). Mudstone is typically rare, but is more common near the top of the unit. The Rainbow Forest beds are typically 3-10 m thick, but were locally observed to be over 15 m thick. In some areas the top of the unit is difficult to determine due to interfingering with the overlying Jim Camp Wash beds and poor exposure.

Sandstone within the Rainbow Forest beds is typically medium-grained but ranges from fine- to coarse-grained. Conglomerate is locally abundant, with as much as 70% being extrabasinal volcanic clasts. Sandbodies are typically multi-storied with scoured surfaces separating individual stories, and they are moderately to well-indurated. Individual stories have W/Ts that are generally less than the sand bodies as a whole (20-30; rarely up to 50). Petrified wood is pervasive. The brightly-colored petrified wood deposits at Giant Logs, Long Logs and Crystal Forest (Fig. 3) are all located within the Rainbow Forest beds.

The Rainbow Forest beds exhibit an erosional relationship with the underlying Blue Mesa Member. Scours are typically broad and shallow. Deacon (1990) reported scours with as much as 7 m of local relief at the base of the Sonsela, but it is unknown by the author if the scours in question were in the Rainbow Forest beds as used here or in another unit of the Sonsela, such as the large ribbons in the Jim Camp Wash beds discussed below. The scours appear to be associated with the depositional sequence responsible for the overlying sand body rather than being of regional significance. The Rainbow Forest beds grade into and locally interfinger with the overlying Jim Camp Wash beds.

The Rainbow Forest beds can be distinguished from the underlying Blue Mesa Member by the more texturally mature nature of sandstone (to a lesser extent by the compositional maturity), the local presence of coarse- to very coarse-grained sandstone, the presence of large percentages of extrabasinal clasts (particularly the locally abundant volcanic clasts), predominance of preserved large-scale crossbedding, and sheet-like nature. The Rainbow Forest beds can be distinguished from the Jim Camp Wash beds by the sheet-like nature, greater percentage of extrabasinal clasts, lower percentages of mudstone, and lack of variability in mudstone coloration. The Rainbow Forest beds can be distinguished from the Flattops One bed by the generally lighter color, greater percentage of volcanic gravel-sized clasts and greater distribution of brightly-colored petrified wood in the Rainbow Forest beds, and position between the Jim Camp Wash beds and the Blue Mesa Member.

Jim Camp Wash beds—The Jim Camp Wash beds are the medial muddy interval of the Sonsela Member as defined in this study. The term Jim Camp Wash beds is used here in the sense of Heckert and Lucas (2002b), except for a preference for informal nomenclature (see above). Revisions are made to the definition to clarify lithologic variability within the unit and distinguish the unit on lithologic criteria that will allow for more utility when conducting regional studies.

Similarity of features and lateral equivalence has led to the inclusion of facies assemblages D and E within the Jim Camp Wash beds. Although mudstone in facies assemblage D is more common than in most facies assemblage E sections, the mudstone/sandstone ratios are still anomalous for Chinle strata outside of the Sonsela Member in the vicinity of PEFO. The facies architectures of prevalent ribbon and thin sandstones surrounded by mud and silt with complex cut-and-fill architecture are also more similar between facies assemblages D and E than to any other portion of the Chinle Formation. However, Heckert and Lucas (2002b) assign the interval included within facies assemblage D to the Blue Mesa Member and within facies assemblage E to the Painted Desert Member of their Petrified Forest Formation (= "upper" Petrified Forest Member of Akers et al., 1958, Stewart et al., 1972b; Billingsley, 1985; Billingsley et al., 1985; see Fig. 3). In the area west and south of Agate Mesa (Fig. 3) facies assemblages D and E were found to grade into one another allowing strict stratigraphic correlation, supporting the interpretation made by lithologic comparisons that they are related units. The presence of the unique siliceous horizon in both facies assemblages also supports the correlations proposed here.

The Jim Camp Wash beds are herein defined as a heterogenic sequence of mudstone, sandstone and conglomerate possessing numerous ribbon and thin sheet sand bodies, local large ribbon sand bodies and high degrees of variation in color, grain-size, and morphological features within mudstone units located between the sand- and conglomerate-dominated Rainbow Forest and Flattops One beds. The type section is maintained as units 3-6 of the Giant Logs section of Heckert and Lucas (2002b). Sections Agate Mesa West 1, Mountain Lion Mesa 1, Dry Wash North and Blue Mesa 1 (Appendix A) are proposed as reference sections to show lateral variabil-

ity. The unit can be distinguished from other units of the Chinle Formation by its nearly equal percentages of sandstone and mudstone, prevalence of sandstone ribbons with deeply scoured bases, common heterolithic intervals, lateral variability in coloration, and general lack of lateral continuity of facies. The unit is typically between 20 and 40 m thick. The disparity in thickness is largely the result of variations in the thickness of the underlying Rainbow Forest beds and the overlying Flattops One bed. The Jim Camp Wash beds can be distinguished from other units of the Sonsela by its higher mudstone content, prevalence of ribbon sandstone architecture and position between laterally extensive sheet sandstones (i.e., the Rainbow Forest and Flattops One beds).

The Jim Camp Wash beds may be the most distinctive unit of the Sonsela Member and be useful in regional identification, particularly where the lower, upper, or both, sandy intervals may be absent. The near equal percentage of sandstone and mudstone (ratios ranging from 0.5 to 2.5, but typically 1.5) is unique in the Chinle Formation in the vicinity of PEFO. The combination of cut-and-fill architecture, abundance of heterolithic deposits, wide lateral variability in mudstone characteristics, sandstone "tiers", presence of small and large ribbon- and thin sheet-sandstone bodies in close lateral and stratigraphic proximity, and the siliceous horizon also appear to be distinctive.

Large ribbon sandstone and conglomeratic bodies can be confused with the sandstone and conglomerate of the Rainbow Forest and Flattops One beds because of similarity in composition and internal architecture. The large ribbon sandstone bodies of the Jim Camp Wash beds can be distinguished by the low W/T, more prevalent and deeper basal scours, dearth of multiple stories and lateral contiguity with mudstone units that match the description of the Jim Camp Wash beds. The mudstone units of the Jim Camp Wash beds can be distinguished from those of the Rainbow Forest and Flattops One beds by their greater abundance and variability in coloration, more abundant purple and red, predominant cut-and-fill architecture, abundance of heterolithic deposits, and thin, interbedded sheet sandstone bodies.

Creber and Ash (1990) first noted the presence of the siliceous horizon between the Rainbow Forest and Flattops One intervals and commented on its stratigraphic potential. They also found the horizon at a similar stratigraphic position in Texas, Utah and elsewhere in northeastern Arizona, and describe it as the result of an interval of increased fungal attack on plants during the Late Triassic. I also observed the layer in a similar position above a possible Rainbow Forest beds equivalent near Paria, Utah (see Woody, 2003). Unfortunately, the cut-and-fill architecture of the Jim Camp Wash beds has locally removed this horizon so that it is typically seen as a discontinuous horizon, limiting its local utility. However, the recognition of a single interval of increased siliceous preservation in areas as dispersed as Arizona, Texas, and Utah suggests that this layer may prove useful in identifying intervals stratigraphically equivalent to the Jim Camp Wash beds in other Upper Triassic strata in the western United States.

Flattops One bed —The Flattops One bed is the uppermost sandstone interval of the Sonsela Member at PEFO. Roadifer (1966) originally defined three Flattops sandstones above his "Jim Camp Wash zone" in the "upper" Petrified Forest Member. Roadifer mentioned that the Jim Camp Wash zone had a sandstone body that was more prominent than the rest and capped the mesa "north of Highway 260 (now Highway 180), just west of the south entrance to the Park" (Roadifer, 1966, p. 23). Billingsley (1985) defined four Flattops sandstones, with Flattops sandstone #1 being the lowest persistent sandstone within the "upper" Petrified Forest Member. This study indicates that the Flattops sandstone #1 as mapped by Billingsley et al. (1985) encompasses a ~10 m thick interval, including the mesa north and west of the Rainbow Forest Museum (i.e. the mesa of Roadifer's Jim Camp Wash zone). It would appear by the descriptions of Roadifer and the observations presented here that Flattops sandstone #1 of Billingsley et al. is probably the same unit as Roadifer's Jim Camp Wash zone (Heckert and Lucas, 2002b). Most workers subsequent to Billingsley (1985) have used his terminology (e.g., Espegren, 1985; Ash, 1987; Long and Murry, 1995; Therrien and Fastovsky, 2000), which will be followed here.

Flattops Sandstone #1 (*sensu* Billingsley, 1985; Billingsley et al., 1985) was named the Agate Bridge Bed by Heckert and Lucas (2002b) and revised to include the traditional Sonsela Sandstone bed that caps Agate Mesa. Espegren (1985) commented on the fact that the Flattops sandstone #1 bed was more similar to outcrops traditionally identified as the Sonsela than it was to the other Flattops sandstones. I disagree with Heckert and Lucas (2002b) that the term "Agate Bridge Bed" is preferable to the more engrained term "Flattops One". The type section of the Agate Bridge Bed is located near the Rainbow Forest Museum where the term Flattops One has had a long history of usage (Billingsley, 1985; Billingsley et al., 1985; Espegren, 1985; Long and Murry, 1995; Therrien and Fastovsky, 2000). The only difference in the usage of Heckert and Lucas (2002b) is to correlate the unit to outcrops traditionally associated with the Sonsela, such as at Agate Mesa. However, as has been previously discussed, this study has found that the Flattops One interval is correlative to the sandstone on top of both Agate and Blue Mesas.

It is my opinion that maintaining tradition of usage and only clarifying relationships provides more utility to future workers than a litany of nomenclatural designations. Refining the definition of the Flattops One bed to include these very similar (see below) and likely interfingering regions traditionally assigned to either the Sonsela Sandstone bed or the Flattops sandstone #1 provides stability to the nomenclature while enhanc-

ing its utility. Additionally, confusion would be avoided if new outcrops are discovered that change the interpretation of the relationship of these beds, or regional relationships contradict the recent findings of this study or Heckert and Lucas (2002b).

Flattops One bed includes facies assemblages F and G and is here defined as a series of closely spaced, laterally extensive, sheet-like deposits of multistoried sandstone and conglomerate (of both extrabasinal and intrabasinal origin) with prevalent internal scours and minor sandstone and mudstone lenses that directly overlie the Jim Camp Wash beds and underlie the Petrified Forest Member (as restricted below). The overall architecture is of laterally and slightly vertically amalgamated channel complexes (Deacon, 1990; Woody, 2003). Section Mountain Lion Mesa 1 is proposed as the type section. Sections Blue Mesa 1, Agate Mesa West 1, Old 180 4, Crystal Forest and Dry Wash are given as reference sections (Appendix A). The Flattops One bed ranges in thickness from ~5-20 m.

All of the sandbodies mapped by Billingsley et al. (1985) possess sheet-like morphologies and similar lithologies, and thus are interpreted as being genetically related. These sandbodies are included in facies assemblage G. Laterally equivalent units capping Agate Mesa and Blue Mesa (*contra* Heckert and Lucas, 2002b; see Figs. 8 and 9) have been included in facies assemblage F. The two facies assemblages appear to slightly inter-tongue in the Crystal Forest area, with facies assemblage F being more prevalent in the northern portion. Facies assemblage F possesses an unconformable relationship with underlying assemblages D and E, while facies assemblage G possesses either an unconformable or gradational basal contact depending on location. Characteristics of lateral continuity, alluvial architecture, sedimentary structures, general lack of mudstone, sandstone composition and texture and stratigraphic position can be used to distinguish these two facies assemblages from other units of the Chinle Formation, and thus warrant their inclusion within the same lithostratigraphic unit.

Support of the inclusion of the Flattops One bed within the Sonsela Member comes from high percentages of sandstone, alluvial architecture of sheet sandstones with dominant large- to moderate-scale crossbedding and internal scouring between stories, and presence of relatively high percentages of extrabasinal clasts. Distinction between the Rainbow Forest beds and the Flattops One bed can be difficult. The most ubiquitously observed criterion is stratigraphic location within the Sonsela Member. Where that criterion is not ascertainable, then designation of the Flattops One bed should be made by its tendency to be tan in color rather than light gray, tendency to be more indurated, less abundant volcanic clasts relative to chert clasts, more common intrabasinal clasts (although intrabasinal clasts are locally absent), thinner average story, greater abundance of internal scour, greater evidence of lateral amalgamation, more common mudstone lenses in the lower and upper portions relative to the middle portion, and the prevalence of gray mudstone rather than dusky blue mudstone. The Flattops One bed can be distinguished from the Jim Camp Wash beds by its greater percentages of sandstone, greater lateral continuity of large sandstone bodies (W/T >30), greater evidence of lateral amalgamation (cf., Bridge and Leeder, 1979; Friend et al., 1979), predominance of multiple stories within sandbodies, tendency to be better lithified, dominance of gray mudstone (where present) and lack of lateral variability of mudstone units. Even though the sandstone bodies that comprise the Flattops One bed have basal scours, the unit largely grades into the underlying Jim Camp Wash beds, particularly south of Mountain Lion Mesa, making the lower contact difficult to identify in some sections. The base of the Flattops One bed should be placed at the first multistoried sandbody possessing W/T ratios in excess of 30. The contact should be considered interfingering where sandstone lenses or tongues meeting the above description are overlain by mudstone with high degrees of variability and/or possesses abundant sandstone ribbons with W/T <15. The Flattops One bed can be distinguished from the Flattops sandstones in the Petrified Forest Member by its lighter coloration (gray to tan, rather than reddish gray), greater abundance of extrabasinal clasts, internal architecture, generally coarser nature, average paleocurrents to the east and north as opposed to northwest (Espegren, 1985; Woody, 2003) and its position at the top of the Jim Camp Wash beds.

Petrified Forest Member

The Petrified Forest Member has previously been divided into a "lower" and an "upper" portion (Cooley, 1957; Akers et al., 1958; Stewart et al., 1972a, 1972b), which included all of the previously described strata. The author here restricts the use of the term Petrified Forest Member in the immediate vicinity of PEFO to include only the "upper" portion as used by previous workers. Lucas (1993) proposed the term Painted Desert Member of the Petrified Forest Formation for the same strata when he elevated the Chinle to group status. However, the term Painted Desert Formation was originally used to describe a portion of what is now the Glen Canyon Group (Ward, 1905; Darton, 1910; Repenning et al., 1969; Stewart et al., 1972a). The author feels that a restriction of a widely used term rather than the reuse of an antiquated term will cause the minimal amount of confusion when adapting the new nomenclature. Additionally, the restriction of the Petrified Forest Member in the vicinity of PEFO would corroborate with its usage and described lithology throughout much of the outcrop belt, including the type section.

Although the Petrified Forest Member was named for the PEFO area, the type section is near Zion National Park in southern Utah (Gregory, 1950). Throughout much of the outcrop belt, the Petrified Forest Member does not posses lithologies similar to the "lower" part (Blakey and Gubitosa, 1983; Dubiel, 1991, 1992, 1994; see above). Exclusive of north-

ern Arizona, the southern Monument Valley area of Utah and westernmost New Mexico, the Sonsela Member and its probable equivalents lie directly on equivalents of Gregory's (1917) original division D (i.e., Monitor Butte and Bluewater Creek Members) or cut through them (e.g., Stewart et al., 1972b; Repenning et al., 1969; Lucas et al., 1997). Thus the type section of the Petrified Forest Member would include only the "upper" part of the member, in accordance with its use here. In fact, the absence of the "lower" Petrified Forest Member between the Monitor Butte and Bluewater Creek (=lower red) Members and the Moss Back Member (a probable equivalent of the Sonsela) was used as supportive evidence for the use of the term Monitor Butte Member up to the base of Sonsela Member within PEFO (Dubiel et al., 1999); also negating the differentiation of "lower" and "upper" portions of the Petrified Forest Member.

At this time it is unclear as to the detailed correlations between the Petrified Forest Member and other members in the area separating the type section and PEFO. Until these correlations can be verified it is the author's opinion that the Petrified Forest Member should be restricted to the interval between the Sonsela Member and the first laterally persistent limestone that marks the base of the Owl Rock Member at PEFO. This restriction would eliminate the original terms "lower" and "upper" Petrified Forest Member, and maintain utility and distinction between the differing lithologies of the Blue Mesa and Petrified Forest Members as used in this study. This approach also alleviates the problems of inclusion produced by raising the rank of the Sonsela to a member.

As here restricted the Petrified Forest Member in the vicinity of PEFO is an interval of deep red and purple mudstone and subordinate, laterally-continuous sandstone with only locally significant proportions of extrabasinal clasts. Facies assemblage H is assigned to the Petrified Forest Member (restricted). The lower contact with the underlying Sonsela Member is broadly gradational. The Petrified Forest Member in the PEFO area, as restricted, can be distinguished from the Blue Mesa Member by its predominantly red coloration, moderately- to well-lithified sheet sandstone bodies with high degrees of lateral continuity, general greater lateral continuity of units, and dominance of vertic features (cf., Driese and Foreman, 1992) in the paleosols. The Petrified Forest Member can be distinguished from the Sonsela Member by its greater lateral continuity of units, predominance of red coloration, less abundant sandstone, dearth of ribbon sandstone bodies and heterolithic deposits, and smaller amounts of variability in mudstone units.

CONCLUSIONS

This study supports the use of member rank for the Sonsela Member of the Chinle Formation. The Sonsela Member within PEFO was found to have a tripartite subdivision similar to that described for the type section (Akers et al., 1958) and recently within PEFO (Heckert and Lucas, 2002b). However, this study disagrees with Heckert and Lucas (2002b) regarding nomenclature of the upper bed, lateral correlations, and the propriety of formal vs. informal nomenclature. Informal nomenclature is preferred by the author due to difficulties in regional correlation, partially due to local absence of units and rapid lateral facies variations. In my opinion this approach maximizes tradition of usage and utility on a local level, but does not constrain regional stratigraphic studies with excessive or rigid nomenclature.

Within the Sonsela Member the basal sandstone-dominated interval is informally referred to as the Rainbow Forest beds, and in PEFO consists of at least two laterally persistent sandstone and conglomerate bodies and minor mudstone lenses. The medial unit is informally referred to as the Jim Camp Wash beds, and consists of near equal percentages of sandstone and mudstone with predominant cut-and-fill architecture. Sandstone is found as large ribbon (3-20 m thick), small ribbon (<3 m thick) and thin (<2 m thick) sheet sandstone bodies. Mudstone is highly variable in character and lateral persistence. Heterolithic deposits of intercalated mudstone and sandstone are abundant in the unit. The Jim Camp Wash beds locally grade into and interfinger with both the underlying Rainbow Forest beds and overlying Flattops One bed. The upper sandstone-dominated unit is informally referred to as Flattops One bed, and consists of an interval of laterally persistent sandstone bodies with locally interbedded lenses of mudstone.

The Blue Mesa Member underlies the basal unconformity of the Sonsela Member. The term Blue Mesa Member is provisionally retained from Lucas (1993) based upon its distinctive lithology and distribution in northeast Arizona, westernmost New Mexico and the southern Monument Valley region of Utah. Further work on lithostratigraphic correlation between the Blue Mesa Member and type Monitor Butte and Petrified Forest Members needs to be completed to confirm the regional utility of the Blue Mesa Member.

The Petrified Forest Member as revised in this study is gradational with the underlying Sonsela Member. The Petrified Forest Member is restricted in the vicinity of PEFO to the red mudstone-dominated interval between the top of the Sonsela Member and the base of the Owl Rock Member. This restriction is warranted because of previous studies that

have shown that regionally, including near the type area, the Petrified Forest Member does not contain lithologies similar to the underlying Blue Mesa and Sonsela members (Repenning et al., 1969; Stewart et al., 1972b; Blakey and Gubitosa, 1983; Dubiel, 1994; Lucas et al., 1997).

The proposed nomenclature is based upon lithologic unity as elucidated by the NASC (NACSN, 1983) and is consistent both lithologically and stratigraphically as demonstrated by mapping at a 1:24,000 scale of the southern portion of PEFO (Woody, 2003). The revised nomenclature in this study provides a robust and consistent framework to base future stratigraphic and sedimentological studies on, both locally and regionally. Future identification of the Sonsela Member should be made by comparison of local facies assemblages with those of the units above and below. Contrary to most previous studies that recognized the Sonsela Member as only large sandstone bodies (Billingsley et al., 1985; Deacon, 1990), the Jim Camp Wash beds may be the most regionally recognizable subunit of the Sonsela Member, particularly where large sandstone and conglomerate bodies are either abundant or absent. A distinctive siliceous horizon also appears to be significant as a regional marker bed within the Jim Camp Wash beds, although it is locally removed by the cut-and-fill architecture that is so prevalent in the unit.

ACKNOWLEDGMENTS

This work was completed as a partial fulfillment of a M.S. degree at Northern Arizona University. The author would like to express gratitude to Ron Blakey, Nancy Riggs, and Barry Albright for discussions on content and course; Bill Parker for numerous dialogues regarding Chinle stratigraphy and deposition and for funding help; and the staff of PEFO, particularly Karen Beppler-Dorn, Pat Thompson, Pat Jablonsky, Dan Slais, and the late Superintendent Micki Hellickson. Reviews by Sid Ash, Russell Dubiel, Randy Irmis and Bill Parker significantly improved the manuscript. Portions of an early version have benefited by revisions from Mary Kraus. Funding was provided by the Colorado Plateau Cooperative Ecosystems Study Unit, Rocky Mountain Section-Society of Economic Paleontologists and Mineralogists, and the Friday Lunch Clubbe (Alumni of Northern Arizona University).

REFERENCES

Akers, J. P., M. E. Cooley, and C. A. Repenning. 1958. Moenkopi and Chinle formations of Black Mesa and adjacent areas, p. 88-94. In R. Y. Anderson and J. W. Harshbarger (eds.), New Mexico Geological Society Guidebook. Volume 9. New Mexico Geological Society.

Allen, J. R. L. 1965. A review of the origin and characteristics of recent alluvial sediments. Sedimentology, 5:89-191.

Ash, S. R. 1972. Plant megafossils of the Chinle Formation, p. 23-43. In C. S. Breed, and Breed, W. J. (eds.), Investigations in the Triassic Chinle Formation. Volume Museum of Northern Arizona Bulletin 47. Museum of Northern Arizona, Flagstaff, AZ.

Ash, S. R. 1986. Fossil plants and the Triassic-Jurassic boundary, p. 21-30. In K. Padian (ed.), The Beginning of the age of dinosaurs: Faunal Change across the Triassic-Jurassic Boundary. Cambridge University Press, Cambridge.

Ash, S. R. 1987. Petrified Forest National Park, Arizona, p. 405-410, Geological Society of America, Rocky Mountain Section, Centennial Field Guide. Geological Society of America, Boulder, CO.

Ash, S. R. 1992. The Black Forest Bed, a distinctive rock unit in the Upper Triassic Chinle Formation, northeastern Arizona. Journal of the Arizona-Nevada Academy of Science, 24-25:59-73.

Ash, S. R., and G. T. Creber. 1992. Paleoclimatic interpretation of the wood structures of the trees in the Chinle Formation (Upper Triassic), Petrified Forest National Park, Arizona, USA. Palaeogeography, Palaeoclimatology, Palaeoecology, 96:297-317.

Ash, S. R., and G. T. Creber. 2000. The Late Triassic *Araucarioxylon arizonicum* trees of the Petrified Forest National Park, Arizona, USA. Palaeontology, 43:15-28.

Aslan, A., and W. J. Autin. 1998. Holocene flood-plain soil formation in the southern lower Mississippi Valley: Implications for interpreting alluvial paleosols. Geological Society of America Bulletin, 110:433-449.

Billingsley, G. H. 1985. General stratigraphy of the Petrified Forest National Park, Arizona, p. 3-8. In E. H. Colbert and R. R. Johnson (eds.), The Petrified Forest through the Ages. Museum of Northern Arizona, Flagstaff.

Billingsley, G. H., and W. J. Breed, assisted by S. R. Ash. 1985. Preliminary map of Petrified Forest National Park. unpublished.

Blakey, R. C., and R. Gubitosa. 1983. Late Triassic paleogeography and depositional history of the Chinle Formation, southern Utah and northern Arizona, p. 57-76. In M. W. Reynolds and E. D. Dolly (eds.), Mesozoic paleogeography of the west-central United States. Rocky Mountain Section-Society of Economic Paleontologists and Mineralogists, Denver.

Blakey, R. C., and R. Gubitosa. 1984. Controls of sandstone body geometry and architecture in the Chinle Formation (Upper Triassic), Colorado Plateau. Sedimentary Geology, 38:51-86.

Blodgett, R. H. 1988. Calcareous paleosols in the Triassic Dolores Formation, southwestern Colorado, p. 103-121. In J. Reinhardt and W. R. Sigleo (eds.), Paleosols and weathering through geologic time; principles and applications. Volume 216. Geological Society of America, Boulder.

Blodgett, R. H., and K. O. Stanley. 1980. Stratification, bedforms, and discharge relations of the Platte braided river system, Nebraska. Journal of Sedimentary Petrology, 50:139-148.

Bown, T. M., and M. J. Kraus. 1987. Integration of channel and floodplain suites, I. Developmental sequence and lateral relations of alluvial paleosols. Journal of Sedimentary Petrology, 57:587-601.

Bown, T. M., and M. J. Kraus. 1993. Time-stratigraphic reconstruction and integration of paleopedologic, sedimentologic, and biotic events (Willwood Formation, Lower Eocene, northwest Wyoming, USA). Palaios, 8:68-80.

Bridge, J. S., and M. R. Leeder. 1979. A simulation model of alluvial stratigraphy. Sedimentology, 26:617-644.

Brierley, G. J. 1996. Channel morphology and element assemblages: a constructivist approach to facies modelling, p. 263-298. In P. A. Carling, and Dawson, M.R. (ed.), Advances in Fluvial Dynamics and Stratigraphy. John Wiley & Sons, Chicester.

Bristow, C. S. 1996. Reconstructing fluvial channel morphology from sedimentary sequences, p. 351-371. In P. A. Carling and M. R. Dawson (eds.), Advances in Fluvial Dynamics and Stratigraphy. John Wiley and Sons, Chichester.

Colbert, E. H. 1972. Vertebrates from the Chinle Formation, p. 1-11. In C. S. Breed and W. J. Breed (eds.), Investigations in the Triassic Chinle Formation. Museum of Northern Arizona, Flagstaff.

Cooley, M. E. 1957. Geology of the Chinle Formation in the upper Little Colorado drainage area, Arizona and New Mexico. Master's, University of Arizona, Tucson, 317 p.

Cooley, M. E. 1958. The Mesa Redondo Member of the Chinle Formation, Apache and Navajo Counties, Arizona. Plateau, 31:7-15.

Cooley, M. E. 1959. Triassic stratigraphy in the state line region of west-central New Mexico and east-central Arizona, p. 66-73. In

J. E. J. Weir and E. H. Baltz (eds.), West-central New Mexico. Volume 10. New Mexico Geological Society, Socorro.

Creber, G. T., and S. R. Ash. 1990. Evidence of widespread fungal attack on Upper Triassic trees in the southwestern U.S.A. Review of Palaeobotany and Palynology, 63:189-195.

Darton, N. H. 1910. A reconnaissance of parts of northwestern New Mexico and northern Arizona. United States Geological Survey, Reston, 435, 88 p.

Deacon, M. W. 1990. Depositional analysis of the Sonsela Sandstone Bed, Chinle Formation, Northeast Arizona and Northwest New Mexico. Unpublished M.S. thesis, Northern Arizona University, Flagstaff, 128 p.

Deluca, J. L., and K. A. Eriksson. 1989. Controls on synchronous ephemeral- and perrenial-river sedimentation in the middle sandstone member of the Triassic Chinle Formation, northeastern New Mexico, U.S.A. Sedimentary Geology, 61:155-175.

Demko, T. M. 1994. Candy-striped teepees: sedimentology and plant taphonomy of a Triassic channel-levee-crevasse complex, Petrified Forest National Park, Arizona. Geological Society of America Annual Meeting, 6:10-11.

Demko, T. M. 1995a. Taphonomy of fossil plants in Petrified Forest National Park, Arizona, p. 37-51, Fossils of Arizona. Volume 3. Mesa Southwest Museum, Mesa.

Demko, T. M. 1995b. Taphonomy of fossil plants in the Upper Triassic Chinle Formation. Unpublished Ph.D. dissertation, University of Arizona, Tucson, 274 p.

Demko, T. M., R. F. Dubiel, and J. T. Parrish. 1998. Plant taphonomy in incised valleys: implications for interpreting paleoclimate from fossil plants. Geology, 26:1119-1122.

Dickinson, W. R. 1981. Plate tectonic evolution of the southern Cordillera. Arizona Geological Society Digest, 14:113-135.

Dickinson, W. R., L. S. Beard, G. R. Brakenridge, J. L. Erjavec, R. C. Ferguson, K. F. Inman, R. A. Knepp, F. A. Lindberg, and P. T. Ryberg. 1983. Provenance of North American Phanerozoic sandstones in relation to tectonic setting. Geological Society America Bulletin, 94:222-235.

Driese, S. G., and J. L. Foreman. 1992. Paleopedology and paleoclimatic implications of Late Ordivician vertic paleosols, Juniata Formation, southern Appalachians. Journal of Sedimentary Research, 62:71-83.

Dubiel, R. F. 1991. Depositional environments of the Upper Triassic Chinle Formation in the eastern San Juan Basin and vicinity, New Mexico. United States Geological Survey Professional Paper 1808, 22 p.

Dubiel, R. F. 1992. Sedimentology and depositional history of the Upper Triassic Chinle Formation in the Uinta, Piceance, and Eagle basins, northwestern Colorado and northeastern Utah. United States Geological Survey Professional Paper B 1787-W, 25 p.

Dubiel, R. F. 1994. Triassic deposystems, paleogeography, and paleoclimate of the Western Interior, p. 133-168. In M. V. Caputo, J. A. Peterson, and K. J. Franczyk (eds.), Mesozoic Systems of the Rocky Mountain Region, USA. Rocky Mountain Section - Society of Economic Paleontologists and Mineralogists, Denver.

Dubiel, R. F., S. T. Hasiotis, and T. M. Demko. 1999. Incised valley fills in the lower part of the Chinle Formation, Petrified Forest National Park, Arizona: Complete measured sections and regional stratigraphic implications of Upper Triassic rocks, p. 78-84. In V. L. Santucci and L. McClelland (eds.), National Park Service Paleontological Research Technical Report. Volume NPS/NRGD/GRDTR-99/03. National Park Service.

Dubiel, R. F., J. T. Parrish, J. M. Parrish, and S. C. Good. 1991. The Pangaean megamonsoon - evidence from the Upper Triassic Chinle Formation, Colorado Plateau. Palaios, 6:347-370.

Duchaufour, P. 1982. Pedology. George Allen & Unwin Ltd., London, 448 p.

Espegren, W. A. 1985. Sedimentology and petrology of the upper

Petrified Forest Member of the Chinle Formation, Petrified Forest National Park and vicinity, Arizona. Unpublished M. S. thesis, Northern Arizona University, Flagstaff, 228 p.

Ethridge, F. G., R. L. Skelly, and C. S. Bristow. 1999. Avulsion and crevassing in the sandy, braided Niobrara River: complex response to base-level rise and aggradation, p. 179-191. In N. D. Smith and J. Rogers (eds.), Fluvial Sedimentology VI. Blackwell Science, Oxford.

Fastovsky, D. E., M. M. Jones, F. Therrien, A. S. Herrick, and K. Mcsweeney. 2000. Thick B-horizons in Late Triassic paleosols, Chinle Formation, Petrified Forest National Park, Arizona, USA. Abstracts with Programs - Geological Society of America, 32(7):11.

Friend, P. F., M. J. Slater, and R. C. Williams. 1979. Vertical and lateral building of river sandstone bodies, Ebro Basin, Spain. Journal Geological Society London, 136:39-46.

Good, S. C. 1993. Stratigraphic distribution of the mollusc fauna of the Chinle Formation and molluscan biostratigraphy zonation, p. 155-160. In S. G. Lucas and M. Morales (eds.), The Nonmarine Triassic. Volume 3. New Mexico Museum of Natural History and Science, Albuquerque.

Gottesfeld, A. S. 1972. Paleoecology of the lower part of the Chinle Formation in the Petrified Forest, p. 59-72. In C. S. Breed and W. J. Breed (eds.), Investigations in the Triassic Chinle Formation. Volume 47. Museum of Northern Arizona, Flagstaff.

Gregory, H. E. 1917. Geology of the Navajo Country: a reconnaissance of parts of Arizona, New Mexico and Utah. United States Geological Survey Professional Paper 93, 161 p.

Gregory, H. E. 1950. Geology and geography of the Zion Park Region Utah and Arizona. United States Geological Survey Professional Paper 220, 200 p.

Harshbarger, J. W., C. A. Repenning, and J. H. Irwin. 1957. Stratigraphy of the uppermost Triassic and the Jurassic rocks of the Navajo country. United States Geological Survey Professional Paper 291, 74 p.

Hasiotis, S. T., R. F. Dubiel, and T. M. Demko. 2001. Shinarump incised valley cut-and-fill deposits, paleosols, and ichnofossils in the lower part of the Upper Triassic Chinle Formation, Petrified Forest National Park, Arizona; it really does exist, and it has regional stratigraphic implications. Abstracts with Programs - Geological Society of America, 33(4):23.

Hazel, J. 1991. Alluvial architecture of the Upper Triassic Chinle Formation, Cane Springs Anticline, Canyon. Unpublished M. S. thesis, Northern Arizona University, Flagstaff, 149 p.

Heckert, A. B., and S. G. Lucas. 1996. Stratigraphic description of the Tr-4 unconformity in west-central New Mexico and eastern Arizona. New Mexico Geology, 18:61-70.

Heckert, A. B., and S. G. Lucas. 1997. No Moenkopi Formation sediments in the Petrified Forest National Park, Arizona. Abstracts with Programs - Geological Society of America, 29:14.

Heckert, A. B., and S. G. Lucas. 1998a. The oldest Triassic strata exposed in the Petrified Forest National Park, Arizona, p. 129-134. In V. L. Santucci and L. McClelland (eds.), National Park Service Paleontological Research. Volume NPS/NRGD/GRDTR-98/01. Department of the Interior, National Park Service, Geological Resources Division.

Heckert, A. B., and S. G. Lucas. 1998b. Stratigraphic distribution and age of petrified wood in Petrified Forest National Park, Arizona, p. 125-129. In V. L. Santucci and L. McClelland (eds.), National Park Service Paleontological Research Technical Report. Volume NPS/NRGRD/GRDTR-98/01. National Park Service.

Heckert, A. B., and S. G. Lucas. 2002a. Lower Chinle Group (Upper Triassic:Carnian) stratigraphy in the Zuni Mountains, west-central New Mexico, p. 39-60. In A. B. Heckert and S. G. Lucas (eds.), Upper Triassic Stratigraphy and Paleontology. Volume 21. New Mexico Museum of Natural History and Science, Albuquerque.

Heckert, A. B., and S. G. Lucas. 2002b. Revised Upper Triassic stratigraphy of the Petrified Forest National Park, Arizona, U.S.A., p. 1-35. In A. B. Heckert and S. G. Lucas (eds.), Upper Triassic Stratigraphy and Paleontology. Volume 21. New Mexico Museum of Natural History and Science, Albuquerque.

Jackson, R. G. 1978. Preliminary evaluation of lithofacies models for meandering alluvial streams, p. 543-576. In A. D. Miall (ed.), Fluvial Sedimentology. Volume 5. Canadian Society of Petroleum Geologists, Calgary.

Jones, M. 2000. Paleosols of the Carnian-Norian boundary interval, Petrified Forest National Park. Unpublished M. S. thesis, University of Rhode Island, Kingston, 178 p.

Klappa, C. F. 1980. Rhizoliths in terrestrial carbonates: classification, recognition, genesis, and significance. Sedimentology, 27:613-629.

Kraus, M. J. 1987. Integration of channel and floodplain suites, II. Lateral relations of alluvial paleosols. Journal of Sedimentary Petrology, 57:602-612.

Kraus, M. J. 1997. Lower Eocene alluvial paleosols: pedogenic development, stratigraphic relationships, and paleosol/ landscape associations. Palaeogeography, Palaeoclimatology, Palaeoecology, 129:387-406.

Kraus, M. J. 1999. Paleosols in clastic sedimentary rocks: their geologic applications. Earth Science Reviews, 47:41-70.

Kraus, M. J., and A. Aslan. 1993. Eocene hydromorphic paleosols: significance for interpreting ancient floodplain processes. Journal of Sedimentary Petrology, 63:453-463.

Kraus, M. J., and B. Gwinn. 1997. Facies and facies architecture of Paleogene floodplain deposits, Willwood Formation, Bighorn Basin, Wyoming, USA. Sedimentary Geology, 114:33-54.

Kraus, M. J., and L. T. Middleton. 1987. Dissected paleotopography and base-level changes in a Triassic fluvial sequence. Geology, 15:18-21.

Kraus, M. J., and T. M. Wells. 1999. Recognizing avulsion deposits in the ancient stratigraphic record, p. 251-270. In N. D. Smith and J. Rogers (eds.), Fluvial Sedimentology VI. Blackwell Science, Oxford.

Lawton, T. F. 1994. Tectonic setting of Mesozoic sedimentary basins, Rocky Mountain Region, United States, p. 1-25. In M. V. Caputo, J. A. Peterson, and K. J. Franczyk (eds.), Mesozoic Systems of the Rocky Mountain Region, USA. Rocky Mountain Section- Society of Economic Paleontologists and Mineralogists, Denver.

Lehman, T. M. 1994. The saga of the Dockum Group and the case of the Texas/New Mexico boundary fault, p. 37-47. In J. Ahlen, J. Peterson, and A. L. Bowsher (eds.), Geologic activities in the 90s. Volume 150. New Mexico Bureau of Mines and Mineral Resources, Socorro.

Litwin, R. J., A. Traverse, and S. R. Ash. 1991. Preliminary palynological zonation of the Chinle Formation, southwestern U.S.A., and its correlation to the Newark Supergroup (eastern U.S.A.). Review of Palaeobotany and Palynology, 68:269-287.

Long, R. A., and P. A. Murry. 1995. Late Triassic (Carnian and Norian) tetrapods from the southwestern United States. New Mexico Museum of Natural History and Science Bulletin 4:1-254.

Long, R. A., and K. Padian. 1986. Vertebrate biostratigraphy of the Late Triassic Chinle Formation, Petrified Forest National Park, Arizona: preliminary results, p. 161-169. In K. Padian (ed.), The Beginning of the age of dinosaurs: Faunal change across the Triassic-Jurassic Boundary. Cambridge University Press, Cambridge.

Lucas, S. G. 1991. Correlation of Triassic strata of the Colorado Plateau and southern High Plains, New Mexico, p. 47-56. In B. Julian and J. Zidek (eds.), Field guide to geologic excursions in New Mexico and adjacent areas of Texas and Colorado. Volume 137. New Mexico Bureau of Mines and Mineral Resources, Socorro.

Lucas, S. G. 1993. The Chinle Group: revised stratigraphy and chronology of Upper Triassic nonmarine strata in the western United States, p. 27-50. Volume 59. Museum of Northern Arizona, Flagstaff.

Lucas, S. G. 1998. Global Triassic tetrapod biostratigraphy and biochronology. Palaeogeography, Palaeoclimatology, Palaeoecology, 143:347-384.

Lucas, S. G., O. J. Anderson, and A. P. Hunt. 1994. Triassic stratigraphy and correlations, southern High Plains of New Mexico-Texas, p. 105-123. In J. Ahlen, J. Peterson, and A. L. Bowsher (eds.), Geological Activity in the 90s. Volume 150. New Mexico Bureau of Mines and Mineral Resources, Socorro.

Lucas, S. G., and S. N. Hayden. 1989. Triassic stratigraphy of west-central New Mexico, p. 191-211. In O. J. Anderson, S. G. Lucas, D. W. Love, and S. M. Cather (eds.), Southeastern Colorado Plateau. Volume 40. New Mexico Geological Society, Socorro.

Lucas, S. G., A. B. Heckert, and J. W. Estep. 1999. Correlation of Triassic strata across the Rio Grande rift, north-central New Mexico, p. 305-310. In F. J. Pazzaglia and S. G. Lucas (eds.), Albuquerque Geology. Volume 50. New Mexico Geological Society, Socorro.

Lucas, S. G., A. B. Heckert, J. W. Estep, and O. J. Anderson. 1997. Stratigraphy of the Upper Triassic Chinle Group, Four Corners Region, p. 81-107. In O. J. Anderson, B. S. Kues, and S. G. Lucas (eds.), Mesozoic Geology and Paleontology of the Four Corners Region. Volume 48. New Mexico Geological Society, Socorro.

Lucas, S. G., and A. P. Hunt. 1989. Revised Triassic stratigraphy in the Tucumcari Basin, east-central New Mexico, p. 150-169. In S. G. Lucas and A. P. Hunt (eds.), Dawn of the age of dinosaurs in the American Southwest. New Mexico Museum of Natural History and Science, Albuquerque.

Lucas, S. G., and A. P. Hunt. 1993. Tetrapod biochronology of the Chinle Group (Upper Triassic), western United States, p. 327-329. In S. G. Lucas and M. Morales (eds.), The Nonmarine Triassic. Volume 3. New Mexico Museum of Natural History and Science, Albuquerque.

Marriott, S. B. 1996. Analysis and modelling of overbank deposits, p. 63-93. In M. G. Anderson, D. E. Walling, and P. D. Bates (eds.), Floodplain Processes. John Wiley & Sons Ltd.

Marriott, S. B., and V. P. Wright. 1993. Paleosols as indicators of geomorphic stability in two Old Red Sandstone alluvial suites, South Wales. Journal of the Geological Society, London, 150:1109-1120.

Miall, A. D. 1977. A review of the braided-river depositional environment. Earth-Science Reviews, 13:1-62.

Miall, A. D. 1985. Architectural-element analysis: a new method of facies analysis applied to fluvial deposits. Earth Science Reviews, 22:261-308.

Murry, P. A. 1990. Stratigraphy of the Upper Triassic Petrified Forest Member (Chinle Formation) in Petrified Forest National Park, Arizona, USA. Journal of Geology, 98:180-189.

Murry, P. A., and R. E. Kirby. 2002. A new hybodont shark from the Chinle and Bull Canyon formations, Arizona, Utah and New Mexico, p. 87-106. In A. B. Heckert and S. G. Lucas (eds.), Upper Triassic Stratigraphy and Paleontology. Volume 21. New Mexico Museum of Natural History and Science, Albuquerque, NM.

NACSN. 1983. North American Stratigraphic Code. American Association of Petroleum Geologists Bulletin, 67:841-875.

Nanson, G. C., and K. Page. 1983. Lateral accretion of fine-grained concave benches in meandering rivers, p. 133-143. In J. D. Collinson and J. Lewin (eds.), Modern and Ancient Fluvial Systems. Volume 6. Blackwell Science, Oxford.

Parsons, B., D. J. P. Swift, and K. Williams. 2003. Quaternary facies assemblages and their bounding surfaces, Chesapeake Bay mouth: an approach to Mesoscale stratigraphic analysis. Journal of Sedimentary Research, 73:672-690.

Pipujol, M. D., and P. Buurman. 1994. The distinction between ground-water gley and surface-water gley phenomena in Tertiary paleosols of the Ebro Basin, NE Spain. Palaeogeography, Palaeoclimatology, Palaeoecology, 110:103-113.

Pipujol, M. D., and P. Buurman. 1997. Dynamics of iron and calcium carbonate redistribution and palaeohydrology in middle Eocene alluvial paleosols of the southeast Ebro Basin margin (Catalonia, northeast Spain). Palaeogeography, Palaeoclimatology, Palaeoecology, 134:87-107.

Pizzuto, J. E. 1987. Sediment diffusion during overbank flows. Sedimentology, 34:301-318.

Repenning, C. A., M. E. Cooley, and J. P. Akers. 1969. Stratigraphy of the Chinle and Moenkopi Formations, Navajo and Hopi Indian reservations Arizona, New Mexico, and Utah. United States Geological Survey Professional Paper 521-B, 33 p.

Retallack, G. J. 1997. Dinosaurs and dirt, p. 345-359, Proceedings Dinofest International. Dinofest International, Phoenix, AZ.

Roadifer, J. E. 1966. Stratigraphy of the Petrified Forest National Park. Unpublished Ph.D. dissertation, University of Arizona, Tucson, 152 p.

Slingerland, R., and N. D. Smith. 2004. River avulsions and their deposits. Annual Review of Earth and Planetary Sciences, 32:257-285.

Smith, N. D., T. A. Cross, J. P. Dufficty, and S. R. Clough. 1989. Anatomy of an avulsion. Sedimentology, 36:1-23.

Steiner, M. B., and S. G. Lucas. 2000. Paleomagnetism of the Late Triassic Petrified Forest Formation, Chinle Group, western United States: further evidence of "large" rotation of the Colorado Plateau. Journal of Geophysical Research, 105:25791-25808.

Stewart, J. H. 1957. Proposed nomenclature of part of Upper Triassic strata in southeastern Utah. American Association of Petroleum Geologists Bulletin, 41:441-465.

Stewart, J. H., F. G. Poole, and R. F. Wilson. 1972a. Changes in Nomenclature of the Chinle Formation on the southern part of the Colorado Plateau: 1850s-1950s, p. 75-103. In C. S. Breed and W. J. Breed (eds.), Investigations in the Triassic Chinle Formation. Volume 47. Museum of Northern Arizona, Flagstaff.

Stewart, J. H., F. G. Poole, and R. F. Wilson. 1972b. Stratigraphy and origin of the Chinle Formation and related Upper Triassic strata in the Colorado Plateau Region. United States Geological Survey Professional Paper 690, 336 p.

Therrien, F. 1999. Theropod mortality in the Late Triassic Chinle Formation: a comparison of Petrified Forest National Park (Arizona) and Ghost Ranch (New Mexico). Unpublished M. S. thesis, University of Rhode Island, Kingston, 258 p.

Therrien, F., And D. E. Fastovsky. 2000. Paleoenvironments of early tetrapods, Chinle Formation (Late Triassic), Petrified Forest National Park, Arizona. Palaios, 15:194-211.

Therrien, F., A. S. Herrick, M. M. Jones, G. D. Hoke, and D. E. Fastovsky. 1999. Paleoenvironmental changes in the Chinle Formation as seen in vertebrate localities of the Petrified Forest National Park, Arizona. Abstracts with Programs - Geological Society of America, 31(2):72.

Thomas, R. G., D. G. Smith, J. M. Wood, J. Visser, E. A. Calverley-Range, and E. H. Koster. 1987. Inclined heterolithic stratification — terminology, description, interpretation and significance. Sedimentary Geology, 53:123-179.

Vepraskas, M. J. 1994. Redoximorphic Features for Identifying Aquic Conditions. North Carolina Agricultural Research Service, 301, 33 p.

Ward, L. F. 1905. Status of the Mesozoic floras of the United States. United States Geological Survey Professional Paper 48, 616 p.

Witkind, I. J., and R. E. Thaden. 1963. Geology and uranium-vanadium deposits of the Monument Valley area, Apache and Navajo Counties, Arizona. United States Geological Survey Professional Paper 1103, 171 p.

Woody, D. T. 2003. Revised geological assessment of the Sonsela

Member, Chinle Formation, Petrified Forest National Park, Arizona. Unpublished M.S. thesis, Northern Arizona University, Flagstaff, 207 p.

Wright, V. P., and M. E. Tucker. 1991. Calcretes: an introduction, p. 1-22. *In* V. P. Wright and M. E. Tucker (eds.), Calcretes. Volume 2. International Association of Sedimentologists, Oxford.

Zuber, J. D. 1990. Geochemistry and sedimentology of paleosols in the upper Petrified Forest Member, Chinle Formation, Petrified Forest National Park, Arizona. Unpublished M. S. thesis, Northern Arizona University, Flagstaff, AZ, 152 p.

APPENDIX A – Description of measured sections. All UTM locations given using NAD 27 CONUS datum.

Section Agate Mesa West 1

Base of section, UTM Zone 12S, E607822, N3860933, at top of Rainbow Forest beds.

Total thickness (m)   **Unit-lithology. Upper contact.**

Chinle Formation,
Sonsela Member,
Rainbow Forest beds:

.1+   AA-light purple (weathered) medium-grained sandstone; fresh surfaces are moderate purple with small, pale gray, spherical mottles; slightly friable; contains local pebble sized chert clasts (predominantly yellow to brown, but some black and orange) — only exposed in wash so thickness is not known, or variations, but a subtle change in gradient of the wash indicates that is most likely a laterally persistent unit. Covered.

9.3   AB-covered

Jim Camp Wash beds:

10.38   A-gray-green mudstone containing local large mottles of deep maroon mudstone; weathers to very pale gray; small (<1 mm) rhizoliths are common; red portions contain very weakly developed slickensides and are slightly coarser grained. Gradational.

11.65   B-deep, dusky-purple mudstone containing small (~1 X 0.8 mm) ped structures with a slightly redder coloration, decreasing up section; fissility increases as grain size decreases up section; rhizoliths are somewhat common locally, often in association with gray-green mottles; upper surface looks very similar to lower surface. Sharply gradational.

12.93   C-gray, nearly pure claystone with dusky red mottles; silt sized mica flakes are concentrated near the middle of the unit where the mottles are larger and purple coloration is also present in addition to the red; unit grossly resembles A. Gradational.

17.43   D-unit is almost identical to unit B; but because it is thicker these lithologic variations were seen — increase in mottling, and addition of purple colored mottles at 2.2 m for 0.4 m then decreases; the upper portion contains large pale gray mottles surrounding rhizoliths in a pure claystone with complex "net-like" mottling of deep dusky purple and ~30% greenish gray mottles surrounding black material or

purely randomly; very poorly developed ped structures and moderately developed slickensides are seen in this upper portion; and uppermost portion has yellow-brown mottles associated with a unidentified metallic mineral with a blue sheen. Sharply gradational.

17.98   E- Identical to unit C. Gradational.

21.11   F-moderate dusky red mudstone with thin lenses and layers of light gray to almost white muddy silt; weathers to moderate to pale dusky red slope; the muddy silt layers are more concentrated near the top where they are thicker and more persistent, with a deeper red and finer-grained claystone as the interlayers; 0.7 m from the top is a band (0-40 cm thick) of highly mottled purple mudstone, this unit thickens and becomes more prominent on the southern flank of the ridge and is sharply overlain by the upper unit described below; this purple mudstone is mottled with red, purple and light gray and minor amounts of yellow-gray; small (~0.5 mm) ped structures are common, and decrease along with the mottling down-section; mottling becomes predominantly reddish down-section as the grey mottles disappear and the purple becomes more subdued. Gradational.

22.03   G-light dusky purple to dusky blue mudstone to fine-grained sandstone; gray mottles increase up-section to around 0.7 m where they are predominant in a slightly silty sand matrix, mottles in this section are dull red and purple with finer grain size; mottles decrease upward into a gray-green layer of silty very fine-grained sand. Sharp.

22.75   H-deep dusky purple mudstone; nearly identical to unit B. Broadly gradational.

24.38   I-dusky red mudstone with large amounts of gray-green mottles; mottles are often but not unanimously in bands forming slightly lighter-colored lenses on the slope; these bands are slightly coarser (muddy siltstone). Broadly gradational.

26.13   J-nearly identical to I, but with lenses of dusky red mudstone with almost no mottling 0.3-0.5 m thick and 2-4 m wide; becomes gray-green in upper 0.5 m with increased mottling; small (<1 mm) silicified rhizoliths are common in the red lenses and bands increasing in size at the upper portion; break in section. Gradational.

27.61   K-variable colored mudstone; grades from red with green mottles to deep purple with red and green-gray mottles to purple with lots of green-gray mottles associated with silicified rhizoliths (1-3 mm in diameter). Gradational.

30.79   L-moderate purple mudstone; gray-green mottles increase in size and abundance up-section to a point of approximately equal volumes to the purple mudstone then decrease rapidly; in this portion rhizoliths are rare, but do occur as nearly "hair-like" ribbons of silicified material; 1.2 m from the top, the mottles are <10% and directly associated with well-preserved rhizoliths around 1 mm in diameter; for 0.4 m mottles decrease and become spherical to slightly oblong in a moderate- to pale-dusky purple matrix with small ill-developed slickensides; the uppermost 10 cm is purple with increasing irregular, green-gray mottles to pure green-gray. Erosional.

Flattops One bed: (Entire unit M has a highly variable thickness, several meters difference are observed in the adjacent buttes; predominantly due to variability in erosion on the top of the buttes.)

32.09   Ma-medium- to coarse-grained sandstone and conglomerate; slightly friable and pale gray, weathers to white; very poorly sorted; granules to pebbles of chert throughout, often defining cross-sets (very low angle trough), small amounts of volcanic clasts also seen locally, substantially larger (both median =5 cm and mode=6.5 cm averages) than the chert pebbles (<3 cm); conglomerate content and size increases upward. Erosional.

32.89   Mb-shallow scour of low angle cross-bedded conglomerate interbedded with clean sandstone; forms a small ledge. Sharp.

34.39   Mc-fine- to medium-grained, moderately sorted sandstone, coarse sand-sized chert grains are common in the coarser grained portions; locally small pebble chert clasts help define low-angle, tabular cross-bedding. Erosional.

35.89   Md-granule to pebble conglomerate; base is marked by pebble to small cobble sized, well-rounded to subrounded chert clasts, some small (<2 cm) volcanic clasts (<20% volume), and some very large (10-35 cm) deep red with some small gray-green mottles, fine-grained, well-cemented sandstone clast that are well-rounded; granules in the unit are well-rounded purple mudstone clasts and <10% chert granules; lower portion is horizontally laminated; medial portion is small-scale, moderate-angle, trough crossbedded dominated by granules, upper portion is moderate-scale and -angle tabular cross-bedded granule to pebble, with some small cobbles of purple mudstone, conglomerate; locally grading into moderately well sorted, medium-grained sandstone with large-scale, moderate-angle cross-sets defined by coarser grains and conglomerate sized clasts. Erosional.

39.29   Me-poorly sorted conglomerate with low-angle, large-scale tabular crossbedding and horizontal laminations; some laminations are well-sorted, coarse-grained sandstone only; sandstone laminations increase up-section to become nearly exclusive, but in medium- to coarse-size fractions, but with pebbles to small cobbles (predominantly of chert) and better-cemented, very coarse-grained sandstone helping to define some laminations.

Top of Flattops One bed (top of mesa)
Top of section, UTM Zone:12S, E607511, N3860954.

Section Blue Mesa 1

Base of section, UTM Zone 12S, E614277, N3866793.

Total thickness (m)   Unit-lithology. Upper contact.

Chinle Formation,
Blue Mesa Member:
.30   A-dusky blue, slightly silty claystone; some blocky to elongate, moderately-developed peds; some small (<1 mm) pale green mottles; very sparse, small (1 mm to 1cm) calcareous nodules; weathers to low rounded slopes covered by talus, mostly clasts. Covered.

1.4   B-covered. Covered

Sonsela Member,
Rainbow Forest beds:
6.53   C-gray sandstone; lower 3 m is medium- to fine-grained sandstone with broad lenses in the upper part of small pebble and granule chert clasts; base has some fragmentary fossil material; upper 2 m is fine-grained sandstone; grains in both are subangular to subrounded and predominantly quartz, but also include red chert fragments (unsure of feldspar %); sedimentary structures dominated by large-scale, low-angle trough cross-bedding where they are seen (usually not visible); weathers to pinkish gray to very pale purple with a ledge and slope morphology. Sharp.

8.02   D-fining upward sequence; base is 5 cm of mudstone rip-up clast bearing medium-grained sandstone; grades upward to well-sorted, very fine-grained sandstone; fresh surfaces are very pale grayish-purple with pale gray-purple on weathered slopes; thin lenses of mudstone similar to the rip-up clasts are seen at the base. Sharp.

Jim Camp Wash beds:
9.03   E-pale greenish-gray claystone; minor amounts of slickensides present; grades upward into very pale dusky red, fissile shale with some irregular subspherical mottles; grades upward into pale dusky red, silty mudstone with moderate amounts of mottling; weathers to an irregular, moderately-steep slope of pinkish- and purplish-gray; topmost 4 cm is a small ledge of clay with abundant mottles and increased cementation, dusky red in color with weakly developed, small (<1 cm) ped structure; rhizoliths, up to 5 cm in diameter, are seen at the top and bottom of unit. Sharp.

9.51   F-pale dusky red, slightly sandy siltstone, very weakly laminated, lots of large green-gray, subspherical mottles; unit coarsens up by the addition of more sandy material; weathers to a moderate slope. Sharp.

9.86   G-dull red-brown mudstone with a fair amount of gray-green mottling, but with some dusky purple irregular mottles as well; small but fairly well-developed ped structures; very weak laminations, and maybe even ripple laminations are faintly seen locally; rhizoliths up to 8 cm long, 0.8 cm in diameter are common, as are fine rhizoliths (<1 mm) in hand sample; preservation is siliceous and some of the finer ones may be preserved as carbonaceous material. Abruptly gradational.

10.39   H-dull red, silty sandstone; weak, relict ripple lamination; large green-gray mottles grades up-section to slightly coarser silty sand with fine-grained sand sized mica grains becoming very common near the top. Sharp.

12.00   I-dusky purple claystone; well developed slickensides; some small subspherical to irregular green-gray mottles, sometimes following rhizoliths that are 1 mm to 1 cm in diameter, colors usually follow the larger ones; hand samples shows numerous "root hair" sized siliceous rhizoliths; some irregular mottles are slightly calcareous; upper portion has increasing mottles producing a lighter color on the weathered slope and more rhizoliths, but of the same size, "root hairs" however are not as common; weathers to a steep, irregular dusky red-purple slope with "blotches" of pale purple to gray from mottles. Gradational.

18.32 J-deep dusky purple claystone with moderate to large amounts of irregular mottling and small rhizoliths; grades laterally in 5 m to deep purple mudstone with large subspherical mottles and no rhizoliths; small (5 mm diameter, 2 cm long) possible burrows (meniscate); entire unit grades upward into dusky blue; weathers to moderate slope with irregular coloration, with less mottling from 1.5-3 m; at 4.5 m poorly-developed calcareous nodules are at the center of mottles, large, but sparsely distributed slickensides, and cm scale blocky to irregular peds(?); by 5 m no sign of the peds or slickensides was observed. Abruptly gradational.

18.93 K-pale green-gray, poorly-sorted, fine-grained sandstone; black grains nearing medium-grain size are common (~20%) along with mica gains (~15%), the rest of the grains seem to be fairly normal composition, Qtz, feldspar, etc.; weathers to very pale gray, steep slope. Broadly gradational.

19.22 L-light greenish-gray to light dusky purple mudstone; well-developed, small (~5 mm) peds, which are either greenish-gray or purple; the gray ones are siltier than the purple; weathers to a pale gray-purple steep slope. Abruptly gradational.

20.71 M-dusky purple mudstone; mottles decrease up section. Sharp.

21.62 N-very pale gray, slightly silty claystone. Broadly gradational.

23.98 O-dusky reddish-purple, moderately well-sorted, fine-gained sandstone; pale green-gray mottles in lowest 0.5 m; large (>1 cm) rhizoliths common in lower portion; small rhizoliths seen throughout; faint low-angle, small-scale planar cross-bedding; upper portion is well sorted. Sharp.

25.21 P-pale grayish green mudstone; becomes siltier up-section, where it also has a "network" pattern of pinkish red siliceous mottles; lenticular in nature, not seen off of the ridge (5 X 15 m); similar lenses are seen to the N but not to the S; weathers to moderately steep slope and local knob. Sharp.

26.26 Q-dull red-brown, poorly-sorted, matrix-supported conglomerate; clasts are dark yellow and brown chert; matrix is very muddy and silty; weathers to a low slope, and locally to a very thin ledge; locally the pebbles are in small-scale, high-angle, planar cross-sets. Covered.

29.84 R-dull grayish red-brown, poorly-sorted, fine- to medium-grained sandstone; contains deeper red, dusky red-purple and yellow mottling; yellow often surrounds carbonized plant fragments (up to 3cm in long dimension); grades upward into sandy mudstone with yellow to yellow-orange mottles sometimes surrounding more sand-rich areas. Sharp.

40.12 S-moderately well-sorted, medium-grained sandstone; color is various shades of gray on fresh surfaces; pinkish-gray to pale gray on weathered surfaces; rhizoliths preserved as siliceous and carboniferous material are moderately common in the basal portion; grades into sandy mudstone, largely sandy siltstone; subunit contains local, yellow-tan stripes in a vertical orientation; local lenses of sandy material are present, as are rare lenses of chert granule to small pebble clasts; overall unit fines upward to lenses of claystone, thick lens of 2 m present at top; weathers to steep, very pale gray slope; moderately well indurated on fresh surfaces. Erosional.

Flattops One Bed:

48.63 T- dark gray-brown, well-sorted, medium-grained sandstone; well indurated; local lenses of reddish- to brownish-gray, fine-grained sandstone lenses; color lightens upward on weathered surfaces from tan to yellow-gray to pale gray; high- to moderate-angle, moderate- to large-scale, planar and some trough crossbedding; small pebbles of chert often help define cross-sets; some crossbedding very high angle (>30°); sets are 0.5-2 m high; conglomerate is less prevalent to S of section and up-section; up-section also has more trough cross-bedding (large- to very large-scale, low angle); logs common near base of unit. Erosional, covered by Qd.

Top of Flattops One bed (top of mesa)
Top of section, UTM Zone 12S, E614134, N3866676.

Section Camp Butte

Base of section, UTM Zone 12S, E612581, N3867223.

Total thickness (m)   **Unit-lithology. Upper contact.**

Chinle Formation,
Blue Mesa Member:

4.92 A-blue-green-gray mudstone, nearly pure claystone; color varies slightly on weathering surfaces laterally to dusky blue; fresh surfaces are blue-green and blue-green-gray; a thin fine-grained, green sandstone lens (0-8 cm thick) occurs lateral to the section at 2 m, above the sandstone, but still in the lens, is greenish-gray claystone; measured unit becomes higher in clay content lateral to this scour for about the same thickness, even though the scour doesn't reach the actual section; weathers highly "bentonitic"; *in situ* stumps occur laterally in this unit. Gradational.

8.63 B-dusky blue-purple, slightly silty mudstone; weathered surfaces show diffuse areas of pale dusky blue; fresh surfaces are blue-gray with diffuse mottles of dusky purple; 1-5 mm diameter, weakly developed peds (?) were seen; red nodules covered many surfaces, but were only seen as very diffuse in fresh surfaces, locally they formed thin layers of coalesced, mm-scale nodules on the surface; mottles of dusky blue become dominant at 1-2 m and then decrease above; surface is heavily weathered in most places.

Very broadly gradational; taken as when purple is vastly more common than dusky blue.

16.07   C- deep purple mudstone; bentonite type weathering forming a steep slope; at 0.7 m is a fine-grained, poorly-sorted, gray-purple sandstone (15 cm thick) filling a local, broad scour (traceable for up to 40 m); mottles abruptly decrease above this layer, even where scour isn't present, and are represented as small (<1 cm) spherical mottles with local irregular mottles vs. the large irregular ones noted below and in B; fresh surfaces in this section are deep purple with diffuse areas of reddish purple and dusky blue; mm-scale, very ill-defined ped structures (?) are seen; small slickensides are common; another change is seen at 3-3.5 m where reddish purple mottles drastically increase; mottling overall decreases up-section; and slickensides are not seen above 3.5 m until 6 m; light dusky blue to blue-gray mottles increase drastically to point where there is no purple, just light dusky blue with green-gray mottles; silt content increases as well. Erosional.

Sonsela Member,

Rainbow Forest beds: (Unit D, variable sandstone; wood was not seen in place here, but is seen elsewhere; two large piles of wood fragments were seen on slopes immediately below implying that at least one large log (~1 m) came out of this unit; subunits Dc and Dd not measured precisely due to steepness of slope)

17.57   Da-base is orange-tan on weathered surfaces, dusky blue and yellow-gray, somewhat mottled on fresh; very poorly sorted; largest grains were medium-grained; fine grains were most abundant; bone fragments common in lowest portion; rhizolith fragments and some chert pebbles locally define low-angle, moderate-scale crossbedding; subunit coarsens upward and becomes better sorted, but muddy matrix is still common; weathers to steep slope. Sharp.

19.29   Db-layered medium-grained sandstone, interbedded with material identical to Da; weathers to pale gray to grayish brown ledge and slope; fresh is pale gray to bluish-gray; contact between layers is usually, but not ubiquitously gradational; ledges are moderately-sorted, fine- to medium- grained and become thinner up-section; moderate-angle, moderate- and small-scale, planar and some trough crossbedding, often defined by very pale gray mudstone clasts, locally mudstone rip-ups are up to 30 cm and do not clearly define sets. Gradational.

25.6   Dc- very similar to Da; weathers to extremely steep partially covered slope; details are limited. Sharp.

28.00   Dd-moderately well-sorted, medium-grained sandstone; low- to moderate-angle, tabular crossbedded; angle decreases to very low angle at top; topmost layers may be horizontally laminated; purple mudstone granule-sized (but could be well-rounded, small pebble sized) clasts define many of the cross-sets; weathers to a small cliff given abundance of large talus blocks that partially cover Dc; only seen on this one butte, but other subunits seen elsewhere. Erosional.

Top of Rainbow Forest beds (top of butte)

Top of section, UTM Zone 12S, E612626, N3867120.

Section Crystal Forest

Base of section, UTM Zone 12S, E610591, N3859345.

Total thickness (m)   **Unit-lithology. Upper contact.**

Chinle Formation,
Blue Mesa Member?:
3.00   A-purple claystone; lots of gray-green mottling; some local areas of weak calcareousness in the center of some of the larger (~1 cm) irregularly mottled areas. Covered.

Sonsela Member?
Rainbow Forest beds?:
8.33   B-covered; logs weathering out in situ throughout interval. Covered.

10.95   C- fine-grained, well-sorted (in sand sized fraction, but with clayey matrix), gray-green sandstone; weathers green-gray in steep slopes. Sharp.

Jim Camp Wash beds:
17.16   D-green-gray mudstone; base has 3 layers, decreasing in thickness up section of purple mudstone and silty sandstone with greenish-gray mottles of sandstone; after last purple layer unit grades up into silty mudstone; grades laterally into very fine-grained sandstone with thin (1-5 cm), dull red, silty mudstone lenses; units are deeply weathered with bentonite-type weathering. Sharp.

19.91   E-interbedded mudstone and thin sandstone lenses; sandstones are silty and green-gray to pale reddish-gray, mudstone layers are predominantly dull red to dull red-brown with some green-gray; weathers to pale reddish-gray to moderate dull red; mudstone is generally slightly sandy, but is locally fissile and slightly silty; mottles are very limited in extent. Sharp.

21.69   F-purplish red mudstone overlain by pale dusky purple mudstone with pale gray mottles; lower subunit is 2-15 cm thick; rhizoliths occur throughout, but are especially common at 0.5 m where there is a drastic increase in mottling and rhizoliths on the N side of the outcrop, on the S side the layer is greenish-gray, after 1 m the subunit grades back into pale purple, similar to below; break in section. Gradational.

28.79   G-gray, sandy mudstone interfingering with purple mudstone; in the upper portion the purple forms thin stringers; rhizoliths are sparse but not rare; grades upward into silty mudstone and dark to moderate green to greenish-yellow in lenses; weathers to moderate slope. Erosional.

30.11   H-shallow lens of dark green-gray, fine-grained, poorly- sorted sandstone; slight upward coarsening trend; lens can be traced for 25 m N and 40 m S; wood is common laterally; local chert and some volcanics and quartzite pebbles to cobbles. Sharp.

30.57   I-fine-grained, poorly-sorted sandstone; upper portion contains numerous pebbles with a fine-grained sandy matrix; logs common laterally; break in section. Sharp.

40.73   J-partially covered sequence of lenses.

Ja-moderate green, sandy mudstone; lenticular in nature with internal lenses of lighter green (fine-grained sandstone) and dark greenish-gray mudstone. Sharp.

Jb-more covered than Ja; pale gray-green, fine-grained, poorly-sorted sandstone grading upward into poorly- to moderately-sorted, medium-grained sandstone with sparse small chert pebbles. sharp; taken as first laterally persistent and densely populated pebble conglomerate.

Flattops One bed:

51.44 K-fine- to medium-grained, gray to pale yellow-gray sandstone; most is well sorted; weathers to yellow-tan to tan-brown; low- to moderate-angle, moderate- to very large-scale (>1 m) crossbedding, some small scale, especially up section; moderate amounts of tabular cross-beds also present; some soft-sediment deformation; largest cross-set is 2.3 m high and over 20 m long (epsilon cross-bedding?); small amounts of pebble conglomerate help define some high- to moderate-angle cross-sets; cross-sets form complex interaction with each other, often with widely varying directions between sets; slight cut-and-fill type geometries. Erosional, covered by Qd.

Top of Flattops One bed (top of mesa)

Top of section, UTM Zone 12S, E611669, N3858766.

Section Dry Wash N

Base of section at contact with Blue Mesa Member, UTM Zone 12S, E610014, N3856388.

Total thickness (m)   Unit-lithology. Upper contact.

Chinle Formation,
Rainbow Forest beds:

3.37 A-dull red-gray, very fine-grained sandstone; contains logs at this level on the other side of the wash; locally interbedded with mudstone, claystone and minor silty sandstone; silty sandstone is slightly paler than the rest, claystone is deep red-brown with sparse, very small, spherical mottles; weathers to fairly uniform moderate slope; color variations difficult to see on weathered surfaces; grades laterally into very pale gray, medium-grained sandstone. Sharp.

Jim Camp Wash beds:

4.16 B-very pale gray, fine-grained sandstone filling a local scour surface into dusky purple to slightly purple-gray mudstone with moderate amounts of yellowish green-gray mottles; weathers to steep slope with high degree of bentonite-type weathering. Abruptly gradational.

5.24 C-pale yellow- to greenish-gray claystone (similar in color but paler than the mottles in B); weathers to low slope with very well-developed, bentonite-type weathering. Covered.

12.58 D-moderate dull gray mudstone; some rhizoliths of yellowish material (carnotite?) throughout, but sparse in distribution; highly weathered surface forming an irregular, moderately steep slope covered with bentonite-type weathering; local broad lenses of silty and sandy material are present throughout the section. Sharp.

18.66 E-base is a 0-2 cm thick calcareously cemented, very fine-grained sandstone, locally ripple laminated; sharply overlain by light greenish-gray, silty sandstone; weathered surface has a slightly banded appearance with thin layers of darker and more greenish-gray, very pale to moderate pinkish-gray, and local and minor green; green layers locally weather into very small ledges; the rest is uniform forming a moderate slope; the greenish- and pinkish-gray layers are generally very fine- to fine-grained sandstone, but can be up to medium-grained; pale gray claystone layers are also present. Sharp.

21.08 F-moderate greenish-gray claystone; grades up into silty and sandy mudstone; some (very few) very small rhizoliths; a calcareous layer ~5 cm thick is present at 2.0 m; sandier layers are slightly darker; no other features were seen; weathers to moderate slope of pale greenish-gray. Gradational.

25.08 G- dull dusky purple mudstone with large, gray, irregular mottles; color darkens and mottles decrease upwards from base and then increase again as ~1 cm spherical mottles surrounding nodules. Erosional.

Flattops One bed: (Unit H is a yellow- to brownish-gray sandstone; scoured into by Quaternary sandstone to W and present erosional surface to E.)

25.38 Ia- yellow- to brownish-gray sandstone; base is dark brown weathered, gray on fresh surface, highly-indurated, calcareous pebble conglomerate. Sharp.

27.38 Ib- tan-gray, fine-grained sandstone; weathers to slope, slightly darker in color; moderately well sorted. Erosional.

29.88 Ic-moderate to dark tan, medium-grained sandstone; fresh surfaces are gray; well-sorted, dominated by very low-angle, large-scale, trough crossbedding, horizontal laminations are also common, but the extremely low angle of the crossbedding makes some determination slightly difficult. Gradational.

37.58 Id-partial covered, fine- to medium-grained; generally well-sorted sandstone; local scour-and-fill is prominent between subunits; general trend is to fine upward, although the largest grains are near the top; calcareous pebble and minor granule conglomerate is common in lenses; moderate- to large-scale, low- to moderate-angle, trough and some planar crossbedding is common; weathers to slope and ledge with subspherical, more indurated "concretions" occuring in the coarse end of medium-grained, well-sorted sandstone at the top, commonly separating along low-angle cross-sets into "disks". Erosional.

Top of Flattops One bed (top of butte)

Top of section, UTM Zone 12S, E609792, N3856275.

Section Lots Wife

Base of section, UTM Zone 12S, E610276, N3862740.

Total thickness (m)   Unit-lithology. Upper contact.

Chinle Formation,
Blue Mesa Member:

0.50 A-dull purple mudstone; weakly-defined laminations of pale purple to grayish-green; mottles are abundant; some small <1 cm irregular areas of darker purple and grayish nodules, unit is not calcareous outside of the nodules. Abrupt.

0.95   B-pale greenish-gray, massive siltstone; some surfaces weather to pinkish-gray and have pinkish-gray mottling of mudstone areas (poorly developed peds?); some darker radiating blocky structures (<1 mm) as well as some fine-grained sandstone grains (~10-15%), especially in the top portions. Erosional.

Sonsela Member,
Rainbow Forest beds:

8.37   C-poorly-sorted, medium- to coarse-grained, pale purple-gray sandstone; locally is mottled with dark dusky purple mottles up to ~1 cm; has local small pebbles and granules of dark colored chert defining low-angle cross-sets; some thin, pure conglomerate units are seen infrequently, but can be up to 0.8 m thick; most pebbles are nearly purely intraformational (60-80%), some chert and locally volcanic clasts are also abundant; fines upward into sets; becomes well-indurated at top; low-angle, moderate- to small-scale, trough crossbedding and some planar crossbeds; unit grades into sandstone and interbedded sandstone and silt-stone interval at top. Sharp.

Jim Camp Wash beds:

18.37+   D- purple to purple-red mudstone and silty sandstone in-terval; sand and silt is only in thin (<20 cm) lenses that are pinkish- to pale reddish-gray; mudstone units have only moderate amounts of slickensides at best, and are gener-ally mottled with small, rounded, greenish-gray mottles; some calcareous nodule formation, but not many; the amount of sand and silt layers increases up section and the two thickest lenses are within 0.5 m of each other at the top of this measured portion; mottling increases up-sec-tion to point of light colored sand and silt layers and above have few mottles; these form fining up sequences. Top of section not measured.

Jim Camp Wash beds (incomplete section); sandstone interval above section partially destroyed by erosion in April 2005.

Section Mountain Lion Mesa 1

Base of section at contact with Rainbow Forest beds, UTM Zone 12S, E608482, N3857866.

Total thickness (m)	Unit-lithology. Upper contact.

Chinle Formation,
Sonsela Member,
Jim Camp Wash beds:

7.3   A-mostly covered pale dusky purple to dusky purple mud-stone; slight mottling between the two colors, with minor amount of very pale blue mottles. Sharp.

7.95   B-siliceous horizon (silcrete); predominantly deep red in color, massive to "stringy" chert; locally layered, moderate gray and deep red with minor amounts of purplish tints;

near top is slightly layered with thin interbeds of dusky blue to gray mudstone; this unit rapidly thins away from this area and is only 10 cm ~25 m away, but maintains the 10 cm thickness in all direction for at least 100 m. Sharp.

16.59   C-light dusky purple to dusky blue mudstone; variegated with small mottles of pale dusky blue in purple or dusky red to purple in bluish portions; small lenses of fine-grained sandstone are rare; contacts between the blue and purple portions are large-scale undulatory surfaces and contain mottles of the other color making the boundary diffuse. Covered.

17.79   D-mostly covered; moderate dusky red sandstone and sandy siltstone; is exposed better to N where it contains layers of moderate gray, fine-grained sandstone forming poorly-developed "hoodoo" layers and is capped by dusky red and gray interbeds dipping with low angles to the WSW; not seen to south; section is near southern limit of the unit; this unit taken as a whole appears to have an erosional contact with the underlying unit. Gradational.

21.09   E- pale dusky blue and moderate purplish-red mudstone and siltstone. Erosional.

24.89   F-very poorly-sorted conglomerate, predominantly well-rounded, black and white chert clasts; moderate amounts of red, yellow and orange; the white and black average small cobble size whereas the other colors average me-dium pebble size; matrix is gray silty sand; a thin local layer of the silty sand separated two beds of conglomerate here, but is thicker in other portions of the slope; no sedimen-tary structures were seen; to south it is represented by a thinner layer of predominantly carbonate nodule clasts. Abrupt.

28.11   G- soft, moderate red and purple mudstone; grades to green-ish-gray in upper 1.5 m. Erosional.

Flattops One bed:

36.03   H-light tan to tannish-gray to yellowish-gray sandstone; dominated by tabular crossbedding, local trough cross-sets are abundant; tabular sets are usually around 0.3 m deep and 2 m wide and are of moderate angle ~7-13Ú; troughs are considerably larger (up to 2 m high and several m wide) and are defined by crumbly weathering; local con-glomerate lenses are prevalent especially near the top; nearly uniform up-section increase in conglomerate per-centage; upper layers also contain a larger percentage of carbonate nodule to chert clasts.

Top of Flattops One bed (top of ledge)
Top of section, UTM Zone 12S, E608201, N3858495.

Section Old 180 4

Base of section, UTM Zone 12S, E608325, N3850628.

Total thickness (m)	Unit-lithology. Upper contact.

Chinle Formation,
Sonsela Member,
Jim Camp Wash beds:

1.84   A-generally well-sorted, medium-grained sandstone; color ranges from grayish-pink to pure gray on fresh surfaces; weathers gray-red to pale dusky red in a hoodoo type weathering pattern; contains 2 sets of large-scale, moderate- to high-angle, trough crossbedding; near the top of the unit is a 6 cm thick layer with large (up to 7 cm) clasts of deep red mudstone some with cracks filled with the surrounding sand (same as above and below); just below this some of the cross-sets are defined by thin sets of thin deep red mudstone. Sharp.

4.76   B-dusky red sandy siltstone with interlayers of weakly laminated silty sandstone only a few cm thick at 1.3, 1.8 and 2.1 m (sharp contacts at top and bottom, especially the bottom); the unit fines upward to dark, deep red mudstone with some green-gray mottling; silty sandstone layers are lighter in color due to increased sand content which is greenish-gray and increased green mottling; slickensides are observed throughout but are more developed above the last silty sandstone layer; the upper most portions contain well-developed blocky to slightly rounded ped structures. Sharp.

5.89   C-dull dusky red siltstone with minor amounts of dull gray-green mottling and some well-developed green elongate mottles around partially preserved very fine rhizoliths; mottling increases up-section and small ill-defined nodules begin to form; a well-developed nodule layer is at the top (nodules here are larger up to 4-6 cm, but still discontinuous in nature). Sharp.

6.94   D-deep red to purple mudstone; mottled with increasing greenish mottles up-section; becomes carbonaceous, but doesn't develop truly defined nodules; gradational into siltstone with mudstone mottles; silt is greenish and slightly sandy, especially towards the top; mudstone is same color as below but slightly silty; 2 x5 cm nodules with lobate to discoidal morphology observed in the uppermost portion. Sharp.

6.99   E-well sorted, fine-grained sandstone; pale greenish-gray on fresh surfaces, weathers to dark brown; grains of quartz and some chert (slightly larger) and black accessories from hand sample; grades into a pebble conglomerate 15 m to north. Sharp.

8.37   F-poorly-indurated, moderately well-sorted, medium-grained sandstone; contains some pebble conglomerate laterally; unit laterally is either pure sandstone, pure conglomerate, or interlayers of both as well as maybe some siltstone and mudstone; color is generally yellowish green-gray to grayish-green, with conglomerate layers being dark brown due to the weathered carbonate nodule clasts. Gradational.

9.49   Ga-dark purple mudstone with green mottles often surrounding small clusters of sandstone as the units grade into one another in ~10 cm (shrink-swell features); small (generally <1 cm but up to 2 cm) round nodules become increasingly abundant up section as do well-developed slickensides; small areas of ill-defined rounded ped structures are locally seen in areas of the most developed nodules and slickensides. Gradational.

10.87   Gb-dark purple mudstone; the nodules of Ga begin to coalesce in elongate forms and greenish mottles increase throughout this interval being the most concentrated at the top. Gradational.

13.99   Gc- dark to dull dusky purple mudstone; lighter in color at top; decreasing mottles up-section; green-gray mottling sporadically throughout. Abrupt.

15.46   H-pale greenish-gray mudstone with small fibrous purple mottles in the lower portion; thin, partially solidified rhizoliths throughout, but without reduction halos; upper portion highly weathered- grades to sandy siltstone with abundant small (1-2 cm) nodules, very closely packed nodules and matrix are calcareous in the upper portions. Erosional.

Flattops One bed:

21.81   I-sandstone and conglomerate; base is a thin (~5 cm thick) pebble conglomerate; above this are various layers of sandstone and conglomerate; sandstone is well-sorted, medium- to fine-grained, yellowish-gray and poorly-indurated near the base, often forming a steep slope with small ledges of coarser, more indurated material; conglomerate layers increase upwards, many filling large scours (up to 2.5 m thick) with low-angle, trough cross-bedding; most clasts are carbonate nodules but some layers also contain chert, especially near the top; several segments of logs can be seen on the slopes, ranging from 8 cm to over 30 cm in diameter, mostly brownish in color, but with multiple shades of brown, orangish-red is the brightest color seen. Erosional.

Top of Flattops One bed (capped by Quaternary deposits on the mesa top).

Top of section, UTM Zone 12S, E608365, N3850851.

Section Old 180 W

Base of section, UTM Zone 12S, E602742, N3853275.

Total thickness (m)   **Unit-lithology. Upper contact.**

Chinle Formation,
Blue Mesa Member:

1.50   A-dark purple mudstone with dark green-gray, small, irregular mottles; weathers into a small "blowout" protected by log fragments and cobbles; weathered surface is dusky purple-gray. Sharp.

Sonsela Member,
Rainbow Forest beds:

8.31   B-largely covered; pale gray, moderately-sorted, medium- to fine-grained sandstone at base; purple mudstone with some mottling above; appears to be mostly sandstone with purple mudstone lenses. Covered.

15.23   C-very pale gray, well-sorted, fine-grained sandstone; weathers to steep slope with ledges at top and "hoodoos" on the uppermost slope to west of ledge and small cliff; weathered surfaces are pale gray to pale purple-gray to tan; grains seem similar to many other sandstone in area (quartz, feldspar, black accessories); at 4.5 m there is a ledge 0.3 m thick of non-indurated sand between two indurated ledges, the top surface of the bottom ledge has numerous rhizoliths in it and appears to be mottled to purple; in the interval between these two ledges there appears to be very heavily mottled and partially silicified mudstone, could be clasts (~30 cm) but weathering pattern did not allow a full determination, but suggests mudstone lens; rhizoliths were also common in the hoodoo forming area. Covered.

16.63   D-covered. Covered.

Jim Camp Wash beds:

17.24   E-purple-gray, poorly-sorted (lots of silty and muddy matrix material, but sand sized fraction well sorted), very fine-grained sandstone; weathers to red-gray, low slope; units F-N are not present laterally, E is the entire thickness. Gradational.

17.39   F-purple sandy mudstone; small, irregular, green-gray mottles; weathers to steep slope. Sharp.

17.54   G-dull red silty mudstone; very few mottles; some ~1 cm nodules; weathers to irregular slope. Gradational.

17.98   H-purple-gray, well-sorted, well-rounded, fine-grained sandstone; forms a lens; weathers to reddish-purple-gray moderate slope. Sharp.

18.20   I-deep red, very silty mudstone; forms a lens; weathers to an irregular red color on a moderate slope. Sharp.

18.91   J-fine-grained sandstone, very similar to unit H, but with clasts of mudstone that look like unit I. Sharp.

19.09   K-identical to I. Sharp.

20.41   L-identical to H. Sharp.

20.54   M-identical to I. Sharp.

21.44   N-fine-grained sandstone; identical to H, except for local rhizoliths near the base and that it fines upward to very fine-grained and is gradational with the overlying unit. Gradational.

22.85   O-moderate red, silty mudstone; weathers to steep slope and almost nodular looking rounded knobs on very steep slopes; small, sparse mottles with a fairly even distribution except for them being larger and more sparse at base; branching tubular-like structures (decapod burrows?) filled with material identical to P extend down from P in complex patterns with a concentrated distribution, deepest is to near the base but most are less than 0.5 m;

found throughout the horizon, but complex branches are only seen in this immediate area. Sharp; possible original topography of ~.2 m is seen locally.

23.98   P-dusky blue mudstone; small ~1 cm rhizoliths are common near the base and are much less common in the upper portion, but thin rhizoliths do form "aprons" of "matted" material that extend down in "sheets" from the upper surface, nearly all the way to the base in several locations; these are often surrounded by green to yellow-green colors and are red in color themselves; mottles (pale gray, except those mentioned in association with the quasi-vertical "mats") are generally restricted to just around rhizoliths. Erosional; relief of 40-50 cm locally.

Flattops One bed:

34.38   Q- gray, moderately well- to well-sorted, medium-grained sandstone; weathers to dark tan to blue-gray steep slopes or small cliffs; large logs (up to 2 m in diameter) are observed weathering out of the unit, particularly near the top; low-angle, trough crossbedding of moderate- to large-scale are dominant sedimentary structures; but locally very low-angle, trough and moderate-angle, planar crossbedding, as well has horizontal laminations are important components; complex internal architecture (cut-and-fill); upper 3 m is predominantly conglomeratic and shows the largest scale features (mudstone clasts are very common in the lower portion of this upper 3 m, while chert clasts increase to slightly over 50% in the upper portion, mudstone clasts are also larger in the lower portion); general trend is to coarsen upward, although the largest grains never reach coarse grain size; mudstone clasts at top of unit are very pale gray rather than purple like those below; volcanic clasts (up to 20% of clasts in lenses) are usually slightly larger and more rounded than chert clasts (predominantly yellow and brown); most of the lenses only contain 3 varieties of volcanic clasts, but some contain all of the usual 5, plus at least one possible clast of granite (20-25 cm in diameter) and a possible meta-basalt clast (15 cm in diameter). Erosional, Qd.

Top of Flattops One bed (partially covered in Qd—lens can be traced as a level of splays and sandstones on N side of the road to ~7-10 m below main body of Flattops One bed; roughly equivalent to the first large, sheet-like lens below Flattops One bed on the mesa north of the Rainbow Forest).

Top of section, UTM Zone 12S, E602398, N3853272.

Parker, W. G., Ash, S. R., and Irmis, R. B., eds., 2006.
A Century of Research at Petrified Forest National Park: Geology and Paleontology.
Museum of Northern Arizona Bulletin No. 62.

THE STRATIGRAPHIC DISTRIBUTION OF MAJOR FOSSIL LOCALITIES IN PETRIFIED FOREST NATIONAL PARK, ARIZONA

WILLIAM G. PARKER

Division of Resource Management, Box 2217, Petrified Forest, AZ 86028 <William_Parker@nps.gov>

ABSTRACT – Precise field relocation and documentation of fossil localities in Petrified Forest National Park allows for better resolution of the stratigraphic ranges of taxa thought to have biochronological significance. Palynomorph data suggests that the Sonsela Member of the Chinle Formation is Latest Carnian-Early Norian in age and that the boundary between the Carnian and Norian Stages lies in the lower-middle portion of the member. There is no evidence for a significant unconformity at this boundary and whereas the Sonsela Member fauna appears to be transitional, there appears to be an abrupt change in the flora in this section.

Keywords: Triassic, Petrified Forest, Chinle Formation, Biostratigraphy, fossil localities

INTRODUCTION

ON DECEMBER 3rd, 1853 the geologist Jules Marcou noted "fossil trees imbedded in a layer of hard, thick bedded, gray, pink, and whitish-gray sandstone exposed along Lithodendron Creek" (Marcou, 1855). This is the first direct reference to a specific fossil with an accompanying lithologic description from the Petrified Forest National Park (PEFO) area that can be assigned to a specific stratigraphic interval. It is nearly certain that Marcou was describing the Black Forest bed (Ash, 1992) of the Petrified Forest Member of the Upper Triassic Chinle Formation, a prominent petrified wood bearing layer within the Lithodendron Wash drainage in what is now the northern or Painted Desert portion of Petrified Forest National Park (Fig. 1).

The Chinle Formation in the PEFO region has a thickness of approximately 300 meters (Creber and Ash, 2004) and is currently divided into five units from oldest to youngest: an unnamed basal unit, the Blue Mesa, Sonsela, Petrified Forest, and Owl Rock Members (Fig. 2; Woody, 2003; this volume). The basal unit is exposed only in the Tepees area of the park (Fig. 2) consisting mainly of reddish, silty sandstone, underlying the Blue Mesa Member, has been assigned to the Moenkopi Formation by Dubiel et al. (1999), but probably represents the Mesa Redondo Member (Cooley, 1958) of the Chinle Formation (Parker and Irmis, 2005).

The Triassic faunas of the PEFO area have been discussed in great detail (e.g., Colbert, 1985; Long and Ballew, 1985; Long and Padian, 1986; Murry and Long, 1989; Good, 1998), and more recently by Long and Murry (1995), Irmis (2005), and Parker (2005b). Likewise, the fossil floras have also received much attention (e.g., Daugherty, 1941; Ash, 1972; Ash, 1989; Ash, 2005b) including recent discussions regarding reconstructions of various trees (Ash and Creber, 2000; Creber and Ash, 2004) and arthropod-plant interactions (Ash 1997, 1999, 2000, 2001). Despite this extensive body of work, past attempts at constructing a biochronology of the park, espe-

cially with vertebrate taxa, have been plagued by inconsistencies between various workers with taxonomy of relevant taxa (e.g., Camp, 1930; Long and Ballew, 1985; Lucas and Hunt, 1993; Long and Murry, 1995) and stratigraphic correlations (e.g., Heckert and Lucas, 1998; Dubiel et al., 1999). Furthermore, studies focusing on palynomorphs or magnetostratigraphy have either been part of larger studies on the Chinle Formation (e. g., Litwin et al., 1991) or have focused only on a single stratigraphic unit (e. g., Fischer and Dunay, 1984; Pocock and Vasanthy, 1988; Steiner and Lucas, 2000) thus providing limited detailed information for correlating various strata within the park.

Recently, as part of a comprehensive paleontological inventory, a database of all known paleontological localities has been compiled (Parker, 2002). At this time, over 500 localities have been recorded with at least a third of these being relocated and documented using GPS technology and photography (Parker and Clements, 2004). This paper contains a description of the faunas and floras of some of the more biostratigraphically important localities from the park and places them in the revised stratigraphy advocated by Heckert and Lucas (2002) and Woody (2003; this volume).

Abbreviations.—AMNH, American Museum of Natural History, New York; PEFO, Petrified Forest National Park, Arizona; PFV, Petrified Forest National Park fossil vertebrate locality; PFP, Petrified Forest National Park fossil plant locality; UCMP, University of California Museum of Paleontology.

PREVIOUS BIOSTRATIGRAPHIC WORK

Like Marcou, Ward (1905) also noted the distinct lithology that differentiates the Black Forest Bed from the rest of the Chinle beds, including it in his Leroux Member of the Shinarump Formation. There is some discrepancy regarding the name of this unit because Ward (1905: p. 20) mentions the name Lithodendron Member for the unit that contains the Black Forest Bed petrified logs, yet places the Black Forest Bed in the overlying Leroux Member in his geological column on page 45 ("sandstone ledge with black logs; local"). Nonetheless, this figure represents the first published geologic section for the Chinle Formation and is easily interpreted because Ward's (1905) Shinarump Formation is essentially the equivalent of Gregory's (1917) Chinle Formation, with the top of the modern Sonsela Member forming the top of the Lithodendron Member and the Black Forest bed being situated medially in the Leroux Member, a unit that also includes the modern Owl Rock Member.

Working mainly in Gregory's (1917) divisions C and D of the Chinle Formation (later named the Petrified Forest and Mesa Redondo members [in part], respectively), Camp (1930) proposed biozones for the Chinle based on numerous vertebrate fossils of phytosaurs. This work was continued by Camp and Welles (1956) and later reestablished by Long and Ballew (1985) who also noted the potential biostratigraphic use of aetosaurs in addition to phytosaurs. On the basis of this past work, Lucas (1993) proposed four "land vertebrate faunachrons" (lvf) for Late Triassic terrestrial strata for the southwestern United States, which were formalized by Lucas and Hunt (1993). In ascending order, these consist of an Otischalkian lvf of middle to late Carnian in age and characterized by the phytosaurs "*Paleorhinus*" and *Anghistorhinus* (=*Rutiodon*, see Hungerbühler, 2001), and the aetosaur *Longosuchus*; the Adamanian lvf of latest Carnian age and characterized by the phytosaur *Leptosuchus* (*Rutiodon* of Lucas and Hunt, 1993 and Lucas, 1998) and the aetosaur *Stagonolepis wellesi* (*Calyptosuchus* of Long and Ballew, 1985); the Revueltian lvf of early to middle Norian age and characterized by the phytosaur *Pseudopalatus* and the aetosaur *Typothorax coccinarum*; and the Apachean lvf of Rhaetian age and characterized by the phytosaur *Redondasaurus* and the aetosaur *Redondasuchus*. Lucas and Hunt (1993) and Lucas (1998) established the type fauna of the Adamanian lvf as the Blue Mesa Member fauna of the PEFO area. Lucas (1998) incorporated this regional Late Triassic biostratigraphy into a global Triassic vertebrate biostratigraphy. Recently, these faunachrons have come under close scrutiny and many authors have suggested they are in need of revision because of taxonomic changes and recognized overlaps between some of the index taxa (Lehman and Chatterjee, 2005; Parker and Irmis, 2005; Hunt and Lucas, 2005; Langer, 2005; Rayfield et al., 2005).

Langer (2005) and Rayfield et al. (2005) stressed that many of the current correlations using the lvfs of Lucas (1998) were made on the basis of specimens with dubious taxonomic status. Both authors demonstrated that the Otischalkian and Adamanian lvfs possess similar reference faunas; however, Langer (2005) subsumed the Otischalkian

into his upper Ischigualastian lvf throughout Pangaea based on the presence of "*Paleorhinus*" and the lack of *Leptosuchus*. Rayfield et al. (2005) used a GIS based approach to test the validity of the lvfs for the Late Triassic proposed by Lucas and Hunt (1993) and concluded that there was little support for the use of proposed vertebrate index taxa, mainly due to taxonomic instability and discouraged the use of "grade-level" associations of taxa.

In response to the discovery of a pseudopalatine phytosaur from strata believed to be Adamanian in age (Hunt and Lucas, 2005), Hunt et al. (2005) revised the division of the Adamanian into to sub-lvfs, the St. Johnsian and the Lamyan, differentiated mainly by the presence or absence of the aetosaur *Typothorax antiquum*. Heckert (this volume) recognizes the Lamyan as a valid sub-lvf, but considers it to be a lower portion of the Revueltian rather than the upper division of the Adamanian. Nonetheless, the validity of the Lamyan rests on the taxonomic validity of *T. antiquum* (see discussion below).

Ash (1976, 1980) proposed three floral zones for the Chinle Formation based on plant megafossils. The oldest biostratigraphic unit, the *Eoginkgoites* zone, is late Carnian in age and in Arizona is restricted to the Shinarump Member. Above this is the *Dinophyton* zone, which is latest Carnian in age and includes the Mesa Redondo and Blue Mesa Members as well as the lower and middle portions of the Sonsela Member. The youngest zone, the *Sanmiguela* zone, is Norian in age and occurs in the Owl Rock Member (Ash, 1987). Recently, Ash (2005a) noted the presence of *Dinophyton* cf. *spinosus* from the Shinarump Member near Cameron, Arizona; however, he also discussed the possibility that these specimens may represent a new species because they lack the spine-like trichomes that are characteristic of *D. spinosus*. Rayfield et al. (2005) argued that the *Eoginkoites* and *Dinophyton* zones contain the same macroflora and should be combined; however, Ash (2005), on the basis of new work, has demonstrated that the floras in the two zones are quite distinct.

Litwin et al. (1991) divided the Chinle Formation into three zones based on fossil palynomorphs. In Arizona, the Shinarump, Mesa Redondo and Blue Mesa Members as well as the basal beds (Rainbow Forest beds and lowermost Jim Camp Wash beds) of the Sonsela Member occur within Zone II. The upper Sonsela (middle and uppermost Jim Camp Wash beds and the Flattops One bed), Petrified Forest and Owl Rock Members occur within Zone III. Zones II and III are equivalent to the New Oxford-Lockatong and lower Passaic-Heidlersburg palynofloral zones of the Newark Supergroup, respectively (Litwin et al., 1991). Zone II is believed to be Late Carnian in age whereas Zone III is considered Norian in age (Litwin et al., 1991).

LITHOSTRATIGRAPHY

Gregory (1917) named the Chinle Formation for Upper Triassic strata in the Chinle Valley of northeastern Arizona. Initially, Gregory divided the Chinle into four parts, to which later workers have applied formal names (Stewart et al., 1972a).

Mesa Redondo Member

Cooley (1958) provided the name Mesa Redondo Member for a reddish, predominantly sandstone unit in the Little Colorado River Valley of Arizona that intertongues with the underlying Shinarump Member as well as the overlying 'lower red' and Blue Mesa Members. Whereas Cooley argued that the Mesa Redondo was distinct from the lower red member, Heckert and Lucas (2003) and Heckert et al. (2005) have argued that they represent the same unit. Lucas and Hayden (1989) applied the formal name Bluewater Creek Member to the 'lower red member' in New Mexico and use of this name has since been extended into eastern Arizona (e.g., Heckert and Lucas, 1997). However, if the Mesa Redondo and Bluewater Creek are synonymous units, the former name has priority (*contra* Heckert and Lucas, 2003).

Heckert and Lucas (1998) assigned reddish strata 20 meters below the Newspaper Sandstone bed in the Tepees area of the park to the Mesa Redondo (Bluewater Creek of their usage) Member, whereas Dubiel et al. (1999) assigned these rocks to the 'mottled strata' that overlies the Moenkopi Formation throughout parts of northeastern Arizona (Stewart et al., 1972b). The basis for the argument of Dubiel et al. (1999) was that a coarse-grained sandstone unit overlying the reddish unit in the park represents the Shinarump Member. Therrien et al. (1999) also considered this sandstone to represent the Shinarump; however, recent field investigations of this unit by the author demonstrate that these 'Shinarump' beds pinch out laterally into bluish beds of the Blue Mesa Member, suggesting that they instead represent a distinct facies in that unit. Furthermore, better exposures of the unit that Dubiel et al. (1999) assigned to the 'mottled strata' are present outside of the park to the west. This unit is stratigraphically above Shinarump Member exposures in and around the city of Holbrook, and are therefore part of the Chinle Formation (pers. obs.). Thus, Heckert and Lucas (1998) were probably correct in assigning this unit to the Mesa Redondo Member, although a direct correlation to the type section of the Mesa Redondo Member is impossible.

Blue Mesa Member

Lucas (1993) named strata in Petrified Forest National Park that underlie the basal sandstone of the Sonsela Member the Blue Mesa Member . The Blue Mesa Member is characterized by its lighter coloration and its weathering profile, forming low rounded badlands (Woody, 2003). The Blue Mesa member represents the

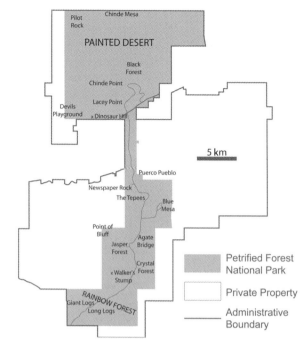

Figure *1*. Map of Petrified Forest National Park showing major geographical areas discussed in the text.

lower portion of what was previously known as the lower Petrified Forest Member (Akers et al., 1958). It is important to note that Lucas' (1993) Blue Mesa Member is part of his Petrified Forest Formation and his original description and type section includes much of what is now included within the Sonsela Member. Therefore, Woody (2003; this volume) redefined this unit to reflect this change.

Recent authors have assigned portions of the Blue Mesa Member (in addition to the Newspaper Rock bed) to the Monitor Butte (e. g., Demko et al. 1998) and Mesa Redondo Members (Dubiel et al., 1999) but did not justify these assignments in detail. Therefore, retention of these strata in the Blue Mesa Member as advocated by Heckert and Lucas (2002) and Woody (this volume) is preferred for this study pending further investigation.

Newspaper Rock bed.—The Newspaper Rock bed is a prominent local marker horizon within the Blue Mesa Member (Fig. 1). The Newspaper Rock bed mainly outcrops in the Tepees/Blue Mesa portions of the park and extends eastwards past the 2004 park boundary, and is also present southwest of the Tepees at the base of Point of Bluff (Fig. 1). This unit consists of interfingering fine-grained ripple-laminated sandstone, greenish-gray mudstones ("leaf shale beds" of Stagner, 1941), and reddish pedogenic siltstones (Fig. 3; Dubiel et al., 1999). Dubiel et al. (1999) interpreted these facies as representing incised valley fills in the Chinle depositional system. Note that I consider the Newspaper Rock bed to constitute all of these interfingering facies following Dubiel et al. (1999), whereas Billingsley (1985) and Heckert and Lucas (2002) restricted the unit to only the sandstone facies. However, I disagree with Dubiel et al. (1999) that this unit is assignable to the

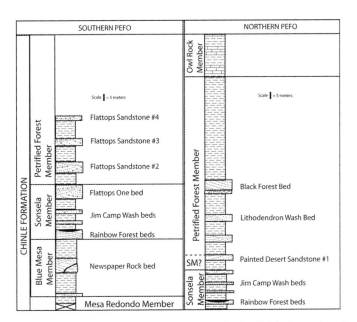

Figure 2. Generalized stratigraphic columns for the Chinle Formation of Petrified Forest National Park showing the relations of beds and members in the southern and northern portions of the park. These columns are not intended to demonstrate correlations between beds, but do display true thicknesses of the units. Adapted from Murry (1990), Lucas (1993), and Heckert and Lucas (2002).

Monitor Butte Member, and instead consider it part of the Blue Mesa Member (Heckert and Lucas, 2002; Woody, 2003, this volume).

Sonsela Member

Lucas (1993) originally raised the Sonsela Sandstone bed to member status, but did not modify its stratigraphic definition. Heckert and Lucas (2002) revised and expanded the Sonsela Member to include the medial sandy interval of the Chinle Formation that has a maximum thickness of 40 meters in the park and consists of a basal sandstone unit, a medial siltstone and sandstone unit, and an upper sandstone (the traditional Sonsela Sandstone bed). Woody (2003; this volume) independently came to the same conclusion, revised the identifying lithologic criteria, provided an alternative correlation throughout park strata, and described informal nomenclature for the Sonsela Member that is preferred for this study. The upper sandstone (Flattops One bed) includes the "Sonsela Sandstone bed" of Akers et al. (1958) and the Flattops Sandstone #1 of Billingsley (1985). The lower sandstone unit (Rainbow Forest beds) consists of the Rainbow Forest bed of Billingsley (1985) and the "Camps Butte" sandstone of Murry (1990). In the past, the medial portion has been assigned to both the upper portion of the 'lower Petrified Forest Member' and the lower portion of the 'upper Petrified Forest Member' (Billingsley, 1985; Murry, 1990; Long and Murry, 1995). Woody (2003; this volume) provided a detailed facies analysis of the Sonsela Member.

The Sonsela Member is also widely exposed in the Devils Playground area of the park where the 'Brown Sandstone' of Billingsley (1985) may represents the upper sandstone unit; however, direct correlations to beds in the southern portion of the park are not presently possible.

Petrified Forest Member

Woody (2003; this volume) restricted the Petrified Forest Member to its upper portion of which had been previously known as the 'upper Petrified Forest Member' (Billingsley 1985). This includes all strata between the top of the Sonsela Member and the base of the Owl Rock Member. In Petrified Forest National Park, the Petrified Forest Member can be distinguished mainly by its predominantly reddish color.

Black Forest Bed.—The thin distinctive white and pink unit containing black petrified logs that Marcou and Ward recognized in the vicinity of Lithodendron Wash was noted many years later by Cooley (1959) and Roadifer (1967) both of whom referred to it as a tuff bed. It was called the Black Forest Tuff by Billingsley (1985) and the Black Forest Sandstone Bed on the unpublished geologic map of the park by Billingsley, et al. (1985). Ash (1992) formally named and described the unit the Black Forest Bed (Fig. 2). The Black Forest Bed has a maximum thickness of 12.6 meters and is located approximately 130 meters above the top of the Sonsela Member and approximately 110 meters below the Owl Rock Member (Ash, 1992). The Black Forest Bed consists of a basal nodular conglomerate and an upper white to pink tuffaceous sandstone. Riggs et al. (2003) published a radiometric date for this unit, using detrital zircons, of 213±1.7 ma, which is early Norian in age (Gradstein et al., 2005).

Owl Rock Member

Limited exposures of this unit occur within Petrified Forest National Park. The most prominent exposure, on Chinde Mesa (Fig. 2), has a thickness of 80 meters (Ash, 1992). No vertebrate or plant fossils have been collected from Owl Rock exposures in the park although elsewhere in Arizona the Owl Rock is highly fossiliferous (Kirby, 1991).

BIOSTRATIGRAPHY

Mesa Redondo Member

No fossils have been found to date in the Mesa Redondo Member of PEFO, mainly because of the limited outcrop exposure. However, a wealth of vertebrate material has been collected from Mesa Redondo (=Bluewater Creek) exposures near St. Johns, Arizona, most notably from the *Placerias* quarry (Long and Murry, 1995). Significant fossils from this locality include the metoposaurid *Buettneria perfecta*, the aetosaurs *Stagonolepis wellesi* and *Desmatosuchus haplocerus*, the phytosaur *Leptosuchus*

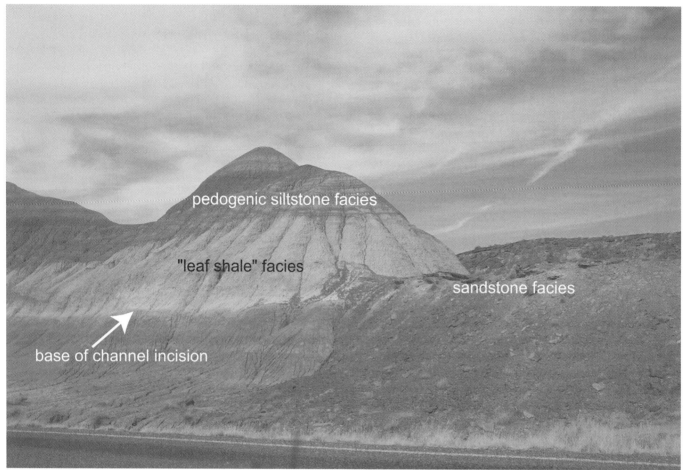

Figure 3. Photograph of the Newspaper Rock bed from the Tepees are showing relationship of the three distinct facies that make up the unit.

adamanensis, the 'poposaur' *Poposaurus gracilis*, and the dicynodont *Placerias hesternus*.

Blue Mesa Member

No fossils, plant or animal, have been recovered from strata in PEFO that are below the level of the Newspaper Rock bed. The basal portion of the sandstone facies of the Newspaper Rock bed contains preserved woody material, but whole logs are extremely rare throughout the unit. Trace fossils are common. The only possible vertebrate fossils known from the "leaf shale" facies of the Newspaper Rock bed are some small possibly shark egg cases described elsewhere in this volume by Axsmith. Invertebrate fossils from the "leaf shale" facies include crayfish, conchostracans, and insects (Miller and Ash, 1988). Blue Mesa Member strata above the Newspaper Rock bed are extremely fossiliferous containing numerous vertebrate, invertebrate, and locally abundant petrified logs and in situ stumps (Fig. 4).

PFP 001 - This locality was discovered in the early 1930s by workers building the main park road and is the main locality (UCMP P3901-1) of Daugherty (1941). It is located in the greenish mudstone facies of the Newspaper Rock bed, the "leaf shales" of Stagner (1941). This site is important not only for the diversity and abundance of plant fossils, but also

because of the preservational quality; many of the species are known from complete leaves and the epidermis and cuticle are preserved on many of them. This is the type locality for numerous plant fossils including the fern-like foliage *Cladophlebis yazzia* Ash (1973) and *Sphenopteris arizonica* Daugherty emend. Ash (1999), the ferns *Clathropteris walkeri* Daugherty emend. Ash (1970a), *Phlebopteris smithii* Daugherty (1941), *Wingatea plumosa* (Daugherty) Ash (1970a); the possible ginkgoalean *Baiera arizonica* Daugherty (1941), the seeds *Samaropsis puerca* Daugherty (1941), and *Carpolithus chinleana* Daugherty (1941). Biostratigraphically significant fossils include the fern *Todites fragilis* Daugherty emend. Ash (1970a), the fern-like foliage *Marcouia neupteroides* (Daugherty) Ash, and *Cladophlebis daughertyi* Ash (1970a), as well as the bennettitalean *Zamites powellii* all of which characterize the *Dinophyton* floral zone of Ash (1980). The enigmatic plant fossil *Dinophyton spinosus* also occurs at this site.

PFP 002 - This locality is a short distance west of PFP 001 and was reported by Daugherty (1941). It occurs in the same unit as the previous locality and contains a similar flora and includes many specimens of the horsetail *Equisetites bradyi* Daugherty, 1941. This is the type locality of the conifer *Podozamites arizonicus* Daugherty (1941). Palynomorphs have also been collected from this site, including *Equisitosporites*

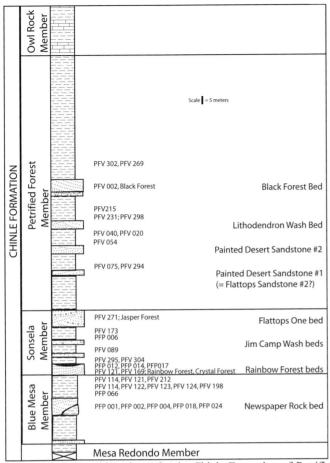

Figure 4. Stratigraphic column for the Chinle Formation of Petrified Forest National Park showing the locations of prominent fossil localities. Adapted from Lucas (1993).

chinleanus Daugherty (1941), which is characteristic of palynomorph zone II of Litwin et al. (1991) and suggests a Carnian age for this flora.

PFP 004 – This locality is a short distance east of locality PFP 001 and contains a large flora that includes most of the species recognized at that locality together with several other noteworthy fossils including the bennettitalean pollen-bearing structure *Androcycas santuccii* Watson and Ash (this volume), the pollen bearing organ *Creberanthus bealeii* Axsmith and Ash, this volume), the large horsetail cone *Equicalostrobus chinleana* (Daugherty) Grauvogel-Stamm and Ash, 1999, the unusual pollen bearing organ *Pramelreuthia yazzi* Ash and Litwin, 1994. The locality also contains carapaces of chonchostracans, beetle elytra, crayfish, and possible shark egg cases (Miller and Ash, 1988; Axsmith, this volume).

PFP 017 - This locality is southeast of Billings Gap on top of an elongate bluff capped by a thick cross-bedded sandstone unit. Past workers (Billingsley et al., 1985; Long and Murry, 1995) have considered this sandstone to represent the traditional Sonsela Sandstone bed (=Flattops One bed of Woody, this volume); however, recent investigations by the author suggest that this horizon represents the Rainbow Forest beds. This site is significant because it provided the "Sonsela Sandstone Bed" palynomorph

sample (R4341) of Litwin et al. (1991). This site contains the palynomorph taxa *Plicatisaccus badius*, *Camerosporites secatus*, and *Cycadopites stonei*, which are representative of palynomorph zone II and considered by Litwin et al. (1991) to indicate a Carnian age for this flora.

PFP 018 - This site is north of a large archaeological site known as Puerco Pueblo and is also in the greenish mudstone facies of the Newspaper Rock bed. This locality contains the leaf *Marcouia neuropteroides* and shoots of *Dinophyton spinosus*, which are characteristic of the *Dinophyton* zone of Ash (1980). It also contains many of the other species found at locality PFP 001 as well as *Araucarites rudicula* Axsmith and Ash, this volume, *Podozamites* n. sp., and *Ginkgoites* n. sp. In addition it contains specimens of the seed fern leaf *Sphenopteris arizonica* Daugherty emend. Ash, 1999 that show evidence of having been attacked by insects (Ash, 1999).

PFP 022 - This locality is in a narrow dry wash about 600 meters west of PFP 001 and is at the same horizon as the previously discussed localities. It was discovered by the wife of the Chief Ranger in 1985 when she observed freshly exposed fossil leaves in a block that had fallen from the wall of the wash. The cycad leaf, *Aricycas paulae* Ash, 1991, which came from this locality was named after her (Paula Andress). Other significant taxa from this locality include *Cladophlebis daughertyi* and *Zamites powellii*.

PFP 066 - Blue Mesa Stump Field. This site is located several meters above the Newspaper Rock bed and is just below a greenish mudstone horizon that contains many of the vertebrate localities of the Blue Forest area (e.g., PFV 122). The lithology of PFP 066 is a bluish pedogenic mudstone that is common in the Blue Forest area and often contains insitu stumps, most likely of *Araucarioxylon arizonicum* (Ash and Creber, 1992). Jones and Ash (this volume) document a stump from this locality that appears to have been charred by fire.

PFV 114 - Blue Forest General Area. Many of Charles Camp's 1921 and 1923 collections fall under this locality number (UCMP V7038). Most of the fossils consist of phytosaur and metoposaur material, including good skull material of *Buettneria perfecta* and *Leptosuchus adamanensis*. An isolated tooth (UCMP 175149) represents the only occurrence of the pseudosuchian *Revueltosaurus hunti* from Petrified Forest National Park.

PFV 121 (in part) - Phytosaur Basin E. This locality was collected by Charles Camp in 1921 and consists of beds from both the Blue Mesa and lower Sonsela Members. Camp collected a skull (UCMP 27007) and partial skeleton (UCMP 27008) of *Leptosuchus adamanensis* from the Blue Mesa Member beds (Camp, 1930).

Hunt (1998) reported the collection of a partial aetosaur skeleton from the Blue Mesa Member in the same horizon as UCMP 27007. This specimen has never been formally described, but Hunt (1998) refers it to *Typothorax antiquum*, a taxon described by Lucas et al. (2002) from the Santa Rosa Formation of New Mexico. This specimen (PEFO uncat) is only a few meters stratigraphically below the base of the Sonsela Member and represents the lowest occurrence of *Typothorax* in the park.

Typothorax antiquum was described by Lucas et al. (2002) for a partial skeleton from the Santa Rosa Formation of New Mexico. According to these authors, *T. antiquum* can be differentiated from *T. coccinarum* on the basis of: 1) paramedian plates with a lower width to length ratio (~2-3:1); 2) pitting of the paramedian plates that is less dense and with larger pits; and 3) a more robust ilium. However, examination of the type material shows that many of the dorsal paramedian plates of *T. antiquum* (e.g., Lucas et al. 2002:figs. 3d, f) actually have width to length ratios higher than 3:1 and even more than 4:1 in some plates. Lower ratio plates assigned to the dorsal region (Lucas et al., 2002:figs. a, e, g) have the crescentic shape, faint ornamentation, and slightly medially offset boss that is characteristic of cervical plates (Martz, 2002). The plates considered to be cervical paramedians by Lucas et al. (2002: figs. a-c) are actually caudal paramedians and a lateral plate (Martz, 2002). Moreover, the density and coarseness of the ornament pitting varies highly among specimens of *Typothorax coccinarum* (pers. obs.). Finally, robustness of the ilium is also a highly variable character and could be equally attributed to individual variation, ontogeny, or sexual dimorphism rather than taxonomic variation (see PFV 231 discussion below), given that few complete *T. coccinarum* ilia are known. Therefore, *T. antiquum* is considered here to be a junior synonym of *T. coccinarum*.

PFV 122 – Dying Grounds. This site is stratigraphically several meters lower than PFV 121 in an extremely fossiliferous greenish mudstone horizon that contains numerous fossil localities. The Dying Grounds is significant for its microvertebrate fauna (Murry, 1989; Heckert, 2004). Recently, the author recognized a proximal end of a femur (PEFO 34347) that had been collected from this locality in the 1990s. This specimen is important because it represents a dinosauriform similar to *Silesaurus* (Dzik, 2003) and *Eucoelophysis* (Nesbitt et al, submitted), and represents the earliest unambiguous occurrence of a *Silesaurus*-like dinosauriform in North America (Parker et al., this volume).

PFV 123 – Annie's Canyon. Charles Camp collected the holotype specimen of *Machaeroprosopus* (=*Leptosuchus*) *adamanensis* (UCMP 26699) (Camp, 1930) from this locality in 1921. It is at the same stratigraphic horizon as Crocodile Hill (PFV 124) and the Dying Ground (PFV 122), stratigraphically high in the Blue Mesa Member.

PFV 124 – Crocodile Hill. Charles Camp excavated this quarry in 1923 and recovered numerous specimens, including many metoposaurs and phytosaurs. Murry (1989) described the microvertebrates from this locality, and Philip Vancleave probably also collected the type specimen of the enigmatic archosauromorph *Vancleavea campi* from here (Long and Murry, 1995). Important specimens include numerous skull and pectoral elements referable to *Buettneria perfecta* and at least two skulls of *Leptosuchus adamanensis* (UCMP 27070).

PFV 198 – Blue Mesa N. Long and Ballew (1985) documented *Dematosuchus haplocerus* from only six localities within PEFO, commenting on the rarity of this taxon. Subsequent examination of the material from these localities by the author determined that none of the material was actually referable to *Desmatosuchus*. Nonetheless, in recent years *Desmatosuchus haplocerus* material has been recovered from three sites in the park. PFV 198 is located north of Blue Mesa and is situated approximately 8 meters above the red pedogenic facies of the Newspaper Rock bed. Plate fragments from this locality (PEFO 31177) are referable to *D. haplocerus* (Parker and Irmis, 2005). This locality is in the same horizon as PFV 122 and represents the lowest stratigraphic occurrence of *Desmatosuchus* in the park.

PFV 212 – Dinosaur Ridge N. This locality is located in the uppermost portion of the Blue Mesa Member, just a few meters below the Sonsela Member and is within Charles Camp's "Phytosaur Basin" locality (PFV 121). Hunt et al. (1996) documented theropod material from this locality; however, it has never been described. This site contains one of the few occurrences of *Desmatosuchus haplocerus* from the park (PEFO 26668) (Parker and Irmis, 2005) and represents the highest stratigraphic occurrence of that taxon. *Stagonolepis wellesi* is also present at this locality.

Sonsela Member

The recently expanded Sonsela Member (Heckert and Lucas, 2002; Woody, 2003) encompasses strata in the park previously assigned to both the upper and lower Petrified Forest Members (Billingsley, 1985). Many of these strata are fossiliferous and contain numerous biostratigraphically important localities.

Rainbow Forest beds.—PFV 121 (in part). Phytosaur Basin E – Charles Camp collected an interclavicle (UCMP 27009) of *Buettneria perfecta* from the whitish sandstone that represents the base of the Sonsela Member (Camp Butte sandstone = Rainbow Forest beds) in the Blue Forest area. Parker and Irmis (2005) figured a partial plate of *Typothorax* (PEFO 26694) from the same unit, assigning it to *Typothorax coccinarum* based on the dorsoventral flexion of the plate and the coarse pitting. Hunt et al. (2005) consider this plate to be indeterminate to species. Under either interpretation, this plate represents the second lowest occurrence of *Typothorax* from the park. Although, *Typothorax* plates occur widely throughout the Sonsela Member (Long and Murry, 1995), many are too fragmentary to assign to a specific species *contra* Hunt et al. (2005), who assign all *Typothorax* specimens from the Sonsela to *T. antiquum* without providing any discussion supporting these referrals. Nonetheless, as discussed previously, *T. antiquum* cannot be adequately differentiated from material of *T. coccinarum* and therefore all known *Typothorax* material is assigned to the latter taxon.

PFV 169 – Battleship NW. Two distinct lithologies of the Rainbow Forest beds are found at this locality, a cross-bedded, weakly lithified sandstone and a laterally equivalent sandy mudstone. Significant fossils from these facies include a partial skeleton of *Stagonolepis wellesi* (PEFO 31217), paramedian plate fragments of *Paratypothorax* sp. (UCMP 126960), and a left squamosal (PEFO 23333) and partial skull (PEFO 34034) of *Leptosuchus adamanensis*. This locality represents the lower stratigraphic occurrence of *Paratypothorax*.

Rainbow Forest – Thousands of colorful logs characterize the area known as the Rainbow Forest, all of which are currently considered to represent *Araucarioxylon arizonicum*. These logs mainly derive from the Rainbow Forest beds; however, to the northeast, along old Highway 180, many logs of *Araucarioxylon* can also be seen weathering from the Jim Camp Wash beds.

Jim Camp Wash beds.—Crystal Forest – This site also contains a large petrified wood accumulation mostly referable to *Araucarioxylon arizonicum* (however, see Savidge and Ash, this volume). The logs occur at various levels in both the Rainbow Forest bed and the Jim Camp Wash beds.

PFV 295 – Jablonsky Site. This site is located in a grayish mudstone that is a few meters about the Rainbow Forest beds near Mountain Lion Mesa. Significant fossils from this site include the skull of a new species of *Pseudopalatus* (Parker and Irmis, this volume) and paramedian plates of *Typothorax coccinarum*. This site represents the lowest unequivocal stratigraphic occurrence of both taxa.

PFV 304 – Milkshake Quarry. This site is located in the southern portion of the park and is situated approximately five meters above the Rainbow Forest bed and approximately 10 meters below the siliceous layer described by Creber and Ash (1992) and Woody (2003, this volume). In 2004, a relatively complete carapace of *Stagonolepis* sp. was collected from this site. Potential apomorphies of the osteoderms suggest that this may represent a new species (Parker and Irmis, 2005); however, the specimen is still being prepared. This is the highest occurrence of *Stagonolepis* in the park.

PVF 089 – Bowman Locality. This locality is also in the southern end of the park and is situated approximately 6 meters above PFV 304. Significant taxa from this locality include *Buettneria perfecta*, *Typothorax coccinarum.*, *Paratypothorax*

sp., *Pseudopalatus pristinus*, and an indeterminate saurischian dinosaur.

PFP 006 – Walker's Stump. In January, 1936, park naturalist Myrl Walker partially excavated a 'standing' stump of *Araucarioxylon* from the Flattops area of the park (Walker, 1936). Preliminary investigations in 1935 and a second partial excavation in 1936 recovered cycad and conifer leaves, scales, and seeds (Walker, 1936). Walker (1936) felt that the close association of a trunk in place and conifer leaves strongly suggested that the leaves and stem (trunk) belonged to the same tree. Daugherty (1941) assigned the cycad leaves to *Otozamites* (=*Zamites*) *powellii* and the conifer leaves to *Pagiophyllum newberryii*, which Ash (1970c) later assigned to a new species, *Pagiophyllum simpsonii*. Many years later this stump was reinvestigated by S. R. Ash and it was noted that the stump is inclined at an angle of about 17 degrees from the vertical in contrast with other in situ stumps in the park, most of which are nearly vertical (S. R. Ash, pers. commun., 2006). According to Ash (pers. commun., 2006) this may indicate that the stump was rafted to its present location and pushed over slightly by the current of water when the root caught on the bottom of the stream. After the eruption of Mt. St. Helens several stumps were observed in similar positions in the flood damaged areas including one that was deposited upright on a section of paved highway (S. R. Ash, pers. commun., 2006). Nonetheless, the discovery of this stump set people to thinking about the possibility of there being other standing stumps and eventually such stumps were recognized in both the Blue and Black forests.

PFV 173 – Crystal Forest Buttes. This site is located east of Crystal Forest and 12 meters below the Flattops One bed. Significant fossils from this locality include a partial carapace of *Paratypothorax* sp. (PEFO 3004) (Hunt and Lucas, 1992) and two squamosals of *Leptosuchus* sp. (UCMP 126998; UCMP 139554). This locality represents the highest occurrence of *Leptosuchus* in the park, exclusive of the Devils Playground area (see discussion below).

PFV 268 - Clambodia. This locality is situated in Rainbow Forest approximately 40 meters below the Flattops One bed. Significant taxa include *Paratypothorax* sp. and *Typothorax coccinarum*.

Flattops One bed.—Jasper Forest – Numerous specimens of the conifer *Araucarioxylon arizonicum* are encased in the Flattops One bed. These logs weather in sections and subsequently slide and tumble into the valley below, which is commonly known as the Jasper Forest.

PFV 271 – This locality in the southern end of the park is just above the Rainbow Forest residential area. In the 1990s, park staff discovered a phytosaur skull in a fallen sandstone block just below and originally from the Flattops One bed. Hunt et al. (2002) disagreed on the taxonomic assignment of the specimen and described this skull alternatively as either *Nicrosaurus* sp. or *Pseudopalatus* sp. This specimen (PEFO 31205) has subsequently been collected and partially prepared, demonstrating that it represents a specimen of *Pseudopalatus* sp. (Parker, 2005b). Note that Parker (2005b:44) erroneously lists this specimen as PEFO 31218. This specimen is the only vertebrate body fossil known from the Flattops One bed.

Petrified Forest Member

Woody (this volume) restricted the Petrified Forest Member in PEFO to strata originally referred to as the upper portion of the Petrified Forest Member (Billingsley, 1985). Laterally persistent sandstone beds are common in this unit and have been used as marker beds (e.g., Billingsley, 1985; Long and Murry, 1995). Sandstone beds in the southern end of the park are informally known as the Flattops sandstones, whereas those in the northern end of the park are informally called the Painted Desert sandstones (Billingsley,1985). Direct correlation of these beds between the northern and southern ends of the park is extremely difficult; however it appears that Painted Desert Sandstone #1 and Flattops Sandstone #2 are roughly equal (pers. obs.). Alternatively, Therrien and Fastovsky (2000) correlated the Painted Desert Sandstone #1 with the Flattops Sandstone #3, approximately 25-30 meters of vertical difference from my interpretation.

A volcaniclastic unit that represents the highest mappable sandstone bed of the Petrified Forest Member in the north end of the park was named the Black Forest Bed by Ash (1992). Riggs et al. (2003) determined a radiometric date of 213±1.7 ma for this bed using detrital zircons. The Black Forest Bed contains a large concentration of logs that are assigned to *Araucarioxylon arizonicum* Knowlton, 1888, *Schilderia adamanica* Daugherty, 1934, *Woodworthia arizonica* Jeffrey, 1910. Vertebrates from the Black Forest Bed include pseudopalatine phytosaurs and *Typothorax coccinarum*. The presence of *Paratypothorax* (Long and Murry, 1995) from this horizon is based on an undiagnostic fragment.

PFV 075 – Karen's Point. This locality is in the Flattops area of the park and situated just above Flattops Sandstone #2. Significant taxa from this site include the aetosaurs *Typothorax coccinarum* and "*Desmatosuchus*" *chamaensis* (Parker and Irmis, 2005). "*D.*" *chamaensis* is otherwise only known from New Mexico in the Petrified Forest Member of the Chama Basin and the Bull Canyon Formation of Quay County (Zeigler et al., 2002). Parker (2003, in press) determined that "*D.*" *chamaensis* does not represent a valid species of *Desmatosuchus* and is instead referable to a new genus closely related to *Paratypothorax*.

PFV 070 – Flattops NW. This locality is also in the Flattops area of the park and is located at the top of Flattops Sandstone #2. Significant specimens from this site include well-preserved paramedian plates of *Typothorax coccinarum*.

PFV 294 – Delaney Tank NE. This locality is just west of Point of Bluff and is situated stratigraphically just above

the Flattops Sandstone #2. In 1962, the MNA collected a partial lateral plate (MNA V697) of *Desmatosuchus* from this locality that Long and Ballew (1985) interpreted as a cervical lateral plate of *D. haplocerus*. Parker (2005a) determined that it was instead from the dorsal lateral region and represented the only known Arizona occurrence of *Desmatosuchus smalli*. *Typothorax coccinarum* also occurs at this locality.

PFV 040 – Dinosaur Hill. The fauna of the Dinosaur Hill locality has been extensively discussed by Padian (1986, 1990), Murry and Long (1989), Parrish (1991), Long and Murry (1995); Hunt et al. (1998), and Heckert (2004). Significant taxa from this locality include *Coelophysis* sp., *Hesperosuchus agilis*, *Apachesaurus gregorii*, *Pseudopalatus* sp., *Typothorax coccinarum*, and *Revueltosaurus callenderi*.

PFV034 – Billingsley Hill. This site is located approximately 450 meters due north of and is 6 meters stratigraphically lower than PFV 040. This locality contains *Pseudopalatus* sp., *Typothorax coccinarum*, and *Apachesaurus gregorii*. More importantly, this site is the type locality for *Kraterokheirodon colberti*, an enigmatic tetrapod known only from this locality and from a second locality near St. Johns, Arizona that is situated either low in the Blue Mesa Member or high in the Mesa Redondo (=Bluewater Creek) Member (Irmis and Parker, 2005).

PFV 020 – Dinosaur Hollow. This locality is roughly at the same stratigraphic horizon as PFV 040, but 6 kilometers to the northeast. This is the type locality of the basal saurischian *Chindesaurus bryansmalli* (Long and Murry, 1995). Long and Murry (1995) and unpublished field notes from Long also document a partial skeleton of *Shuvosaurus* (=*Chatterjeea*) from this locality, although this specimen is lost. Other taxa occurring at this locality include *Typothorax coccinarum* and *Apachesaurus gregorii*.

PFV 215 – Zuni Well Mound. This site is stratigraphically 18 meters above PFV 040, 1.8 km to the northeast, and is located just slightly above the Lithodendron Wash bed of Heckert and Lucas (2002) (=Painted Desert Sandstone #3 of Billingsley, 1985). Significant fossils from this locality include a centrum of a large metoposaurid, material of *Apachesaurus gregorii*, and teeth of *Revueltosaurus callenderi*. Also recovered from this site was a partial skeleton of the diapsid *Vancleavea* sp. (Parker and Irmis, 2005) and purported theropod material (Hunt and Wright, 1999).

PFV 231 – The Giving Site. Stratigraphically this site is approximately 6 meters above PFV 040 and PFV 020, and 12 m below PFV 215. The fauna at this locality is quite diverse and represents only the second cooccurrence of both *Coelophysis* sp. and *Chindesaurus bryansmalli* (Parker and Irmis, 2005). Other taxa include indeterminate pseudopalatine phytosaurs, adult and juvenile specimens of *Typothorax*, *Vancleavea* sp., *Shuvosaurus* sp.,

Postosuchus, Revueltosaurus callenderi, and an indeterminate crocodylomorph. The *Typothorax* material is of special interest because the juvenile material (*Typothorax coccinarum*) is the first juvenile aetosaur material from the Chinle Formation that can be unambiguously referred to a previously known taxon. This material is referable to *Typothorax coccinarum* because of the pitted ornamentation, high width/length ratio, and pronounced dorsoventral flexion of the paramedian armor (Martz, 2002; Lucas et al, 2002). An almost complete sacrum with associated armor and vertebrae of an adult specimen of *Typothorax* (PEFO 33967) displays similarities with *Typothorax antiquum* (e.g., broader neck of the robust ilium, flat paramedian plates with a low width-length ratio, and coarser pitting of the plate ornamentation). This would represent the highest stratigraphic occurrence of this taxon and suggest that its stratigraphic range overlaps with *T. coccinarum*. Nevertheless, because *Typothorax antiquum* cannot be adequately diagnosed and differentiated from *T. coccinarum*, this specimen is interpreted here as representing a specimen of *T. coccinarum* and the low-width length ratio of the plates is attributable to their position in the carapace (i.e. pelvic or anterior caudal).

PFV 298 – *Revueltosaurus* Quarry. This locality is at roughly the same horizon as PFV 231. The quarry is dominated by the remains of the pseudosuchian *Revueltosaurus callenderi*, including collected material from a minimum of a dozen individuals (Parker et al., 2005). Vertebrae and other elements of a single specimen of *Shuvosaurus* sp. were also collected from this locality.

PFV 002 – Black Forest. This is a widespread area covering several kilometers of exposures of the Black Forest Bed (Ash, 1992). This reworked volcaniclastic unit is highly fossiliferous. A large petrified wood deposit known as the Black Forest contains the trees *Araucarioxylon arizonicum, Shilderia adamanica,* and *Woodworthia arizonica.* To date, *Shilderia* and *Woodworthia* have only been found in the Black Forest Bed (Creber and Ash, 2004). This is the highest documented occurrence of plant fossils in the park. Fossil vertebrates are also common and include *Typothorax coccinarum* and *Pseudopalatus* sp. Long and Murry (1995) listed *Paratypothorax* sp. as being present in the Black Forest Bed; however, this assignment is based on an undiagnostic specimen.

PFV 269 – Judy's Luck. This locality is stratigraphically about 12 meters above the Black Forest bed and with PFV 302 represents the highest documented occurrence of vertebrates in the park. The fauna includes indeterminate archosaurs including phytosaurs and aetosaurs, as well as the temnospondyl *Apachesaurus gregorii.*

PFV 302 – Rabbit Foot Hills. This locality is at the same stratigraphic horizon as PFV 269. It represents the highest documented occurrence of *Typothorax coccinarum* in the park.

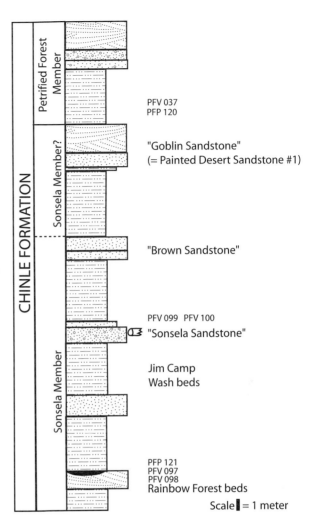

Figure 5. Stratigraphic column for the Chinle Formation in the Devils Playground area of Petrified Forest National Park, showing the locations of prominent fossil localities. Adapted from Murry (1990).

DEVILS PLAYGROUND AREA

Because of a discontinuity of the outcrop sections and local geologic structure it is difficult to directly correlate strata between the southern and northern portions of the park (Billingsley, 1985). This is especially true for the "Devils Playground" area, which is located north of Interstate 40 on the western park boundary. The main exposures in the Devils Playground area are lower stratigraphically than the rest of the northern portion of the park . Most of the exposures possess a lithology that is characteristic of the Sonsela Member, but bed correlations are tentative because there are many more sandstone bodies than observed in the southern portion of the park. For example, Billingsley (1985) named a prominent ledge-forming sandstone in the area the Brown Sandstone and assigned it to a stratigraphic position equivalent to the Newspaper Rock bed. Subsequently, Murry (1990) correlated a wood bearing sandstone unit in the area to the Flattops One bed (traditional Sonsela Sandstone bed). Recent investigation by the author suggests that the Brown Sandstone may actually be equivalent to the Flattops One bed (but see Raucci et al., this volume) and

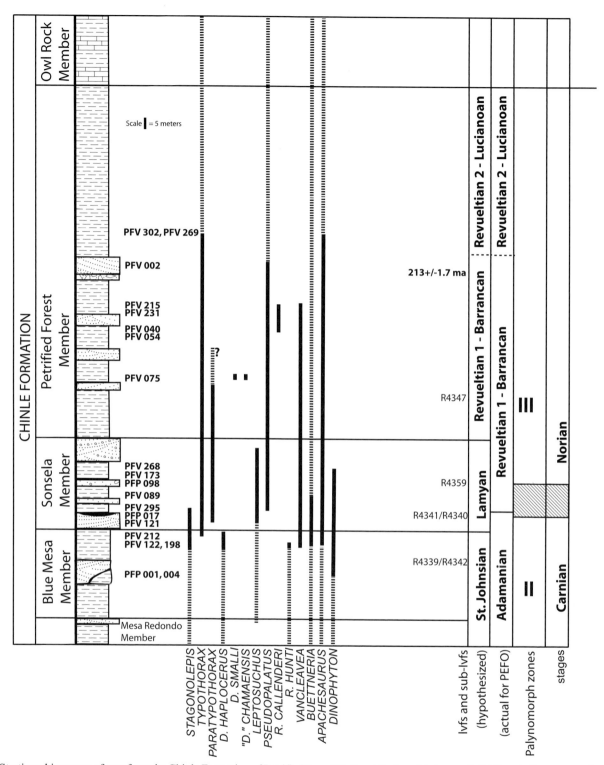

Figure 6 Stratigraphic ranges of taxa from the Chinle Formation of Petrified Forest National Park and Arizona. Solid lines indicate ranges between unambiguous occurrences. Dashed lines with question marks indicate possible range extensions. Dashed lines without question marks indicate range extensions from occurrences at other localities in Arizona. Palynomorph ranges and sample numbers (with R prefix) are from Litwin et al. (1991); hypothetical land vertebrate faunachron ranges are from Hunt et al. (2005); the U/Pb radiometric date for the Black Forest Bed is from Riggs et al. (2003).

that the bed considered by Murry (1990) to represent the "Sonsela Sandstone bed" is in the Jim Camp Wash beds. Most of the outcrop in the lower part of the section clearly represents this unit (Jim Camp Wash beds), a correlation that is supported by the paleontology. Therefore, I tentatively correlate the Brown Sandstone with the Flattops One bed, an unnamed sandstone at the base of the section to the Rainbow Forest beds, and the medial mudstone and sandstones to the Jim Camp Wash beds (Fig. 4).

Long and Murry (1995) refer to a prominent hoodoo-forming sandstone in the area as the "goblin sandstone". Recent stratigraphic work has suggested that this sandstone is equivalent to the Painted Desert Sandstone #1 of Johns (1988) (Heather Jones, written commun., 2004; Raucci et al., this volume) (Fig. 4). The mudstone layer directly overlying the "goblin sandstone" contains an early Norian palynoflora (R. Litwin, written commun.).

Sonsela Member

Rainbow Forest beds.—PFV 098 – Fossil Garden. In 1927, Charles Camp excavated several phytosaur skulls from a sandy flat he named "the fossil garden". Most of this material is indeterminate but at least one of the specimens (UCMP 27181) represents a small individual of *Leptosuchus crosbiensis.* Long and Murry (1995) list the presence of *Desmatosuchus* and *Stagonolepis* from this locality; however, the material is poorly preserved and not diagnostic.

PFP 121 – This locality is in a dark mudstone that is scoured into an underlying sandstone that floors locality PFV 098. *Dinophyton spinosus* is common at this locality. The flora of this site is undescribed but is similar to floras found at localities just above the Rainbow Forest beds in Crystal Forest and along old Highway 180 and contains a Late Carnian palynoflora (R. Litwin, written commun.).

Jim Camp Wash beds.—PFV 097 - Saurian Valley. This is the type locality of the phytosaur "*Machaeroprosopus*" *lithodendrorum* (=*Leptosuchus crosbiensis*). Contrary to Long and Murry (1995), *Desmatosuchus haplocerus* and *Stagonolepis wellesi* are not present at this locality; however, *Paratypothorax* sp. is represented by partial paramedian plates (e. g., UCMP 129995).

PFV 099 – Saurian Valley N. This site is situated approximately 8 meters above PFV 097 and is within the top portion of a prominent sandstone capping many of the small benches and buttes in the area. This sandstone contains petrified wood locally and has been correlated to the traditional "Sonsela Sandstone bed" by Murry (1990) and Long and Murry (1995). In 2002, a skull of *Leptosuchus* sp. (PEFO 31218) was collected from this locality.

PFV 100 - This site is at the same stratigraphic horizon as PFV 099. In 1946, the American Museum of Natural History collected a phytosaur skull from this locality, which has not yet been prepared (Long and Murry, 1995). In 1985, a crew from the UCMP collected a metoposaur skull from a few meters east of the AMNH site. In 2005, a skull of *Leptosuchus sp.* (PEFO 34239) was collected a little farther to the east. This specimen represents the same taxon as the skull from PFV 099 and both are either robust specimens of *L. adamanensis* or small specimens of *L. gregorii.* These skulls represent the highest occurrence of *Leptosuchus* in the Devils Playground area.

Petrified Forest Member

PFV 037 – Hell Wash. This locality is located above the "goblin sandstone" (Long and Murry, 1995) and contains pseudopalatine phytosaurs, *Typothorax coccinarum*, and *Paratypothorax* sp.

DISCUSSION

Precise relocation and documentation of fossil specimens and historic localities allows for more accurate determination of stratigraphic ranges of taxa in the Chinle Formation of Petrified Forest National Park. Resolution is still low pending a more rigorous stratigraphic study of the park (Albright et al., in prep) and completion of an accurate geological map (Raucci et al., this volume). Figure 5 shows the ranges of vertebrate taxa considered to have stratigraphic value, not only in PEFO, but regionally and even globally (Hunt and Lucas, 1993; Lucas and Heckert, 1996; Lucas, 1998; Hunt et al., 2005). These taxa are plotted by lowest and highest occurrences by locality and cross-referenced with palynomorph data from Litwin et al. (1991) and a radiometric date from Riggs et al. (2003). Carnian and Norian ages are assigned using the palynomorph data from Litwin et al. (1991); however, new magnetostratigraphic correlations between Europe and the eastern U.S. suggest that both of the palynofloras may be Norian in age (Muttoni et al., 2004).

Hunt et al. (2005) accounted for the newly determined transitional fauna of the Sonsela Member (Woody and Parker, 2004), as well as a recent discovery of pseudopalatine phytosaurs in an Adamanian assemblage in New Mexico (Hunt and Lucas, 2005), by subdividing the Adamanian land-vertebrate faunachron (lvf) into two sub-lvfs. The St. Johnsian and Lamyan sub-lvfs differ in the presence or absence of *Pseudopalatus* and *Typothorax* (Hunt et al., 2005) with the start of the Lamyan defined as the first appearance of *Typothorax antiquum* and the end defined as the first appearance of *Typothorax coccinarum*. These authors hypothesized that all of the Jim Camp Wash beds of Sonsela Member in PEFO were Lamyan in age; however, previous authors defined the beginning of the Revueltian with the first appearance of *Pseudopalatus* (Lucas and Hunt, 1993; Lucas, 1998). Because I do not consider *T. antiquum* to represent a distinct taxon, I do not recognize the Lamyan sub-lvf; however, even if *T. antiquum* is valid, its first occurrence in PEFO would be from the upper portion of the Blue Mesa Member, and the first unambiguous occurrence of *T. coccinarum* would be at PFV 268, which is about 50 meters below the top of the Sonsela Member. This stratigraphic range differs greatly from that presented by Hunt et al. (2005), who considered all of the Jim Camp Wash beds *Typothorax* specimens to assignable to *T. antiquum,* and thus indicative of the Lamyan. Moreover, if the beginning of the Revueltian is defined by the FAD of *Typothorax*, then the upper portion of the Blue Mesa Member and the entire Sonsela Member would be Revueltian. I prefer the original definition placing the beginning of the

Revueltian at the FAD of *Pseudopalatus*; in which case the lowest Jim Camp Wash beds, the Rainbow Forest beds, and the Blue Mesa Member would be Adamanian, not Revueltian. This definition is preferred because it more closely matches what is seen for the palynomorph zones (although I admit that it is not necessary for the fauna and flora records to match), provides a Norian age for the Revueltian as was originally conceived (Lucas and Hunt, 1993), and maximizes stability of the definitions of the lvf system by honoring historical usage.

This study finds that *Desmatosuchus haplocerus* and *Revueltosaurus hunti* are restricted to the Adamanian. *Pseudopalatus* is restricted to the Revueltian (by definition). *Typothorax coccinarum* occurs in the Adamanian and Revueltian. *Leptosuchus* displays a similar pattern, although *L. adamanensis* is more common in the Adamanian, whereas *L. crosbiensis* only occurs in the Revueltian. It is important to note that *Leptosuchus* and *Pseudopalatus* only overlap due to stratigraphic correlation and that these taxa have never been recovered together from the same locality. The occurrence of *Pseudopalatus* in the Los Esteros Member of the Santa Rosa Formation of New Mexico demonstrates that these and overlying strata are Revueltian in age, although nothing precludes the beginning of the Revueltian from being diachronous across the American Southwest. Because *Leptosuchus* has not been documented from strata overlying the Los Esteros Member, there is no reason to modify the lvf scheme to account for this "seemingly low" stratigraphic occurrence (*contra* Hunt et al. 2005).

Vertebrate and palynomorph data suggests that at least the lowest portion of the Sonsela Member is Carnian in age, whereas the upper portion of the member is Norian in age. This contrasts with past studies which have considered the Sonsela to be entirely Norian in age (Heckert and Lucas, 2002) or mostly latest Carnian in age (Hunt et al., 2005). Thus, the Carnian/Norian boundary is located approximately in the lower-middle portion of the member (Fig. 5; Woody and Parker, 2004). Furthermore, a transitional period for both the fauna and flora appears to roughly coincide with this interval. There is no evidence for a sizeable unconformity at the Carnian/Norian boundary (the Tr-4 unconformity of Lucas, 1993) (Woody, this volume). Alternatively, if the recent correlation by Muttoni et al. (2004) is correct, all Chinle Formation strata in the park would be Norian in age. Nonetheless, this study suggests that the boundaries of the proposed Late Triassic faunachrons do not correspond with stratigraphic boundaries in the Chinle Formation as proposed by previous workers (Fig. 5).

CONCLUSIONS

The Blue Forest Member contains palynomorphs and plant fossils that pertain to palynomorph Zone II of Litwin et al. (1991) and the *Dinophyton* floral zone of Ash (1970), both of which are believed to be Carnian in age. The vertebrate fauna is dominated by the metoposaurid *Buettneria perfecta*, the aetosaur *Stagonolepis wellesi*, and the phytosaur *Leptosuchus adamanensis*. *Desmatosuchus haplocerus*, *Typothorax coccinarum*, *Revueltosaurus hunti*, and *Vancleavea campi* are also present but rare. A proximal end of a femur from locality PFV 122 represents the earliest unambiguous record of a *Silesaurus*-like dinosauriform in North America.

The lower portion of the Sonsela Member (Rainbow Forest beds and lowest Jim Camp Wash beds) contains a palynomorph fauna that corresponds to palynomorph Zone II of Litwin et al. (1991) and is considered Carnian in age. The fauna of the lower Sonsela Member includes *Stagonolepis wellesi*, *Paratypothorax* sp., *Leptosuchus adamanensis*, *Leptosuchus crosbiensis*, *Pseudopalatus* spp., and *Typothorax coccinarum*.

The upper portion of the Sonsela Member (upper Jim Camp Wash beds and Flattops One bed) contain a palynomorph flora that corresponds to palynomorph Zone III of Litwin and Ash (1991) and is therefore Norian in age. The fauna of the upper Sonsela Member contains *Typothorax coccinarum*, *Paratypothorax* sp., *Leptosuchus adamanensis*, *Pseudopalatus pristinus*, and possibly *Leptosuchus crosbiensis*.

The Petrified Forest Member contains palynomorphs that correspond to Zone III of Litwin et al. (1991) and is therefore Norian in age. The vertebrate fauna is dominated by *Typothorax coccinarum*, *Paratypothorax* sp., *Apachesaurus gregorii*, and *Pseudopalatus* spp. *Revueltosaurus callenderi* and *Vancleavea* sp. are common at several localities in the Painted Desert area but have not been recovered from the Flattops region. *Desmatosuchus smalli*, "*Desmatosuchus*" *chamaensis*, *Coelophysis* sp., and *Chindesaurus bryansmalli* are also present but rare.

Stratigraphic determination of taxon ranges demonstrates that phytosaur taxa are may still be useful as index taxa for the Chinle Formation within PEFO despite evidence of an "Adamanian" pseudopalatine phytosaur in New Mexico. The Revueltian should continue to be defined using the FAD of *Pseudopalatus* following Lucas and Hunt (1993), Lucas (1998), and Lucas et al. (2002), rather than the FAD of *Typothorax coccinarum* as has been advocated by Hunt et al. (2005). Accordingly the Adamanian should be defined as the FAD of *Leptosuchus* as originally conceived. That these taxa overlap in the Sonsela Member simply strengthens the argument for a transitional fauna and flora of the Sonsela Member (Woody and Parker, 2004; Hunt et al., 2005) that may correspond with the Carnian-Norian boundary. *Typothorax* "*antiquum*" cannot be adequately differentiated from *T. coccinarum* using unambiguous autapomorphies and therefore I consider it to be a junior synonym of *T. coccinarum*. Consequently, I do not recognize the division of the Adamanian lvf into the St. Johnsian and Lamyan sub-lvfs. It appears as if assignment of fragmentary plates to *T.* "*antiquum*" by past authors (Lucas et al., 2002: Hunt et al., 2005) was biased by a stratophenetic approach rather than determination of diagnosable characters.

This study suggests that aetosaurs may not be as useful for biostratigraphy as previously hypothesized (e.g., Lucas and Hunt, 1993) because *Typothorax* overlaps with both *Stagonolepis* and *Desmatosuchus haplocerus*, and should not be used to define lvfs, although they may have limited use as index taxa. Furthermore, evidence from this study as well as Chatterjee and Lehman (2005), Langer (2005), and Rayfield et al. (2005) show that these lvfs only have local to regional utility and extreme caution should be used when applying them globally.

ACKNOWLEDGMENTS

Discussions with Daniel Woody, Randall Irmis, Sterling Nesbitt, and Andy Heckert were helpful. Daniel Woody, Randall Irmis, Sterling Nesbitt, Andy Heckert, and Michelle Stocker assisted with fieldwork. Reviews by Randall Irmis and Sid Ash greatly improved the manuscript. Fieldwork was funded by the Federal Recreation Act Fee Program and the Petrified Forest Museum Association. This is PEFO paleontological contribution number 16.

REFERENCES

Akers, J. P., Cooley, M. E., and C. A. Repenning. 1958. Moenkopi and Chinle Formations of Black Mesa and adjacent areas. New Mexico Geological Society Guidebook, 9:88-94.

Ash, S. R. 1966. The Upper Triassic Chinle flora of the southwest United States. Unpublished Ph.D dissertation, University of Reading, England, 223 p.

Ash, S. R. 1967. Preliminary results of a reinvestigation of the Chinle megaflora New Mexico and Arizona (Abstract), p. 20. In Geological Society of America, Rocky Mountain Section, 20th Annual Meeting, Program.

Ash, S.R. 1970a. Ferns from the Chinle Formation (Upper Triassic) in the Fort Wingate area, New Mexico. U.S. Geological Survey Professional Paper, 613-D, 52 p.

Ash, S.R. 1970b. *Dinophyton*, a problematical new plant genus from the Upper Triassic of southwestern United States. Palaeontology, 13:646-663.

Ash, S. R. 1970c. *Pagiophyllum simpsonii*, a new conifer from the Chinle Formation (Upper Triassic) of Arizona. Journal of Paleontology, 44:945-952.

Ash, S.R. 1972. Plant megafossils of the Chinle Formation, pp. 23-43. In C.S. Breed and W.J. Breed (eds.), Symposium on the Chinle Formation. Museum of Northern Arizona Bulletin 47.

Ash, S. R. 1973. Two new plants from the Petrified Forest of Arizona. Journal of Paleontology, 47:46-53.

Ash, S. R. 1980. Upper Triassic floral zones of North America, p. 153-170. In Dilcher, D. L., and T. N. Taylor (eds.), Biostratigraphy of Fossil Plants. Dowden, Hutchinson, and Ross, Inc., Stroudsburg, Pa.

Ash, S. R. 1987. The Upper Triassic red bed flora of the Colorado Plateau, western United States. Journal of the Arizona-Nevada Academy of Science, 22:95-105.

Ash, S. R. 1989. A catalog of Upper Triassic plant megafossils of the western United States through 1988, pp. 189-222. In Lucas, S. G. and Hunt, A. P., (eds.), Dawn of the Age of Dinosaurs in the American Southwest. New Mexico Museum of Natural History, Albuquerque.

Ash, S. R. 1991. A new pinnate cycad leaf from the Upper Triassic Chinle Formation of Arizona. Botanical Gazette, 152:123-131.

Ash, S. R. 1992. The Black Forest Bed, a distinctive unit in the Upper Triassic Chinle Formation, northeastern Arizona. Journal of the Arizona-Nevada Academy of Science, 24/25:59-73.

Ash, S. R. 1997. Evidence of arthropod-plant interactions in the Upper Triassic of the southwestern United States. Lethaia, 29:237-248.

Ash, S.R. 1999. An Upper Triassic *Sphenopteris* showing evidence of insect predation from Petrified Forest National Park, Arizona. International Journal of Plant Science, 160:208-215.

Ash, S. R. 2000. Evidence of oribatid mite herbivory in the stem of a Late Triassic tree fern from Arizona. Journal of Paleontology, 74:1065-1071.

Ash, S. R. 2001. Plant-animal interactions: herbivory, pp. 424-426. In Briggs, D. E. G., and Crowther, P. R., (eds.), Palaeobiology II.

Blackwell Science Ltd., Oxford.

Ash, S. R. 2005a. A new Upper Triassic flora and associated invertebrate fossils from the basal beds of the Chinle Formation, near Cameron, Arizona. PaleoBios, 25:17-34.

Ash, S. R. 2005b. Synopsis of the Upper Triassic flora of Petrified Forest National Park and vicinity. Mesa Southwest Museum Bulletin, 9:53-62.

Ash, S.R. and G. Creber. 2000. The Late Triassic *Araucarioxylon arizonicum* trees of the Petrified Forest National Park, Arizona, USA. Palaeontology, 43:15-28.

Billingsley, G. H. 1985. General stratigraphy of the Petrified Forest National Park, Arizona. Museum of Northern Arizona Bulletin, 54:3-8.

Camp, C. L. 1930. A study of the phytosaurs with description of new material from western North America. Memoirs of the University of California, 10:1-174.

Colbert, E. H. 1985. The Petrified Forest and its vertebrate fauna in Triassic Pangaea. Museum of Northern Arizona Bulletin, 54:33-43.

Cooley, M. E. 1958. The Mesa Redondo Member of the Chinle Formation, Apache and Navajo Counties, Arizona. Plateau, 31:7-15.

Creber, G. and S. R. Ash. 1992. A widespread fungal epidemic on Upper Triassic trees in the southwestern United States. Review of Palaeobotany and Palynology, 63:189-195.

Creber, G. T., and S. R. Ash. 2004. The Late Triassic *Schilderia adamanica* and *Woodworthia arizonica* trees of the Petrified Forest National Park, Arizona, U.S.A. Palaeontology, 47:21-38.

Daugherty, L. H. 1941. Upper Triassic flora of Arizona. Carnegie Institute of Washington Publication, 526:1-108.

Demko, T. M., Dubiel, R. F., and J. T. Parrish. 1998. Plant taphonomy in incised valleys: implications for interpreting paleoclimate from fossil plants. Geology, 26:1119-1122.

Dubiel, R. F., Hasiotis, S. T., and T. M. Demko. 1999. Incised valley fills in the lower part of the Chinle Formation, Petrified Forest National Park, Arizona: Complete measured sections and regional stratigraphic implications of Upper Triassic rocks, p. 78-84. In V. L. Santucci and L. McClelland (eds.), National Park Service Paleontological Research Technical Report. Volume NPS/NRGD/GRDTR-99/03. National Park Service.

Dzik, J. 2003. A beaked herbivorous archosaur with dinosaur affinities from the early Late Triassic of Poland. Journal of Vertebrate Paleontology, 23:556-574.

Fisher, M. K., and R. E. Dunay. 1984. Palynology of the petrified Forest Member of the Chinle Formation (Upper Triassic), Arizona. U.S.A. Pollen et Spores, 26:241-284.

Good, S. C. 1998. Freshwater bivalve fauna of the Late Triassic (Carnian-Norian) Chinle, Dockum, and Dolores Formations of the Southwestern United States, pp. 1-27. In Johnson, P. (ed.), Bivalves: an eon of evolution, University of Calgary Press.

Gradstein, F. M., Ogg, J. G., and A. G. Smith. 2005. A Geologic Timescale 2004. Cambridge University Press, Cambridge, 610 p.

Gregory, H. E. 1917. Geology of Navajo Country – A reconnaissance of parts of Arizona. U. S. Geological Survey Professional Paper, 93, 161 p.

Heckert, A. B. 2004. Late Triassic microvertebrates from the lower Chinle Group (Otischalkian-Adamanian: Carnian) southwestern U.S.A.. New Mexico Museum of Natural History and Science Bulletin, 27:1-170.

Heckert, A. B., and S. G. Lucas. 1997. Lower Chinle Group (Adamanian:Latest Carnian) tetrapod biostratigraphy and biochronology, eastern Arizona and west-central New Mexico. Southwest Paleontological Society Symposium Proceedings, 1:13-24.

Heckert, A. B., and S. G. Lucas. 1998. The oldest Triassic strata exposed in the Petrified Forest National Park, Arizona, pp. 129-134. In Santucci, V. L., and L. McClelland (eds.), National Park Service Paleontological Research Volume NPS/NRGD/GRDTR-98/01. National Park Service.

Heckert, A. B., and S. G. Lucas. 2002. Revised Upper Triassic stratigraphy of the Petrified Forest National Park, Arizona, U.S.A. New Mexico Museum of Natural History and Science Bulletin 21:1-36.

Herrick, A. S., Fastovsky, D. E., and G. D. Hoke. 1999. Occurrences of Zamites powellii in oldest Norian strata in Petrified Forest National Park, pp. 91-95. In V. L. Santucci and L. McClelland (eds.), National Park Service Paleontological Research Technical Report. Volume NPS/NRGD/GRDTR-99/03. National Park Service.

Hungerbühler, A. 2001. Status and phylogenetic relationships of the Late Triassic phytosaur Rutiodon carolinensis. Journal of Vertebrate Paleontology, 21(3 Supplement):64A.

Hunt, A. P. 1998. Preliminary results of the Dawn of the Dinosaurs project at Petrified Forest National Park, Arizona, p. 135-137. In Santucci, V. L., and L. McClelland (eds.), National Park Service Paleontological Research Volume NPS/NRGD/GRDTR-98/01. National Park Service.

Hunt, A.P., and S. G. Lucas. 1992. The first occurrence of the aetosaur Paratypothorax andressi and its biochronological significance. Paläontologishe Zeitschrift, 66:147-157.

Hunt, A. P. and S. G. Lucas. 2005. A skull of Pseudopalatus from the Late Triassic (Late Carnian) Santa Rosa Formation of Central New Mexico, p. 28. In New Mexico Geological Society Proceedings Volume, 2005 Spring Meeting, Socorro.

Hunt, A. P., and J. Wright. 1999. New discoveries of Late Triassic Dinosaurs from Petrified Forest National Park, Arizona, p. 96-100. In V. L. Santucci and L. McClelland (eds.), National Park Service Paleontological Research Technical Report. Volume NPS/NRGD/GRDTR-99/03. National Park Service.

Hunt, A. P., Lucas, S. G., and A. B. Heckert. 2005. Definition and correlation of the Lamyan: A new biochronological unit for the non-marine late Carnian (Late Triassic). New Mexico Geological Society Guidebook, 56:357-366.

Hunt, A. P., Lucas, S. G., Heckert, A. B., Sullivan, R. M., and M. G. Lockley. 1998. Late Triassic dinosaurs from the Western United States. Geobios, 31:511-531.

Irmis, R. B. 2005. The vertebrate fauna of the Upper Triassic Chinle Formation in northern Arizona. Mesa Southwest Museum Bulletin, 9:63-88.

Irmis, R. B., and W. G. Parker. 2005. Unusual tetrapod teeth from the Upper Triassic Chinle Formation, Arizona. Canadian Journal of Earth Sciences, 42:1339-1345.

Johns, M. E. 1988. Architectural element analysis and depositional history of the Upper Petrified Forest Member of the Chinle Formation, Petrified Forest National Park, Arizona. Unpublished M. S. thesis, Northern Arizona University, 163p.

Jones, T. P., Ash, S. R., and I. Figueiral. 2002. Late Triassic charcoal from Petrified Forest National Park, Arizona, USA. Palaeogeography, Palaeoclimatology, Palaeoecology, 188:127-139.

Kirby, R. E., 1991. A vertebrate fauna from the Upper Triassic Owl Rock Member of the Chinle Formation of Northern Arizona. Unpublished M. S. Thesis, Northern Arizona University, 476 p.

Langer, M. C. 2005. Studies on continental Late Triassic tetrapod biochronology. II. The Ischigualastian and a Carnian global correlation. Journal of South American Earth Sciences, 19:219-239.

Lehman, T., and S. Chatterjee. 2005. The depositional setting and biostratigraphy of vertebrate fossil sites in the Triassic Dockum Group of Texas. Journal of Earth System Science, 114:325-351.

Litwin, R. J. 1986. The palynostratigraphy and age of the Chinle and Moenave Formations, southwestern United States. Unpublished Ph.D dissertation, Pennsylvania State University, 266 pp.

Litwin, R. J., Traverse, A., and S. R. Ash. 1991. Preliminary palynological zonation of the Chinle Formation, southwestern U.S.A., and its correlation to the Newark Supergroup (eastern U.S.A.). Review of Palaeobotany and Palynology, 68:269-287.

Long, R. A. and K. L. Ballew. 1985. Aetosaur dermal armor from the late Triassic of southwestern North America, with special reference to material from the Chinle Formation of Petrified Forest National Park. Museum of Northern Arizona Bulletin, 54:45-68.

Long, R. A., and P. A. Murry. 1995. Late Triassic (Carnian and Norian) tetrapods from the southwestern United States. New Mexico Museum of Natural History and Science Bulletin, 4:1-254.

Long, R. A., and K. Padian. 1986. Vertebrate biostratigraphy of the Late Triassic Chinle Formation, Petrified Forest National Park: preliminary results, pp. 161-169. In Padian, K. (ed.), The beginning of the age of dinosaurs: Faunal change across the Triassic-Jurassic boundary. Cambridge University Press, Cambridge.

Lucas, S. G. 1993. The Chinle Group: revised stratigraphy and chronology of Upper Triassic non-marine strata in the western United States. Museum of Northern Arizona Bulletin, 59:27-50.

Lucas, S. G. 1998. Global tetrapod biostratigraphy and biochronology. Palaeogeography, Palaeoclimatology, Palaeoecology, 143:347-384.

Lucas, S. G. and S. N. Hayden. 1989. Triassic stratigraphy of west-central New Mexico. New Mexico Geological Society Guidebook, 40:191-211.

Lucas, S. G., and A. P. Hunt. 1993. Tetrapod biochronology of the Chinle Group (Upper Triassic), western United States. New Mexico Museum of Natural History and Science Bulletin, 3:327-329.

Lucas, S. G., and A. B. Heckert. 1996. Vertebrate biochronology of the Late Triassic of Arizona. Mesa Southwest Museum Bulletin, 4:63-81.

Lucas, S. G., Heckert, A. B., and A. P. Hunt. 2002. A new species of the aetosaur Typothorax (Archosauria: Stagonolepididae) from the Upper Triassic of east-central New Mexico. New Mexico Museum of Natural History and Science Bulletin, 21:221-233.

Marcou, J. 1855. Resume of a geological reconnaissance extending from Napoleon, at the junction of the Arkansas with the Mississippi to the Pueblo de los Angeles, in California, p. 165-171. In Wipple, A. W., and others, report of the explorations for a railway route, near the 35th parallel of latitude from the Mississippi River to the Pacific Ocean. Report of the Secretary of War communicating the several Pacific Railroad Explorations, U. S. 33rd Congress, 1st session, Executive Document 129, 3:40-48.

Martz, J. W. 2002. The morphology and ontogeny of Typothorax coccinarum (Archosauria, Stagonolepididae) from the Upper Triassic of the American Southwest. Unpublished M.S. thesis. Texas Tech University, Lubbock, 279 p.

Miller, G. L. and S. R. Ash. 1988. The oldest freshwater decapod crustacean from the Triassic of Arizona. Palaeontology, 31:272-279.

Murry, P. A. 1989. Microvertebrate fossils from the Petrified Forest and Owl Rock Members (Chinle Formation) in Petrified Forest National Park and vicinity, Arizona, p. 249-277. In S. G. Lucas and A. P. Hunt (eds.), Dawn of the age of dinosaurs in the American Southwest. New Mexico Museum of Natural History, Albuquerque.

Murry, P. A. and R. A. Long. 1989. Geology and paleontology of the Chinle Formation, Petrified Forest National Park and vicinity, Arizona and a discussion of vertebrate fossils of the southwestern Upper Triassic, pp. 29-64. In S. G. Lucas and A. P. Hunt (eds.),

Dawn of the age of dinosaurs in the American Southwest. New Mexico Museum of Natural History, Albuquerque.

Muttoni, G., Kent, D. V., Olsen, P. E., DiStefano, P., Lowrie, W., Bernasconi, S. M., and F. M. Hernández. 2004. Tethyan magnetostratigraphy from Pizzo Mondello (Sicily) and correlation to the Late Triassic Newark astrochronological polarity timescale. Geological Society of America Bulletin, 116:1043-1058.

Padian, K., 1986. On the type material of *Coelophysis* Cope (Saurischia: Theropoda), and a new specimen from the Petrified Forest of Arizona (Late Triassic: Chinle Formation), pp. 45-60. *In* Padian, K. (ed.), The beginning of the Age of Dinosaurs: Faunal change across the Triassic-Jurassic boundary. Cambridge University Press, Cambridge.

Padian, K. 1990. The ornithischian form genus *Revueltosaurus* from the Petrified Forest of Arizona (Late Triassic; Norian; Chinle Formation). Journal of Vertebrate Paleontology, 10:268-269.

Parker, W.G. 2002. Correlation of locality numbers for vertebrate fossil sites in Petrified Forest National Park, Arizona. New Mexico Museum of Natural History and Science Bulletin, 21:37-42.

Parker, W. G. 2005a. A new species of the Late Triassic aetosaur *Desmatosuchus* (Archosauria: Pseudosuchia). Compte Rendus Palevol, 4:327-340.

Parker, W. G. 2005b. Faunal review of the Upper Triassic Chinle Formation of Arizona. Mesa Southwest Museum Bulletin, 11:34-54.

Parker, W. G. In press. Reassessment of the aetosaur "*Desmatosuchus*" *chamaensis* with a reanalysis of the phylogeny of the Aetosauria (Archosauria: Pseudosuchia). Journal of Systematic Palaeontology 5.

Parker, W. G. and S. Clements. 2004. First year results of the ongoing paleontological inventory of Petrified Forest National Park, Arizona, pp. 201-210. *In* Van Riper, C. III and K. Cole (eds.), The Colorado Plateau: Cultural, Biological, and Physical Research, University of Arizona Press, Tucson.

Parker, W. G. and R. B. Irmis. 2005. Advances in vertebrate paleontology based on new material from Petrified Forest National Park, Arizona. New Mexico Museum of Natural History and Science Bulletin, 29:45-58.

Parker, W. G., Irmis, R. B., Nesbitt, S. N., Martz, J. W., and L. S. Browne. 2005. The pseudosuchian *Revueltosaurus callenderi* and its implications for the diversity of early ornithischian dinosaurs. Proceedings of the Royal Society of London B, 272:963-969.

Parrish, J. M., 1991. A new specimen of an early crocodylomorph (*cf. Sphenosuchus sp.*) from the Upper Triassic Chinle Formation of Petrified Forest National Park, Arizona. Journal of Vertebrate Paleontology, 11:198-212.

Pocock, A. J., and G. Vasanthy. 1988. *Cornetipollis reticulata*, a new pollen with angiospermic features from Upper Triassic (Carnian) sediments of Arizona (U.S.A.) with notes on *Equisetosporites*. Review of Palaeobotany and Palynology, 55:337-356.

Rayfield, E. J., Barrett, P. M., Mcdonnell, R. A., and K. J. Willis. 2005. A Geographical Information System (GIS) study of Triassic vertebrate biochronology. Geological Magazine, 142:327-354.

Riggs, N. R., Ash, S. R., Barth, A. P., Gehrels, G. E., and J. L. Wooden. 2003. Isotopic age of the Black Forest Bed, Petrified Forest Member, Chinle Formation, Arizona: an example of dating a continental sandstone. Geological Society of America Bulletin, 115:1315-1323.

Small, B. J. 1989. Aetosaurs from the Upper Triassic Dockum Formation, Post Quarry, west Texas, p. 301-308. *In* Lucas, S. G. and A. P. Hunt (eds.), Dawn of the age of dinosaurs in the American Southwest, New Mexico Museum of Natural History, Albuquerque.

Stagner, H. R. 1941. Geology of the fossil leaf beds of the Petrified Forest National Monument [Ariz.]. Carnegie Institute of Washington Publication, 526:9-17.

Steiner, M. B., and S. G. Lucas. 2000. Paleomagnetism of the Late Triassic Petrified Forest Formation, Chinle Group, western United States; further evidence of "large" rotation of the Colorado Plateau. Journal of Geophysical Research, B, Solid Earth and Planets, 105:25791-25808.

Stewart, J. H., Poole, F. G. and R. F. Wilson. 1972a. Changes in nomenclature of the Chinle Formation on the southern part of the Colorado Plateau: 1850s-1950s. Museum of Northern Arizona Bulletin, 47:75-103.

Stewart, J. H., Poole, F. G., and Wilson, R. F. 1972b. Stratigraphy and origin of the Chinle Formation and related Upper Triassic strata in the Colorado Plateau region. U.S. Geological Survey Professional Paper, 690, 336 p.

Therrien, F., and D. E. Fastovsky. 2000. Paleoenvironments of early theropods, Chinle Formation (Late Triassic), Petrified Forest National Park, Arizona. Palaios, 15:194-211.

Therrien, F., Jones M. M., Fastovsky, D. E., Hoke, G. D., and A. S. Herrick. 1999. The oldest Triassic strata exposed in Petrified Forest National Park revisited, pp. 101-108. *In* V. L. Santucci and L. McClelland (eds.), National Park Service Paleontological Research Technical Report. Volume NPS/NRGD/GRDTR-99/03. National Park Service.

Walker, M. V. 1936. Report on the excavation of a standing tree. Unpublished Naturalist's Report to the Superintendent, Petrified Forest National Park Archives, 6 p.

Ward, L. F. 1905. Status of the Mesozoic floras of the United States (2nd paper). U.S. Geological Survey Monograph, 48, pt. 1, 616 p.

Woody, D. T. 2003. Revised geological assessment of the Sonsela Member, Chinle Formation, Petrified Forest National Park, Arizona. Unpublished M. S. thesis, Northern Arizona University, Flagstaff, 207 p.

PALEOBOTANY

Parker, W. G., Ash, S. R., and Irmis, R. B., eds., 2006,
A Century of Research at Petrified Forest National Park: Geology and Paleontology.
Museum of Northern Arizona Bulletin No. 62.

ARBORAMOSA SEMICIRCUMTRACHEA, AN UNUSUAL LATE TRIASSIC TREE IN PETRIFIED FOREST NATIONAL PARK, ARIZONA, USA

RODNEY A. SAVIDGE[1] AND SIDNEY R. ASH[2]

[1]Faculty of Forestry and Environmental Management, University of New Brunswick, Fredericton, Canada E3B 6C2 <savi@unb.ca>
[2]Department of Earth and Planetary Sciences, Northrop Hall, University of New Mexico, Albuquerque 87131-1116 <sidash@aol.com>

ABSTRACT – A petrified stem from the Late Triassic Chinle Formation in Petrified Forest National Park, Arizona has a fluted wood surface and spirally distributed branch stubs emerging from within fusiform depressions, giving the stem a coarsely braided appearance similar to some modern *Juniperus* trees. In cross section, the secondary xylem exhibits growth interruptions and comprises jumbled radial files of thick-walled, rounded and semi-rounded tracheids, and infrequent, short, homogeneous, uniseriate rays. Circular, equi-diameter, spatially separated bordered pits occur as linear, uniseriate chains on diagonal and tangential as well as radial walls of the 10-mm-long tracheids. The ray cells have distantly spaced taxodioid, rarely cupressoid, crossfield pits in their thin radial and horizontal walls. Morphological and tracheidoxyl phenotypes of the stem are indicative of a new genus and species, a transient genetic anomaly within a landscape dominated by trees having araucarian wood.

Keywords: Arizona, Chinle Formation, Upper Triassic, conifer, Araucariaceae

INTRODUCTION

PETRIFIED WOOD contains information about form, size, ecophysiological adaptations and fundamental biological processes which once occurred in the living woody plant. Fossil woods can readily be found in the Upper Triassic Chinle Formation of Petrified Forest National Park (PEFO), northeastern Arizona, USA. However, only nine fossil species having secondary xylem have been identified in PEFO, only five of these nine had more than a centimeter of secondary xylem, and no new log-sized species has been described since 1941 (Table 1). Moreover, most of the descriptions of petrified wood in PEFO are based on just one or two specimens and cannot be described as comprehensive. This rudimentary state of knowledge about the petrified woods in PEFO is unfortunate, as paleobotanists recognized more than a century ago that "any description of fossil wood which is to be of use in the future must include an exhaustive analysis of all the characters, both absolute and relative, which have not been proved to be purely fanciful" (Barber, 1898). Counterbalancing the present dearth of information is the responsible management of PEFO woods for ongoing investigation.

Petrified logs of a conifer referred to as *Araucarioxylon arizonicum* Knowlton (1888) are found throughout PEFO as the largest fossils (Table 1). In addition to *A. arizonicum*, several other Triassic *Araucarioxylon* species have been described in North America (Knowlton, 1919). However, as explained by Bamford and Philippe (2001), the name *Araucarioxylon* (*sic*, originally *Araucaroxylon* – Kraus, 1870) is actually invalid according to the rules of the International Code of Botanical Nomenclature (Greuter et al., 1999), and many tracheidoxyls (i.e., permineralized fragments of pycnoxylic secondary xylem – Creber, 1972) formerly ascribed to that genus have been reclassified into *Agathoxylon,* a genus created by Hartig (1848). Further research is needed to decide if *A. arizonicum* should be emended to *Agathoxylon* or another genus, but photomicrographs by Daugherty (1941) of putative *A. arizonicum* wood (from PEFO) are not in good agreement with the original description of *A. arizonicum* wood (also from PEFO) made by Knowlton (1888). It seems probable that some of the large logs in PEFO are species different from *A. arizonicum*.

Although they are smaller and not nearly as abundant as those of *A. arizonicum*, logs of *Woodworthia arizonica* Jeffrey, 1910 and *Schilderia adamanica* Daugherty, 1934 are the type species of two monotypic genera found only in the Black Forest Bed of PEFO, usually in close proximity to logs of *A. arizonicum*. As indicated in Table 2, *W. arizonica* has secondary xylem similar to that of *A. arizonicum* and, like the latter, is thought to have been a conifer, but it is readily distinguished by having numerous short shoots embedded throughout its wood (Jeffrey, 1910; Daugherty, 1941; Creber and Ash, 2004). *S. adamanica* has manoxylic wood containing conspicuously wide herring-bone rays similar to those in the secondary xylem of the extant genus *Ephedra* (Gnetophyta, Ephedraceae), making it entirely distinct from both *A. arizonicum* and *W. arizonica* (Daugherty, 1934, 1941).

Dadoxylon chaneyi (Daugherty, 1941) is a fourth kind of petrified wood in PEFO. However, for similar reasons to those invalidating *Araucarioxylon*, the name *Dadoxylon* is not acceptable within ICBN rules (Bamford and Philippe, 2001). *Dadoxylon* has a history of being applied rather liberally to a heterogeneous group of woods having araucarian features in Pityaceae, Cordaitaceae and Coniferae (Darrah, 1939). In addition, since the early 20th century paleobotanists have shown a tendency to use *Dadoxylon* to refer to Paleozoic woods and *Araucarioxylon* to refer to Mesozoic or more recent woods (Darrah, 1939), although such usage based on geological age was not accepted by all (Seward, 1917). *Dadoxylon* as originally used (Endlicher, 1847) required the presence of large diameter pith, a characteristic of Cordaitales (Seward, 1917; Arnold, 1947; Lepekhina, 1972; Stewart, 1983), whereas *Araucarioxylon arizonicum* as a conifer has small diameter pith (Ash and Savidge, 2004). The specimen described by Daugherty (1941) had a non-discoid pith 16 mm in diameter, surrounded by secondary xylem *c.* 2 cm in radial thickness. As noted by Seward (1917), a discoid pith although common is not an invariable attribute of stems closely allied to the Cordaites. In view of the above problems, we suggest that *Dadoxylon chaneyi* (Daugherty, 1941) be re-examined for its taxonomic affinity.

A fifth kind of wood that was collected a short distance west of the PEFO park boundary is *Lyssoxylon grigsbyi* Daugherty (1941). Daugherty (1941) interpreted *L. grigsbyi* to be a cycadeoid (family Williamsoniaceae) on the basis of a fragment of wood with attached cycad-like bark. However, subsequent research indicated the fossil to be a true cycad (Gould, 1971; Vozenin-Serra, 1979). *Lyssoxylon grigsbyi* has spiral-banded secondary-xylem tracheids, well-spaced circular bordered pits and both uni- and multi-seriate fusiform rays (Table 2). Another cycad, *Charmorgia dijolli* Ash (1985) having a short stubby stem, large diameter pith and a narrow width of araucarian xylem, also is known (Table 1).

The fossil tree stem described here as *Arboramosa semicircumtrachea* n. gen. et n. sp. occurs in the Crystal Forest of PEFO and has phenotypic features distinguishing it from *A. arizonicum*, *W. arizonica*, *S. adamanica*, *D. chaneyi* and *L. grigsbyi* (Table 2). Its stem and tracheidoxyl appear not only to be unique in relation to known petrified logs in PEFO but distinct from all known fossil woods. The integrated morphological/anatomical phenotype points to the tree having been a transitional species, possibly a distant ancestor of trees like our modern junipers.

PREVIOUS INVESTIGATIONS

The first plant fossils to be collected for scientific study from the region that is now contained within the boundaries of Petrified Forest National Park were pieces of petrified wood. As noted by several authors (e.g., Knowlton,1888; Daugherty, 1941; and Ash, 1972), they were collected in 1853 from the Black Forest Bed of the Chinle Formation in Lithodendron Wash in the northern part of the park by members of the U.S. Army Exploring Expedition led by Lt. A. W. Whipple. Tracheidoxyls collected at that time by the German traveler Baldwin Möllhausen were given to the German paleobotanist H. R. Göppert who reported that they were of the Abietina and Araucaria types (Göppert, 1858). In the same book, Göppert

also named one specimen of wood *Araucarites möllhausianus*, but he neglected to describe the species and the name is therefore considered a "nomen nudum" (Ward, 1900, p. 317). Additional specimens collected in the same area by other members of the expedition were turned over to the American geologist W. P. Blake (in Whipple, 1855) who reported that the wood structure was "distinctly" preserved in them, but Blake did not identify the woods. In 1879 two large sections of a log were collected from the Black Forest Bed in the same general area by U.S. Army soldiers under the command of Lt. J. T. C. Hegewald and shipped to the Smithsonian Institution in Washington, D.C., for exhibit (Swaine and Hegewald, 1882). That log was later studied by the American paleobotanist Frank Knowlton who, in 1888, described the tree as *Araucarioxylon arizonicum*. Thereafter, fossil wood having the gross morphology of *A. arizonicum* has been reported from many Upper Triassic localities in the southwest, but the internal anatomy of the wood has only been studied by a few of the later workers. Daugherty (1941) published three photomicrographs of "*Araucarioxylon arizonicum*", but he merely repeated Knowlton's diagnosis in his discussion of the species and did not localize the figured material. The bordered pits in one of the three photomicrographs published by Daugherty (1941) are abietinian, not araucarian, and the other two photomicrographs appear not to be *A. arizonicum* secondary xylem as described by Knowlton (1888) or others subsequently (e.g., Scott, 1961; Turkel, 1968; Ash and Savidge, 2004). Thus, it could well be that Daugherty (1941) unwittingly showed that not all of the large logs in PEFO are in fact *A. arizonicum*. Scott (1961) reported that he had examined petrified wood from an unspecified number of localities in the Upper Triassic of the southwestern USA and concluded that all of it belonged to *A. arizonicum*. Turkel (1968) studied the anatomy of several specimens of petrified wood from PEFO for his PhD degree, but he never published his findings. In recent years, the anatomy of *A. arizonicum*-like wood found in PEFO was described in connection with other studies (Ash and Creber, 1992, 2000; Ash and Savidge, 2004).

Within this background, the fossil described here as *Arboramosa semicircumtrachea* n. gen. et n. sp. was earlier assumed to be the upper part of a stem of an *Araucarioxylon arizonicum* tree (Ash and Creber 2000). However, that interpretation was made without having examined the anatomy of the wood. Our observations make it clear that *Arboramosa semicircumtrachea* is unrelated to *A. arizonicum*.

LOCALITY AND REPOSITORY INFORMATION

The stem described here is embedded in the lower part of the Sonsela Member of the Chinle Formation in Crystal Forest, one of the four areas in PEFO containing large concentrations of fossil wood and, therefore, designated a "forest" (Ash, 1987). The fossil lies in the Jim Camp Wash Beds, the same unit that contains the petrified logs in Crystal Forest (Parker, this volume).

       The site where the stem is situated has been assigned locality number PFP 116 in the collection records of Petrified Forest National Park. Qualified investigators may obtain its exact location from the Chief of Resource Management, Petrified Forest National Park The slides and uncut material removed from the stem are stored in the PEFO fossil collection under catalog number PEFO 34160.

METHODS

       To investigate the wood anatomy of the fossil, small samples were chiselled from several locations along the stem, and transverse, radial and tangential surfaces were cut and ground to 30 μm thickness for microscopy. The images presented here (Figs. 2.1 – 4.9) are based on transmitted light microscopy, using a stage micrometer (precision ±2μm) for measurements. Digitized images of both the micrometer scale and the fossil were enlarged by printing, enabling distance estimates to the nearest 0.1μm from measurements on the prints.

       A piece of the permineralized wood having good anatomical preservation was analyzed for K, U, and Pb contents by electron microprobe (JEOL-733, equipped with Geller automation, 15 kV, probe current 30 nA), using U metal, crocoite and orthoclase as calibration standards. The average K content of the secondary xylem was very low, 0.011 wt.%. Neither U nor Pb was above detection limits (0.04 wt % and 0.03 wt %, respectively).

OBSERVATIONS

Morphological features.–Measurements of the fossil's surface features were made in the field. The exposed surface of the fossil, shown in Figures 1.1and 1.2, reveals a stem *c.* 8 m in length and 55 cm in basal diameter, tapering somewhat to where the top of the tree becomes overlain with bentonite and round-

Table 1–Known megafossils in Petrified Forest National Park, Arizona, having secondary xylem of diameter more than 1 cm. Listed in order of abundance.

Species and Authority	Number of specimens[1]	Diameter (m)	Taxonomic Division	Stratigraphic Horizon[2]	Principal Locations in the park[2]
Araucarioxylon[3] *arizonicum* Knowlton, 1888	>10000	>1	Coniferophyta	Sonsela Mbr	Rainbow, Crystal, and Jasper Forest
Araucarioxylon[3] *arizonicum* Knowlton, 1888	>1000	>1	Coniferophyta	Black Forest Bed, Petrified Forest Mbr	Lithodendron and Dead Washes
Woodworthia arizonica Jeffrey, 1910	>1000	~0.5	Coniferophyta	Black Forest Bed, Petrified Forest Mbr	Lithodendron and Dead Washes
Schilderia adamanica Daugherty, 1934	>1000	~0.5	Coniferophyta	Black Forest Bed, Petrified Forest Mbr	Lithodendron and Dead Washes
Charmogia dijolli Ash, 1985	2	0.01	Cycadophyta	Blue Mesa Member	Tepees Area
Lyssoxylon grigsbyi Daugherty, 1941	1	0.02	Cycadophyta	Blue Mesa Member	Adamana Area
Dadoxylon chaneyi[4] Daugherty, 1941	1	0.02	Coniferophyta	Blue Mesa Member	Tepees Area
Arboramosa semicircumtrachea gen. et sp. nov	1	~0.5	Coniferophyta	Jim Camp Wash beds	Crystal Forest

Notes: [1]Estimates based on the scientific literature and casual field observations. [2] For more complete information on stratigraphic horizons and localities see Parker, this volume. [3]*Araucarioxylon* is an invalid genus (see text). [4]*Dadoxylon* is an invalid genus (see text).

ed pebbles of about 1 cm diameter. Bark is not present, but the outer surface of the secondary xylem is non-eroded and can be assumed to have been in contact with cambium when the tree was alive. The surface wood grain is straight, though slightly sinuous, at both the basal and apical ends of the exposed stem; however, between those positions it spirals upward to the right at an angle of c. 8° from the stem axis. The stem base is not buttressed but is fluted, similar to extant trees within the Cupressaceae (e.g., *Juniperus*, *Taxodium*, and *Thuja* spp.). The branch stubs are positioned within axially oriented fusiform-shaped depressions, or concavities, in the surface wood (Figs. 1.2, 1.3). The manner in which the branches join the stem is unlike that of either *Taxodium* or *Thuja* spp. but is quite similar to that found on older stems of some tree-form junipers, such as *J. virginiana* L. (Figs. 1.4, 1.5). Singular branch stubs occupy some stem depressions, but two or more separated by a few centimeters may also occur in one depression, both on the fossil (Fig. 1.2) and in *J. virginiana* (Fig. 1.4). The branch stubs exhibit only a small increase in diameter over the 8 m from top to base of the fossil. The fusiform depressions with their branch stubs are regularly distributed and could be envisaged as describing either an upward-to-the-left or an upward-to-the-right spiral, again a feature of junipers. The spiralled distribution of branches and the small diameters of the branch stubs are evidence that the tree had a dense crown, possibly conical or columnar in its form.

Tracheidoxyl features.–The secondary xylem is well preserved in some parts of the fossil (Figs. 2, 3, 4). Uniformly thick-walled longitudinal tracheids and homogeneous thin-walled uniseriate ray cells are the only two cell types that could be conclusively identified in the secondary xylem, although scattered axial parenchyma may also be present. Thus, at low magnification (Figs. 2.1, 2.2) the xylem could be confused with Paleozoic Cordaiteae woods, e.g., *Cordaioxylon* or *Mesoxylon*. However, when examined in detail it is more complex than that of cordaites with some quite unusual features. In cross sections of the stem, both the inter-tracheid wall contacts and tracheid lumens rarely exhibit any angularity; generally they are circular, elliptical or semi-circular. Tracheids in adjoining radial files for the most part occupy positions of alternate arrangement, rather than being in ranked tiers (Figs. 2.2, 3.1-3.6). Tracheid diameters vary from <10 to >70 μm. The variable diameters, outlines, arrangement and intercellular spacing give the radial files a jumbled appearance (Figs. 2.2, 3.1-3.3).

Micrometric measurements of the secondary xylem elements provided the following data: single-wall thickness of tracheid secondary walls ranges from 6 to 11 μm, with the S_2 layer being the dominant feature, the S_3 layer c. 2 μm and the S_1 less, c. 1 μm (Figs. 2.8, 3.4-3.6, 4.9). Tracheid tangential diameter at mid-length is c. 55 μm, reaching 70 μm in tracheids of circular cross section (Fig. 2.3). The corresponding width in the radial direction reaches 100 μm in tracheids having semi-circular or elliptical cross sections (Figs. 3.4, 3.6); however, it reduces to as little as 15 μm at growth interruptions (Fig. 2.1), and circular tracheid tips can be less than 10 μm in diameter (Fig. 3.5). Tracheids 10 mm in length are common, and still longer ones were noted (Fig. 2.3). Microfibril angle, measured as the angular deviation from the tracheid long axis, is 32-36° in the S_2 (Figs. 4.1, 4.3- 4.5). The angles in the S_1 and S_3 layers are parallel at c. 45° in the orientation opposing that of the S_2 (Figs. 4.1, 4.4). The microfibrils do not display major checking but have conspicuous parallel striations except in the thin S_1 layer where some waviness is evident (Figs. 4.1, 4.8).

Axial parenchyma may be present (Figs. 2.1, 2.5), and tracheids having presumed resinous 'septa' may rarely be found (Fig. 4.3). Evidence for scalariform ribbing of the walls was encountered in a single longitudinal xylem element (Fig. 4.2); that ribbing could not be well resolved and may be artifactual or indicative of an infrequent cell type distinct from the trilaminate tracheids. Axial resin canals and spiral-banded tracheids were not found in the secondary xylem.

The rays in the secondary xylem consist of uniseriate thin-walled parenchyma, only. Viewed in cross section, the rays are widely spaced, not uncommonly separated by more than 20 radial files of tracheids, although less wide spacing is also seen (Figs. 2.1, 2.2). In tangential section, the number of rays in contact with both sides of an individual 10-mm-long tracheid is fewer than 10, a low frequency compared to what has been observed for extant conifers having tracheids only a mm long (Bannan and Bayly, 1956; Bannan, 1965). The rays in the fossil are short (80 – 400 μm), from one to fifteen and usually four to eight cells in height (Figs. 2.3, 2.4, 2.6). Viewed in tangential section, the ray cells are either elliptical or have compressed horizontal walls, with axial diameter c. 25-30 μm and horizontal width 10-18 μm (Fig. 2.6). Intercellular spaces within rays are not evident, and spaces created by walls of adjoining rounded tracheids commonly are occupied by ray cells (Figs. 2.8, 3.1-3.6). In radial section, the rays comprise homogeneous, thin-walled, tube-like, non-swollen parenchyma cells, usually with ergastic contents (Figs. 2.4, 2.7). Neither ray tracheids nor horizontal resin canals were seen. Where ray cells and axial tracheids contact, the cross-fields in radial

Figure 1. *Arboramosa semicircumtrachea* (*1-3*) and *Juniperus virginia* (*4-5*). *1.* The investigated fossil; a long stem flute can be seen to the right of the hammerhead; *2.* Mid-region of the stem shown in Figure 2.1. Single and multiple branch stubs (arrow heads) having both upward-to-left and upward-to-right spiralling placement exit from fusiform cavities; *3.* Near the apical end of the exposed fossil, showing two or more large fusiform cavities in close proximity (arrow); *4.* Base of *Juniperus virginia* stem showing two branch junctions within a fusiform depression (arrows); *5.* In the upper stem of the same *J. virginia*, the young branches develop prior to the appearance of stem concavities. Scale bars: 2, 3=10 cm; 4=5 cm; 5=2 cm. Images in Figures 1-3 show the holotype, PEFO 34160.

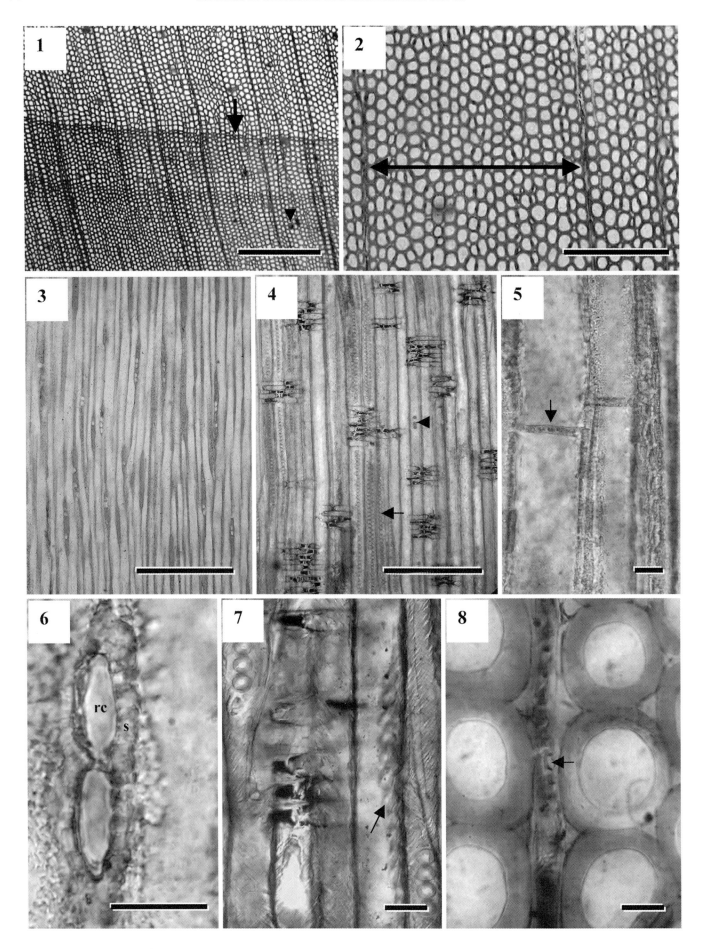

section contain 1 - 6, but usually 4 oculipores equidistantly spaced at *c*. 12 μm apart (Figs. 4.7, 4.8). When four are present, they are positioned at the corners of a square with imaginary connecting lines paralleling the ray cell walls (Fig. 4.8). The long axis of the oculipore aperture is slanted at *c*. 45°. Dimensions of the oculipore border are *c*. 10 μm X 5 μm, with the elliptical aperture > 3 μm wide and extending to 8 μm, never beyond the oculipore border. Similar pitting occurs in the horizontal walls of the ray cells (Fig. 2.8). Pitting of the tangential walls was not seen. By definition, the pits are mostly taxodioid, but cupressoid oculipores having slit-like apertures were also encountered. Borders are not everywhere obvious around the oculipore apertures, and some apertures have an X or V shape, their long axes extending in both the S_1 - S_3 as well as the nearly perpendicular S_2 microfibril directions. Thus, some oopores may also be present, but none were definitively resolved.

Abietinoid bordered pits are abundant in the secondary xylem. Most commonly they occur as long, straight, uniseriate chains of equi-diameter pits, but they are also found in biseriate rank, loosely arranged oppositely or alternately (Figs. 2.4, 2.7, 4.3-4.6). The alignment of pits in the uniseriate chains is parallel to the long axis of the tracheid (Figs. 2.4, 4.3), and a chain of contiguous pits commonly extends for more than a millimeter (Fig. 2.4). The border and aperture of the pits are rounded, usually circular, rarely somewhat flattened horizontally (Fig. 4.3). When in uniseriate rank, the axial distance between bordered pits varies from 3 μm to contacting one another. Where the pits are biseriate and arranged alternately, spaces may or may not separate their margins, so that they can appear to be either abietinoid or araucaroid (Fig. 4.6). Rims of Sanio (crassulae) were not seen.

The horizontal, or circumferential, placement of bordered pits in the walls of tracheids evidently can be at any position where two tracheids are in contact (Figs. 3.1, 3.3). Regardless of where placed circumferentially, bordered pits have the same diameter (16-18 μm) within a narrow range. The bordered-pit aperture (4-5 μm diameter) is generally circular, and a torus is not present. Because of the thickness of the secondary walls, the pit opening tends to be a short cylindrical tunnel extending between the bordered-pit chamber and the lumen (Fig. 3.4). Slit-shaped apertures were infrequently observed and may be artifactual, caused by cell-wall checking. The nature of the bordered pits, manifesting rigid intrinsic

regulation of diameter and vertical alignment but sporadic spacing and placement around the circumference, is unusual.

The rounded tracheids and intercellular spaces seen in cross sections of the fossil recall compression wood (Timell, 1983), as do the relatively steep microfibril angles in the secondary-wall lamellae as seen in longitudinal sections (Figs. 4.1, 4.3-4.5). On the other hand, secondary walls lacking the S_3 layer are characteristic of compression-wood tracheids, and the fossil's secondary walls exhibit tri-laminate S_1, S_2, S_3 layers (Figs. 2.8, 4.9). The spiral checks that are characteristic of the S_2 layer of compression wood are not present in the fossil wood. Moreover, bordered pits are infrequent, even entirely absent, in compression-wood tracheids (Trendelenburg, 1932), whereas the fossil's circular tracheids have abundant bordered pits on all wall surfaces (Figs. 2.4, 2.7, 4.3). When bordered pits do occur in compression wood, the apertures appear to be crossed by diagonal slits that extend beyond the pit annulus and parallel the S_2 microfibrillar orientation within the two adjoining secondary walls (Timell, 1986). In contrast, the apertures in the fossil are circular and do not extend beyond the pit annulus. True compression-wood tracheids tend to be short (Timell, 1986), but the tracheids in the investigated fossil are exceptionally elongated, 10 mm and more in length.

Abrupt, mildly to sharply defined growth interruptions are seen in cross sections of the xylem (Fig. 2.1). The existence of these was determined by measurement to be due to synchronously reduced radial expansion of adjoining cambial derivatives, rather than to an increase in the thickness of the secondary walls, which tend to be uniformly thick throughout the xylem (Fig. 2.1). It cannot be assumed that the rings indicate occurrence of annual cycles of growth and dormancy, as a momentary reduction in radial expansion of cambial derivatives can occur in active cambium in response to a transient limiting supply of an environmental factor, such as water or warmth (Savidge, 1993).

Sections of well-preserved pith were not obtained, but on the basis of both microscopic and macroscopic observation, the pith was of small diameter.

SYSTEMATIC PALEONTOLOGY

Family uncertain
Genus ARBORAMOSA new genus

Figure 2. *Arboramosa semicircumtrachea*. *1*. Cross section showing a growth interruption (arrowed) and evidence for another, less obvious one below. The arrowhead indicates what may be an infrequent resiniferous tracheid or axial parenchyma. Thin section PEFO 34160A1; *2*. Cross section; the arrowed line spans 20+ radial files of tracheids between two rays. Thin section PEFO 34160A1; *3*. Tangential section showing the short, distantly spaced rays. Thin section PEFO 34160C1; *4*. Radial section showing ray heights and the general presence of ergastic material in the ray parenchyma. A long chain of uniseriate pits is indicated by the arrow and an isolated trio by the arrowhead. Thin section PEFO 34160B1; *5*. Tangential section of two septa (one arrowed) indicative of axial parenchyma. Thin section PEFO 34160C1; *6*. Tangential section showing elliptical ray cells (rc) and adjoining secondary wall (s) of a tracheids. Thin section PEFO 34160C1; *7*. Radial section showing bordered pits on diagonally oriented (arrowed) as well as radial walls. Thin section PEFO 34160B1; *8*. Cross section showing taxodioid/cupressoid oculipores (one arrowed) in the horizontal walls of ray cells. Thin section PEFO 34160A1. Scale bars: 1=1 mm; 2-4=0.5 mm; 5=20 μm; 6=25 μm; 7=50 μm; 8=20 μm. All sections made from the holotype PEFO 34160.

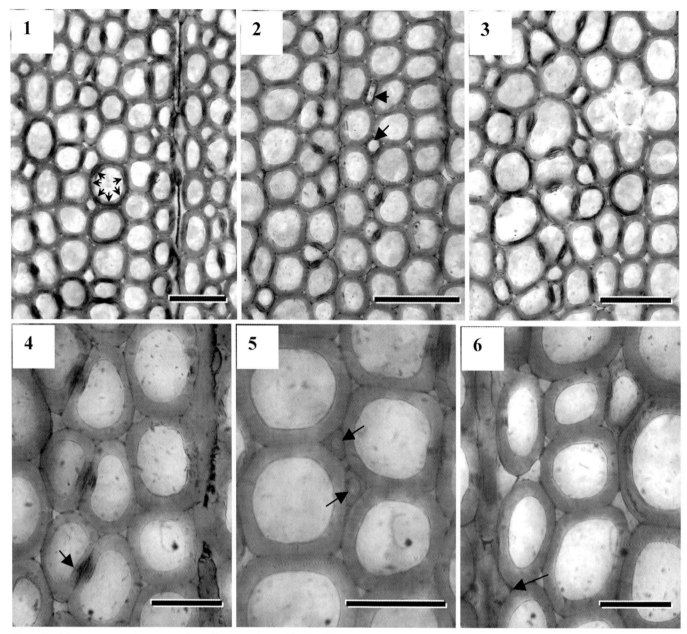

Figure 3. *Arboramosa semicircumtrachea.* Cross sections of the fossil's secondary xylem. *1.* Note the variable diameter but generally thick-walled tracheids. The six arrowheads indicate six bordered-pit pairs at positions around the circumference where the circular tracheid contacts other tracheids; *2.* Tapered tracheid ends (arrowed) can be seen intruding between the radial files. Note the irregular placement of the bordered-pit pairs, conspicuous in the diagonal walls; *3.* Tracheid radial files are poorly organized due to tracheid circularity, variable diameter and intrusive growth; *4.* Semi-rounded tracheids having bordered-pit pairs (one is arrowed) in their straight, diagonally oriented walls; *5.* Small-diameter thick-walled tracheid tips (arrows) occupy locations that otherwise would be intercellular spaces; *6.* Tracheids, particularly where they adjoin rays, exhibit radially stretched, rounded outlines in cross section. The thin primary walls of ray parenchyma cells evidently grow into intercellular spaces between the circular tracheids (arrow). Scale bars: 1-3=100 µm; 4-6=50 µm. All images were made from the holotype, thin section PEFO 34160A1.

Type species.–Arboramosa semicircumtrachea sp. nov. by monotypy.

Diagnosis.–Secondary xylem surface with fusiform-shaped cavities parallel to main stem axis in regular spiralled arrangement; lateral branch stubs egress from fusiform-shaped cavities. Secondary xylem tracheids round to semi-round in transverse section, having bordered pits on all wall surfaces, mixed but mostly abietinian pitting, axial parenchyma present but scarce; xylem pycnoxylic, composed of thin-walled homogeneous uniseriate ray cells, oculipore cross-field pittting; other parenchyma wanting.

Description.–The wood surface of the main stem has a coarsely braided appearance because of its axially oriented fusiform-shaped concavities and the slightly enhanced secondary growth of the stem around the boundaries of those depressions (Figs. 1.1-1.3). The placement of the fusiform concavities is well spaced, precisely regular and could be interpreted as spiralling, either upward-to-the-left or upward-to-the-right, at an angle of *c.* 45° (Fig. 1.2). Branches, or stubs of former branches, connect with the stem within the fusiform depressions. Singular branch stubs occur in some, but two or more may be in close association within the same concavity, one a few cm above the other (Fig. 1.2). The branch stubs generally are of small diameter, being a few centimeters or less on a stem 50 cm in diameter and exhibiting only a small decrease in diameter with increasing stem height, an indication that the branch bases possessed limited capacity for secondary growth when living. Some of the branch bases probably had persisted on the stem of the living tree as dead branch wood. The base of the fossil is grooved, or fluted, in the axial direction over distances exceeding a meter.

Etymology.–The Latin *arbor* (tree) and *ramosa* (branchy) were combined to denote the branchiness of the tree.

Occurrence.–PEFO locality number PFP 116 in the Jim Camp Wash Beds in the Sonsela Member of the Chinle Formation (minimum age of 210 Ma, Riggs et al., 2003).

Discussion.–Branches or branch stubs provide a morphological record of the earlier activity of shoot apical meristems from which the branches originate (Fahn, 1977), as well as that of the vascular cambium, whereas the phenotype of a tracheidoxyl fragment or a decorticated stem or log surface with little or no branching contains only a record of the activity of the lateral meristem (Bannan and Bayly, 1956; Bannan, 1965; Fahn, 1973). The stem morphology is that of extant Cupressaceae, and *Arboramosa* n. gen. fails to satisfy the conditions needed for it to be placed in any recognized Mesozoic conifer, ginkgoalean or cordaitean family on the basis of its tracheidoxyl anatomy. The institution of a new family to include *Arboramosa* n. gen. stem morphology and its novel tracheidoxyl characteristics evidently is in order, but before proposing one, we foresee the need for additional research to characterize the anatomy of pith and primary xylem.

Crowns with densely and spirally arranged branches are common in Cupressaceae, but the manner in which the branches of *Arboramosa* n. gen. connect to the stem within fusiform-shaped concavities (Figs. 1A-1C) is not a general Cupressaceae trait. The form and branch junctions displayed by *Arboramosa* n. gen. are, however, characteristics of some *Juniperus* trees (Figs. 1D-1E). Although *Arboramosa* n. gen. appears to be a juniper-like conifer, the megafossil contains stem-surface features not previously reported in fossilized trees of Triassic age or earlier.

Walchia, Ernestiodendron and *Ortiseia* spp. of the family Walchiaceae (Order Voltziales, Cordaiteae) found in Upper Carboniferous and Permian localities are believed ancestral to living conifers, but unlike the regular spiralled branching found on *Arboramosa* n. gen., those trees had whorled branching patterns (Florin, 1944). The coarsely braided secondary xylem surface and the regular, spiralled distribution of branches on *Arboramosa* n. gen. distinguish it readily from other petrified logs in PEFO. Larger diameter specimens of Upper Triassic *Schilderia adamanica* from the Chinle Formation do have in common with *Arboramosa* n. gen. a fluted stem phenotype (Daugherty, 1941; Creber and Ash, 2004). However, *S. adamanica* does not have branch junctions within fusiform depressions. In addition, *Arboramosa* n. gen. secondary xylem is pycnoxylic whereas that of *S. adamanica* is conspicuously manoxylic. Tracheidoxyl details of *Arboramosa* n. gen. are given emphasis below under the species designation, but some consideration of the history of taxonomical classification is needed here because the names of many genera are based on tracheidoxyl features alone.

Lindley and Hutton (1832) initiated the genus *Pinites* in describing three woods having multiseriate rays, and Witham (1833) used the identical name to describe woods having alternate, polygonal bordered pits (araucarian pitting) on tracheid radial walls. Witham (1833) instituted the genus *Pitus* and distinguished it from *Pinites* on the basis that *Pitus* usually has circular (abietinian) bordered pits in biseriate or triseriate rank, with spaces between the bordered pits, whereas *Pinites* has contiguous hexagonal bordered pits in biseriate or higher rank, like modern species of *Araucaria* and *Agathis*. Although containing many anatomical features of extant conifer woods, both *Pitus* and *Pinites* contain multiseriate as well as uniseriate rays, *Pitus* 4-15 cells in width and *Pinites* 2-5 cells in width (Witham 1833). Technically, therefore, both *Pitus* and *Pinites* are manoxylic woods unlike araucarian or abietinian conifers, but in considering the wood described as *Pinites* by Witham (1833), Göppert (1850) nevertheless decided that it should be renamed *Araucarites*, and he retained the genus *Pinites* to refer to woods similar to those within extant Pinaceae (those which Witham 1833 had described as *Pitus*). Göppert's use of *Araucarites* was in error because Endlicher (1847) had earlier stated that *Araucarites* should not be used to refer to wood of *Araucaria*-like fossils and had instituted *Dadoxylon* to refer to such tracheidoxyls. Moreover, Hartig (1848) had already named the genus *Agathoxylon* (also known as *Dammaroxylon*) on the basis of the same, or very similar, tracheidoxyl features recognized by Göppert (1850) for *Araucarites*. Probably as a result of this nomenclatural confusion, Kraus (1870) later initiated *Araucaroxylon* (sic) from *Araucarites*. Early Devonian specimens that had been designated *Dadoxylon* by Dawson (1871) were subsequently considered to be Paleozoic ancestors, if not equivalents, to *Araucaroxylon* (sic), as were Cordaitae of the Carboniferous and Permian periods (Solms-Laubach 1891). Consequently, both *Dadoxylon* and *Araucarioxylon* are taxonomically invalid (Seward 1917; Philippe, 1993; Bamford and Philippe, 2001) and many Permian and Triassic specimens with those names have been reassigned to the genus *Agathoxylon* named by Hartig (1848).

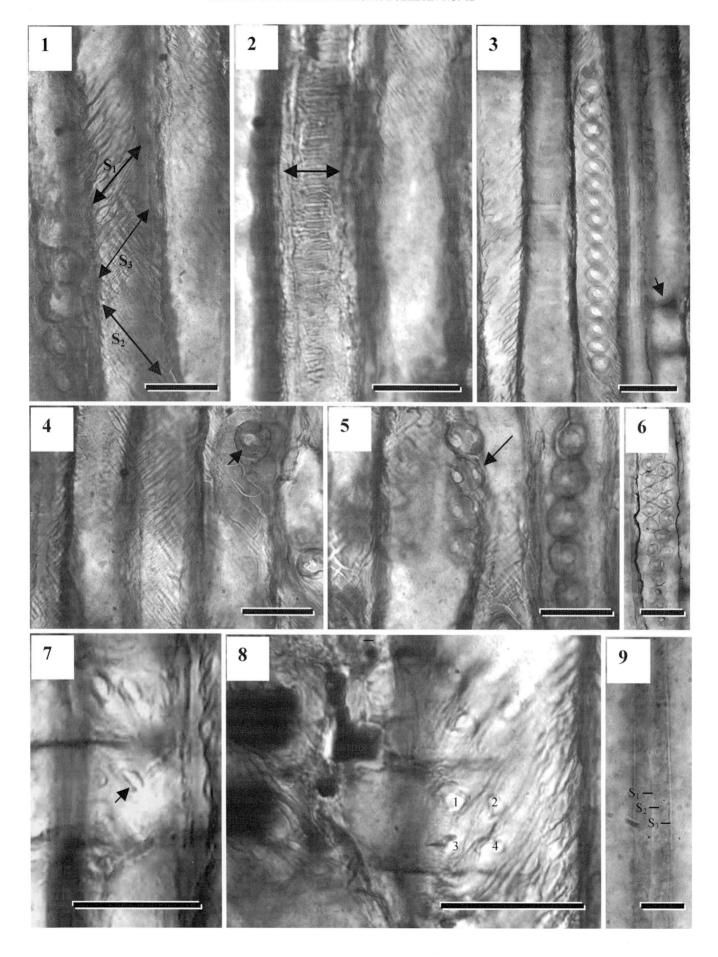

In addition to *Araucarites* and *Pinites*, Göppert (1850) initiated *Cupressinoxylon* and *Taxites* to refer to two additional genera of fossil woods that are anatomically different from *Araucarites* and *Pinites*. *Cupressinoxylon* woods were to resemble those of extant Cupressaceae and Podocarpaceae, *Taxites* woods the Taxaceae. Kraus (1870) subsequently initiated *Cedroxylon* to include woods identical with *Cupressinoxylon* except for lacking resiniferous elements otherwise seen as longitudinal (i.e., axial) parenchyma cells, and various questionable relatives of *Cedroxylon* subsequently were named (Philippe, 2002).

Arboramosa n. gen. secondary xylem superficially satisfies assignment to the genus *Cedroxylon* (Kraus, 1870); however, it actually is quite different from other *Cedroxylon* woods that have been figured (e.g., Stopes, 1915; Morgans, 1999) because of its disorganized radial files, rounded tracheids and circumferentially distributed bordered pits. Moreover, according to Kraus (1870) *Cedroxylon* wood is similar to *Cupressinoxylon* but, as expressed by Bamford and Phillipe (2001), the situation with *Cupressinoxylon* remains a "terrible imbroglio." *Cupressinoxylon* was to be distinguished from the other three types instituted by Göppert (1850) on the basis of having bordered pits separate, in one row, or, if in more than one, the pits of different rows opposite one another, longitudinal parenchyma containing resin present; resin canals absent (Göppert, 1850). When these criteria were applied in practice, it was soon recognized that *Cupressinoxylon* was an artificial supergenus crossing taxonomic boundaries, not only comprising the Cupressaceae but also species in *Abies* and even *Ginkgo biloba* (Barber, 1898). Moreover, the criteria for inclusion in *Cupressinoxylon* failed to adequately embrace some members of the Cupressaceae (Vaudois and Privé, 1971; Bamford and Phillipe, 2001). In view of the continuing revision attending *Cedroxylon* and *Cupressinoxylon*, and taking into consideration the entirely distinctive features of the investigated tracheidoxyl, both of those genera were avoided in the present assignment.

The tracheidoxyl features of *Arboramosa* n. gen. satisfy the unusual dual requirement of taxodioid cross-field pitting and abietinian tracheid radial wall pitting that justified *Protaxodioxylon* as a new tracheidoxyl genus (Bamford and Philippe, 2001). In this respect, *Arboramosa* n. gen. again appears to have affinity with Cupressaceae. However, longitudinal parenchyma cells are common and diagnostic of

Cupressaceae including junipers (Vaudois and Privé, 1971), and that cell type is scarce in *Arboramosa* n. gen. Junipers sometimes exhibit rounded normal-wood tracheids in cross section (Phillips, 1948; McGinnes and Phelps, 1972), but they do not have semi-circular tracheids with one diagonally oriented wall, nor do they produce bordered pits equally on all wall surfaces. These homology shortcomings aside, the major difficulty with assignment of the investigated fossil to *Juniperoxylon* (Houlbert, 1910: *J. turonense* Houlbert) is that fossils of definitive juniper-like wood earlier than the Cenozoic (Tertiary, Middle Eocene) are unknown, and investigations into reproductive structures have raised doubt about the idea that any member of Cupressaceae existed in the Mesozoic or earlier (Watson, 1988). It would be difficult to justify a 160 Ma gap in the fossil record between *Arboramosa* n. gen. as a *Juniperus* predecessor and the existing Cenozoic specimens of *Juniperoxylon*, but more research is clearly needed to determine if the gap can be narrowed. Upper Jurassic *Protocupressinoxylon purbeckensis* was found to have shoots and leaves similar to modern *Thuja plicata* (Cupressaceae), and its wood displays several anatomical features similar to those in wood of *Arboramosa* n. gen., including a scarcity of longitudinal parenchyma and the presence of rounded tracheids. However, semi-circular tracheids with bordered pits on diagonal walls were not reported, and biseriate pitting was described as always opposite (Francis, 1983), making *Protocupressinoxylon purbeckensis* distinct from *Arboramosa* n. gen. Jurassic *Protaxodioxylon* (Bamford and Philippe, 2001) is different from *Arboramosa* n. gen. in having conspicuous longitudinal parenchyma and in having its taxodioid cross-field pit apertures horizontally oriented (see, for example, Morgans, 1999). Similar concerns pertain to Upper Triassic *Taxodioxylon* and *Cupressinoxylon* (Schweitzer,1963; Vaudois and Privé, 1971; Stewart, 1983). In cross sections, rounded tracheids with bordered pits on all wall surfaces are prevalent distinguishing features in *Arboramosa* n. gen., and those features evidently are unknown (or have been overlooked) in *Protaxodioxylon*, *Taxodioxylon* and *Cupressinoxylon*. Petrified tree trunks referred to as *Protojuniperoxylon ischigualastianus* in Upper Triassic (Carnian) deposits of the Ischigualasto Formation in northwestern Argentina are presumed to be unlike *Arboramosa* n. gen., as they were described as those of the Araucariaceae (Romer, 1962). The stem surface features

Figure 4. *Arboramosa semicircumtrachea*. *1.* Microfibril orientations of the somewhat wavy S$_1$, thick S$_2$ and adjoining S$_3$ layers are indicated by the arrowed lines; *2* Horizontally oriented microfibrils are indicated by the arrowed line in a rare xylem cell type (plausibly, an axial parenchyma cell); *3.* A chain of uniseriate circular (abietinoid) bordered pits with circular apertures in a radial wall; a possible resin plug in a tracheid is arrowed; *4.* Singular, isolated abietinoid bordered pits (one arrowed) occur in radial walls; *5.* A bordered pit pair between diagonal walls is arrowed; their diameters are similar to those in radial walls, as evident in the short abietinoid chain above the scale bar; *6.* Tracheid with biseriate pitting; although some pits are araucaroid-like, most are circular and not in contact with one another; *7.* Radial section showing oculipores (taxodioid/cupressoid) in cross fields; a pit border of one is arrowed; *8.* Numbered oculipores in a cross field; four are commonly present and positioned at the points of a square; *9.* Radial section of secondary walls of two adjoining tracheids, showing the very thin S$_1$, thick S$_2$ and thin S$_3$ layers. Scale bars: 1-8=50 μm; 9=20 μm. All images were made from the holotype, thin section PEFO 34160B1.

and branching pattern of *Protaxodioxylon, Taxodioxylon, Cupressinoxylon* and *P. ischigualastianus* evidently remain to be described.

ARBORAMOSA SEMICIRCUMTRACHEA new species
Figures 1.1-1.3, 2-4

Diagnosis.– Pycnoxylic secondary xylem. In transverse section, tracheids in disorganized radial files, circular or elliptical with rounded lumens and intercellular spaces; secondary walls thick with three layers, S_2 thickest, one double wall of adjoining tracheids frequently oriented diagonally rather than radially; equi-diameter bordered pits on all wall surfaces; small diameter tracheid tips intrude into intercellular spaces; axial parenchyma present but infrequent; no longitudinal resin canals; rays uniseriate, infrequent, sometimes separated by 20+ radial files of tracheids; ray cells thin-walled, cylindrical, homogeneous; radial walls extend sideways into intercellular spaces created by adjoining rounded tracheids. In longitudinal sections, circular (abietinoid), equi-diameter bordered pits occur in radial, tangential and diagonal walls of tracheids, torus not evident; uniseriate bordered-pit chains usually long but also occurring as short runs or individual bordered pits; chains linearly aligned parallel to tracheid long axis but curving on diagonal walls; biseriate bordered pits present but uncommon, abietinoid or araucoid where biseriate; transverse septations indicative of axial parenchyma or trabeculae. In radial section, ray cells thin-walled, homogeneous, containing ergastic substances; taxodioid or less commonly cupressoid cross-field pitting with 1-6 usually 4 oculipores per cross field, pit apertures inclined at *c.* 45 degrees. In tangential section, tracheids commonly 10 mm long, non-septated, lacking spiral bands; rays strictly uniseriate, short (80–400 µm), usually 4–8 cells; fewer than 10 rays in contact with both sides of 10 mm-long tracheids; ray cells upright, either elliptical or with compressed horizontal walls; no horizontal resin canals.

Description.– *A. semicircumtrachea* has the characteristic stem morphology of the genus *Arboramosa* (described above), and the species is distinguished by its novel tracheidoxyl anatomy.

Etymology.– The Latin terms *semi* (half), *circum* (around), *trachea* (tracheid) were chosen to describe the semi-circular tracheids seen in cross sections.

Occurrence.– Single holotype specimen (see *Arboramosa* n. gen. above).

Discussion.– Rounded tracheids having three secondary wall lamellae and intercellular spaces like those of *A. semicircumtrachea* can also be found, but not so generally distributed, in normal stem wood of *Juniperus* and *Ginkgo* spp. (Phillips, 1948; McGinnes and Phelps, 1972; Timell, 1983, 1986). Rounded elements and associated intercellular spaces occupy 10 % or less of the surface area in those extant woods,

whereas in *A. semicircumtrachea* it is rare to find anything but rounded tracheids with associated intercellular spaces. Abietinian bordered pitting is largely restricted to the radial walls of *Juniperus* and *Ginkgo* tracheids, whereas abietinian bordered pits are present on all wall surfaces of the rounded tracheids in *A.. semicircumtrachea*. To our knowledge this anatomical phenotype has no precedent. Cross-field pitting in *A. semicircumtrachea* is predominantly taxodioid, less commonly cupressoid (Figs. 2.8, 4.7, 4.8). The distinction between taxodioid and cupressoid pits is based on the width of the aperture *vis-à-vis* the pit border, and it is not uncommon for the aperture width to vary such that both types co-occur. Cupressoid pitting is reportedly diagnostic of *Juniperus* spp. (Panshin and de Zeeuw, 1970), but taxodioid pitting can readily be found also (R. A. Savidge, personal data). *Ginkgo biloba* L. has a mixture of taxodioid - cupressoid pitting (R. A. Savidge, personal data). In terms of numbers of pits and their positioning in the cross field, *G. biloba* is similar to *A. semicircumtrachea* whereas junipers generally have only one or two pits per cross field.

Disorganized radial files of secondary xylem are diagnostic of Ginkgoales (Scott et al., 1962), and in this respect the tracheidoxyl phenotype of *A. semicircumtrachea* more closely resembles ginkgo than juniper. In cross sections of *Ginkgo biloba*, although angular tracheids are the more common, circular or elliptical tracheids having the occasional diagonal wall can sometimes be found (R. A. Savidge, personal data). The conspicuously intruded tips found in *A. semicircumtrachea* indicate abrupt, vigorous elongation of fusiform cambial derivatives. Evidence for abrupt intrusive tip growth is difficult to detect in extant conifers, and the tips evidently extend only marginally as stem diameter growth proceeds (Bannan, 1965; Savidge and Farrar, 1984). Intruded tracheid tips like those found in *A. semicircumtrachea* do occur in cross sections of *G. biloba* secondary xylem (R. A. Savidge, personal data). *A. semicircumtrachea* and *G. biloba* both have uniseriate, short rays. However, *A. semicircumtrachea* ray cells are not bulging or barrel-shaped, but they are conspicuously so in *G. biloba*.

The bordered pits of *A. semicircumtrachea* are equi-diameter and for the most part positioned in the tracheid walls as very well ordered, long linear chains parallel to the tracheid axis. Although the pits have spaces between them, crassulae are lacking. These features distinguish *A. semicircumtrachea* from *G. biloba* and *Juniperus* spp. Bordered pits in *G. biloba* tend to be of variable diameter and, when uniseriate, placed in weakly ordered arrangement on the radial walls (R. A. Savidge, personal data). When ginkgo bordered pits on radial walls of tracheids are biseriate, as they frequently are, they are almost invariably placed opposite one another, with crassulae obvious, and crassulae are also present in junipers (R. A. Savidge, personal data). In *A.*

Table 2. Anatomical features of *Arboramosa semicircumtrachea* compared with those of previously described species in Petrified Forest National Park.

Secondary xylem feature	Arboramosa semicircumtrachea [1]	Araucarioxylon arizonicum [2,4]	Woodworthia arizonica [3,4]	Schilderia adamanica [3,4]	Dadoxylon chaneyi [3]	Lissoxylon grigsbyi [3]
Tracheid radial files	disorganized	well organized	well organized	organized	organized	well organized
Secondary-wall thickness	uniformly thick	variable	variable	uniformly thick	variable	variable
Tracheid (X section)	round/semi-round	angular or round	angular	angular or round	angular	angular
Lumen (X section)	rounded	angular or round	angular	angular or round	angular or round	round
Intercellular spaces	very common	rare to common	rare	occasional	occasional	no
Trabeculae	no	no	no	yes (hyphae?)	yes	no
Spiral-banded tracheids	no	no	no	no	no	yes
Bordered-pit outline	circular/angular	angular/circular	angular/circular	angular/circular	angular/circular	angular
Crassulae	not evident	flattened contacts	flattened contacts	flattened contacts	yes	not evident
Bordered-pit wall placement	on all wall surfaces	radial, sparse on tangental	radial, sparse on tangental	both radial and tangental	both radial and tangental	radial, only
Bordered-pit diameter variation	constant (16-18 μm) on all walls	radial: 20μm tangential: 3μm	radial: 18μm tangential: 9μm	radial: 14x18μm tangential: variable	radial: 9-18μm tangential: c. 6μm	radial: 6-10μm
Bordered-pit chains[5]	uniseriate, long; biseriate, short	uni- and biseriate, short	uniseriate, long; biseriate, short	uni- and biseriate, short	uni- and biseriate, short	uni-, bi-, and triseriate, short
Chain axial organization	linear	scattered	mostly linear	weakly linear	mostly linear	weakly linear
Rays	uniseriate	uni- and biseriate	uniseriate, also short-shoot traces	uni- to multiseriate	uni- to biseriate	uni- to multiseriate
Ray spacing (X section)	6-20 radial files	1-8 radial files	2-10 radial files	1-10 radial files	2-10 radial files	1-6 radial files
Ray height (cell number)	1-15	1-40	1-10	1-12	1-5	4-50
Uniseriate ray width (μm)	10-18	12-30	18	10	18	11
Ray-cell tangential shape	elliptical	circular, flattened	oval, oblong	variable	elliptical	variable
Ray-cell wall thickness	thin	thin	medium	thin	thin to thick	thin to thick
Cross-field pit type	taxodioid/cupressoid	oopores?[6]	taxodioid	taxodioid and oopores	taxodioid	piceoid?[6]
Number of pits/field	1-6 (4 commonly)	elusive[6]	2-8	2-6	1-6	2-5
Cross-field pit orientation	45°	elusive[6]	45°	variable	45°	unstated[6]
Resiniferous tracheids	no, or sparse	yes, common	yes, numerous	no	sparse	no
Axial parenchyma	probably[6]	no	no	yes	no	sparse
Tyloses	no	no	no	no	yes	yes
Horizontal resin canals	no	no	no, short-shoot traces numerous	no	no	yes

Sources and footnotes:
[1] As described herein
[2] Knowlton 1888, Jeffrey 1913
[3] Daugherty 1941
[4] R. A. Savidge, unpublished data
[5] (long, >1 mm; short, < 0.1mm)
[6] Remains to be resolved

semicircumtrachea, where biseriate bordered-pit placement occurs, the pits show no bias toward being opposite one another. They may be alternate and spaced, alternate and adpressed (araucarian-like), or opposite, but regardless of the arrangement, crassulae are not present. Tangential wall pitting of ginkgo and juniper tracheids generally occurs only in the latewood, and when present the pits are of much smaller diameter than the radial wall pits (R. A. Savidge, personal data). In contrast, pit placement in *A. semicircumtrachea* occurs at any location around the tracheid circumference and is everywhere equi-diameter.

Axial, or longitudinal, parenchyma are present to a limited extent in secondary xylem of juniper species and ginkgo (Phillips, 1948; McGinnes and Phelps, 1972; Panshin and de Zeeuw, 1970), and they also appear to be present but rare in *A. semicircumtrachea*. The walls of *A. semicircumtrachea* are generally thick; that is, the xylem lacks the sporadically distributed thin-walled large diameter parenchyma cells commonly found among thicker-walled, smaller diameter tracheids in *G. biloba*. Calcium oxalate crystals, common in the enlarged parenchyma of ginkgo, were not seen in the fossil.

The rounded, multi-pitted tracheids in *A. semicircumtrachea* do not strictly satisfy the definition of compression wood (Timell, 1986). Their prevalence in the wood is nevertheless instructive, providing evidence that the phenomena of cell rounding and concomitant formation of intercellular spaces are probably not factors preventing production of either the S_3 layer or bordered pits during formation of true compression wood in extant conifers. Greguss (1967) considered a Permian specimen of *Araucarioxylon* to have some features of compression wood, and Daugherty (1941) noted that *Dadoxylon chaneyi* contained zones of "rotholz" (German for redwood, synonymous with compression wood), but the only authentic tracheidoxyl compression wood so far observed is from the recent Pleistocene (Morey and Morey, 1969; Timell, 1983, 1986).

Agathoxylon (*Dadoxylon/Araucarioxylon*) genera have been broadly defined to encompass considerable variation (Jeffrey, 1910, 1913; Grambast, 1960; Greguss, 1961, 1967; Lepeckhina, 1972; Mussa, 1982), but even so the latitude is not sufficiently broad to permit inclusion of the qualitative tracheidoxyl features reported here for *Arboramosa semicircumtrachea* n. gen. et n. sp. (Table 2).

GENERAL DISCUSSION

The distinguishing characteristics of tracheidoxyls used by Göppert (1858) to diagnose *Araucarites* and later by Kraus (1870) to diagnose *Araucaroxylon* (*sic*) were 1) bordered pits in one row with contact and mutual compression (i.e., adpression), or alternating in several rows and becoming polygonal from mutual adpression, 2) uniseriate rays, and 3) rims

of Sanio (crassulae) lacking. In other words, the tracheidoxyl was to have araucaroid bordered pits with angular margins similar to those found on the radial walls of tracheids in modern *Araucaria* and *Agathis* spp. and in contrast to the abietinoid pits found in most other conifers. Abietinoid pits in tracheid radial walls are non-adpressed, circularly outlined, and generally are separated by crassulae. Woods exhibiting both araucarian and abietinean bordered pits are of the "mixed" type and are found in the Mesozoic and later (Bamford and Philippe 2001). *A. semicircumtrachea* pitting is mixed but primarily abietinean, except that crassulae are wanting. On this basis, the tree evidently was either transitional from an araucarian to an abietinian conifer or was a genetic anomaly within the largely araucarian realm of PEFO woods. The cell biology/biochemistry of pit formation during xylogenesis evidently involves the biogenesis and placement against developing cell walls of an organelle (Savidge 2000, 2003), but the processes of both bordered-pit and crassula formation remain poorly understood biochemically and genetically. Consequently, it is difficult to rationalize tracheidoxyl development and evolution on the basis of the two kinds of pitting.

The development within *A. semicircumtrachea* of semi-circular tracheids with one wall diagonally oriented, relative to the radial line created by the radial file as seen in cross section, is a novel feature not seen in reports on other tracheidoxyls. As noted above, rounded tracheids with three secondary-wall layers do occasionally occur in normal wood of a few extant conifer species; however, semi-rounded tracheids with one straight diagonally oriented wall occur rarely except in *Ginkgo biloba*. The template for such development evidently arises when one side of a thin-walled, differentiating cambial derivative is compressed (by turgor pressure) against the corresponding walls of two similar cells (one slightly more advanced than the other in its stage of differentiation) within an adjoining radial file (Savidge and Farrar, 1984). The existence of alternately ranked cambial derivatives in adjoining radial files, in conjunction with their different degrees of intercellular bonding, probably provides the fulcrum needed for partially rotating the cells circumferentially as they change from their rectangular outline on the periphery of the cambium to rounded 'tubes' in the zone where they begin to be incorporated into the xylem. The turgor pressure within the cells was obviously sufficient to support attainment of the rounded shape and must also have been a factor contributing to one side becoming flattened to produce the diagonally oriented double-wall contact. Intrusive elongation of tips of primary-walled fusiform cambial derivatives probably occurred during or soon after they had rounded and concomitantly generated intercellular spaces that served as elongation corridors (Hejnowicz, 1961; Savidge and Farrar, 1984).

If enlarged parenchyma with calcium oxalate druses were present in the secondary xylem, if the ray cells were bulging rather than cylindrical, and if the bordered pits were not equi-diameter and when biseriate were opposed to one another with the pairs separated by crassulae, the tracheidoxyl of *A. semicircumtrachea* would likely be aligned with the Ginkgoales. On the basis of leaf impressions, Ginkgoales is believed to date to the Permian, so perhaps it is not far-fetched to imagine *A. semicircumtrachea* as a gingkoalean derivative on its way toward becoming a conifer.

On the other hand, if longitudinal parenchyma were more conspicuous in *A. semicircumtrachea*, and if one were prepared to overlook the general occurrence of rounded tracheids and the circumferential distribution of bordered pits, a case could be made for the tree being in the Cupressaceae and, considering its stem morphological features, possibly even being an ancestor of *Juniperus* spp. The scarcity of longitudinal parenchyma in *A. semicircumtrachea* may not be a major obstacle. Experimentally, fusiform cambial derivatives differentiate as axial parenchyma rather than as tracheids when auxin is in short supply (Savidge and Wareing, 1981; Savidge 1983, 1988), and it is plausible that a minor genetic change in auxin production by leaves or apical meristems is the physiological basis underlying the ability of Cupresseaceae to produce longitudinal parenchyma.

The presence or absence of growth rings or even of partial rings in secondary xylem has frequently been discussed in relation to taxonomic discrimination; however, it should also be considered that growth rings in *A. semicircumtrachea* may be merely adaptive features indicative of the physiological plasticity inherent to woody plants and expressed as needed when climate was non-conducive to ongoing cambial growth (Savidge, 1993). The seasonally mild growing conditions of the PEFO site in the Late Triassic are manifested by the absence of annual growth interruptions in the wood of *A. arizonicum* (Ash and Creber, 1992; Ash and Savidge, 2004).

On the basis of fossil leaves and petrified wood found within PEFO, vascular plant diversity during the Late Triassic included cycadeoids, ginkgoaleans, sphenopsids, ferns, caytonialean pteridosperms and trees possibly related to extant Gnetales (Daugherty, 1941; Krassilov and Ash, 1988; Ash, 1989, 1992, 2001a, 2001b; Creber and Ash, 2004; Pigg et al., 1993). This agrees well with succession inferred by investigations into phytochrome gene sequences from which the divergence period for Gnetatae, Ginkgoatae, and Cycadatae was estimated to be in the Permian and that of the Pinatae in the Triassic (Schmidt and Schneider-Poetsch, 2002). *A. semicircumtrachea*. was an unusual tree and, in relation to its unique secondary xylem, it was a genetic anomaly. *A. semicircumtrachea* appears to be an example of abrupt speciation, possibly arising in response to either a single mutation event or by polyploidisation (Dynesius and Jansson, 2000). Its pronounced branchiness and unusual wood anatomical traits are evidence for pleiotropic control of particular aspects of primary and secondary growth that, until now, have evaded physiological understanding (Savidge, 2001). If the tree's branchiness is considered as evidence for enhanced photosynthesizing capability, and its generally thick-walled tracheids with their abundant bordered pits as evidence for greater stem strength and hydraulic conductivity, *A. semicircumtrachea* appears to have attained a level of physiological fitness exceeding that of any precedent or antecedent conifer. However, excepting the remote possibilities that *A. semicircumtrachea* has affinity with Ginkgoales or *Juniperus*, there is no substantial evidence in the fossil record for the unique wood anatomical traits of *A. semicircumtrachea* having persisted through either anagenesis or cladogenesis, and thus it appears probable that *Arboramosa semicircumtrachea* n. gen. et n. sp. was a short lived species.

CONCLUSIONS

The holotype of a new genus and species of tree named *Arboramosa semicircumtrachea* from Petrified Forest National Park, Arizona, U.S.A., is a genetic anomaly of the Late Triassic Period. The fossil may also be indicative of a new but transient family because its spiralling branch junctions are unique, the first such to be clearly documented in the Mesozoic. The abundant presence of semi-circular tracheids with one straight but diagonally oriented wall, as seen in cross sections, is an entirely novel feature captured in the name of this new species. The nature of the bordered pits, manifesting on the one hand rigid intrinsic regulation of size and vertical placement yet, on the other, little or no control of placement around the circumference, is evidently unprecedented in the fossil record.

ACKNOWLEDGMENTS

We acknowledge with thanks Karen Beppler-Dorn, Chief of Resource Management and William Parker, Paleontologist at Petrified Forest National Park, who authorized and encouraged both of us to conduct research within the Park. Ancel Murphy and Calvin Nash of UNB prepared the slides, and Douglas Hall assisted with the electron probe analyses. Financial support was from the Petrified Forest Museum Association (to SRA) and the Natural Sciences and Engineering Research Council of Canada (to RAS). We are indebted to William Tidwell (Provo, Utah), Marian Bamford (Johannesburg, South Africa), and Marc Phillipe (Lyon, France) for critical reading of the penultimate draft.

REFERENCES

Arnold, C. A. 1947. An introduction to paleobotany. McGraw-Hill, New York and London, 433 p.

Ash, S. R. 1972. The search for plant fossils in the Chinle Formation, p. 23-43. *In* W. J. Breed and C. S. Breed (eds.), Investigations in the Triassic Chinle Formation. Museum Northern Arizona Bulletin 47.

Ash, S. R. 1985. A short thick cycad stem from the Upper Triassic of Petrified Forest National Park, Arizona, and vicinity. Museum of Northern Arizona Bulletin, 54:17-32.

Ash, S. R. 1987. Petrified Forest National Park, Arizona. *In* S. S. Beus (ed.), Centennial Field Guide, Volume 2, Rocky Mountain Section of the Geological Society of America, p. 405-410.

Ash, S. R. 1989. A catalog of Upper Triassic plant megafossils of the western United States through 1988, p.189-222. *In* S. G. Lucas and A. P. Hunt (eds.), Dawn of the Age of Dinosaurs in the American Southwest, New Mexico Museum of Natural History, Albuquerque.

Ash, S. R. 1992. The Black Forest Bed, a distinctive rock unit in the Upper Triassic Chinle Formation, northeastern Arizona. Journal of the Arizona-Nevada Academy of Science, 24/25:59-73.

Ash, S. R. 2001a. New cycadophytes from the Upper Triassic Chinle Formation of the southwestern United States. PaleoBios, 21:15-28.

Ash, S. R. 2001b. The fossil ferns of Petrified Forest National Park, Arizona, and their paleoclimatological implications, p. 3-10. *In* V. L. Santucci and L. McClelland (eds.), Proceedings of the 6th Fossil Resource Conference: National Park Service Geologic Resources Division Technical Report NPS/NRGRD/GRDTR-01/01, Washington, DC.

Ash, S. R., and G. Creber. 1992. Palaeoclimatic interpretation of the wood structures of the trees in the Chinle Formation (Upper Triassic) in the area of Petrified Forest National Park, Arizona, U.S.A. Palaeogeography, Palaeoclimatology, Palaeoecology, 96:299-317.

Ash, S. R., and G. Creber. 2000. The Late Triassic *Araucarioxylon arizonicum* trees of the Petrified Forest National Park, Arizona, USA. Palaeontology, 43:15-28.

Ash, S. R., and R. A. Savidge. 2004. The bark of the Late Triassic *Araucarioxylon arizonicum* tree from Petrified Forest National Park, Arizona. IAWA Journal, 25:349-368.

Bamford, M. K., and M. Philippe. 2001. Jurassic–Early Cretaceous Gondwanan homoxylous woods: a nomenclatural revision of the genera with taxonomic notes. Review of Palaeobotany and Palynology, 113:287-297.

Bannan, M. W. 1965. Ray contacts and rate of anticlinal division in fusiform cambial cells of some Pinaceae. Canadian Journal of Botany, 43:487-507.

Bannan, M. W., and I. J. Bayly. 1956. Cell size and survival in conifer cambium. Canadian Journal of Botany, 34:769-776.

Barber, C. A. 1898. *Cupressinoxylon vectense*; a fossil conifer from the lower greensand of Shanklin, in the Isle of Wight. Annals of Botany, 12:329-361.

Creber, G. T. 1972. Gymnospermous woods from the Kimmeridgian of East Sutherland and from the Sandringham Sands of Norfolk. Palaeontology, 15:655-661.

Creber, G. T., and S. R. Ash. 2004. The Late Triassic *Schilderia adamanica* and *Woodworthia arizonica* trees of the Petrified Forest National Park, Arizona, USA. Palaeontology, 47:21-38.

Darrah, W. C. 1939. Textbook of Paleobotany. Appleton-Century, New York, London, 441 p.

Daugherty, L. H. 1934. *Schilderia adamanica*–a new fossil wood from the petrified forests of Arizona. Botanical Gazette, 96:363-366.

Daugherty, L. H. 1941. The Upper Triassic flora of Arizona. Carnegie Institute of Washington Publication, 526:1-108.

Dawson, J. W. 1871. The fossil plants of the Devonian and upper Silurian formations of Canada. Geological Survey of Canada, Ottawa, Dawson Brothers, Montreal, 92 p.

Dynesius, M., and R. Jansson. 2000. Evolutionary consequences of changes in species' geographical distributions driven by Milankovitch climate oscillations. Proceedings of the National Academy of Sciences USA, 97:9115-9120.

Endlicher, S. 1847. Conspectus coniferarum fossilium, p. 52. *In* S. Endlicher (ed.), Synopsis Coniferarum. Scheitlin and Zollikofer, St.-Gall.

Fahn, A. 1977. Plant anatomy, 2nd ed. Pergamon, Oxford, New York, Toronto, Sydney, Paris, Frankfurt, 611 p.

Florin, R. 1944. Die Koniferen des Oberkarbons und des Unteren Perms. Palaeontographica, 85B:244-456.

Francis, J. E. 1983. The dominant conifer of the Jurassic Purbeck Formation, England. Palaeontology, 26:277-294

Göppert, H. R. 1850. Monographie der fossilen Coniferen. Natuurk. Verhandelingen van de hollandishce Maatschappy der Wetensch. te Harlem, 2 Verzm, vol. 6, Arnz and Company, Leiden, 286 p.

Göppert, H. R. 1858. Über die von Möllhausen mitgebrachten Fragments des Holzes aus dem versteinerten Walde, p. 492. *In* H. B. Möllhausen, (ed.), Tagebuch einer Reise vom Mississippi, nach Küsten der Südsee. Leipzig.

Gould, R. E. 1971. *Lyssoxylon grigsbyi*, a cycad trunk from the Upper Triassic of Arizona and New Mexico. American Journal of Botany, 58:239-248.

Grambast, L. 1960. Étude d'un *Dadoxylon* permian du Congo belge et remarques sur les *Dadoxylon* permo-carbonifères des territoires à flore Gondwana. Musée Royal de l'Afrique Central, Annales Sciences Géologique, 30:11-21.

Greguss, P. 1961. Permische fossile Holzer aus Ungarn. Palaeontographica B, 109:131-146.

Greguss, P. 1967. Fossil gymnosperm woods in Hungary. Akadémiai Kiadó, Budapest,136 p.

Greuter, W., J. McNeill, F. R. Barrie, H. M. Burdet, V. Demoulin, T. S. Filgueiras, D. H. Nicolson, P. C. Silva, J. E. Skog, P. Trehane, N. J. Turland, and D. L. Hawksworth. 1999. International Code of Botanical Nomenclature (St Louis Code). Regnum Vegetabile, Koeltz, Königstein, 138 p.

Hartig, T. 1848. Beiträge zur Geschichte der Pflanzen und zur Kenntnis der norddeutschen Braunkohlen-Flora. Botanisches Zeitung, 6:122–128, 137–141, 166–172, 185–190.

Hejnowicz, Z. 1961. Anticlinal divisions, intrusive growth, and loss of fusiform initials in nonstoried cambium. Acta Societatis Botanicorum Poloniae, 30:729-752.

Houlbert, C. 1910. Les bois des faluns de Touraine. *In* H. D. Ctesse Lecointre (ed.) Les formes diverses de la vie dans les faluns de la Touraine. La Feuille des Jeunes Naturalistes, 40:70-77.

Jeffrey, E. C. 1910. A new araucarian genus from the Triassic. Boston Society of Natural History Proceedings, 34:325-332.

Jeffrey, E. C. 1913. The history, comparative anatomy and evolution of the *Araucarioxylon* type. Proceedings of the American Academy of Arts and Science, 48:531-571.

Knowlton, F. H. 1888. New species of fossil wood (*Araucarioxylon arizonicum*) from Arizona and New Mexico. U.S. National Museum Proceedings, 11:1-4.

Knowlton, F. H. 1919. A catalogue of the Mesozoic and Cenozoic plants of North America. United States Geological Survey Bulletin 696, 815 p.

Krassilov, V., and S. R. Ash. 1988. On *Dinophyton*–protognetalean Mesozoic plant. Paleontographica B, 208:33-38..

Kraus, G. 1870. Bois fossiles de Conifères, p. 363–385. *In* W. P. Schimper (ed.), Traité de Paléontologie Végétale, 2, J. B. Baillière et fils, Strasbourg.

Lepekhina, V. G. 1972. Woods of Palaeozoic pycnoxylic gymnosperms with special reference to north Eurasia representatives. Palaeontographica B, 38:44-106.

Lindley, J., and W. Hutton. 1832. The fossil flora of Great-Britain, vol. 1, J. Ridgway, London, 218 p.

McGinnes,, E. A., and J. E. Phelps. 1972. Intercellular spaces in eastern redcedar (*Juniperus virginiana* L). Wood Science, 4:225-229.

Morey, P. R., and E. D. Morey. 1969. Observations on Epon embedded Griffin Hill peat (Massachusetts), Two Creeks *Picea* (Wisconsin), *Cedrus penhallowii* (Sierra Nevada, California) and *Callixylon* (Delaware, Ohio). Palaeontographica B, 125:73-80.

Morgans, H. S. 1999. Lower and middle Jurassic woods of the Cleveland Basin (North Yorkshire), England. Palaeontology, 42:303-328.

Mussa, D. 1982. Lignitafofloras permianas da Bacia do Paraná, Brasil (Estados de São Paulo e Santa Catarina). 2 volumes. Tese (Doutorado), Instituto de Geociencias, Curso de Pós-Graduação em Geosciences, Universidade Federal do Rio Grande do Sul, Porto Alegre.

Panshin, A. J., and C. De Zeeuw. 1970. Textbook of wood technology, Volume 1, McGraw-Hill, New York, p. 705.

Philippe, M. 1993. Nomenclature générique des trachéidoxyles fossiles mésozoïques à champs araucarioides. Taxon, 42:74–80.

Philippe, M. 2002. Reappraisal of five fossil coniferous wood genera proposed by early American wood anatomists. IAWA Journal, 23:319-326.

Phillips, E. W. J. 1948. Identification of softwoods by their microscopic structure. Forest Products Research Bulletin No. 22, HMSO, London.

Pigg, K. B., W. C. Davis, and S. R. Ash. 1993. A new permineralized Upper Triassic flora from Petrified Forest National Park, Arizona: A preliminary report. *In* S. G. Lucas, and M. Morales (eds.), The Nonmarine Triassic, New Mexico Museum of Natural History and Science Bulletin, 3:411-413.

Riggs, N. R., S. R. Ash, A. P. Barth, G. E. Gehrels, and J. L. Wooden. 2003. Isotopic age of the Black Forest Bed, Petrified Forest member, Chinle Formation, Arizona: An example of dating a continental sandstone. Geological Society of America Bulletin, 115:1315-1323.

Romer, A. S., 1962. The fossiliferous Triassic deposits of Ischigualasto, Argentina. *In* A. S. Romer and C. B. Cox, The fossiliferous Triassic deposits of Ischigualasto, Argentina and preliminary description of *Ischigualastia*, a new genus of dicynodont. Museum of Comparative Zoology, Breviora, 156:1-7.

Savidge, R. A. 1983. The role of plant hormones in higher plant cellular differentiation. II. Experiments with the vascular cambium, and sclereid and tracheid differentiation in the pine, *Pinus contorta*. Histochemical Journal, 15:447-466.

Savidge, R. A. 1988. Auxin and ethylene regulation of diameter growth in trees. Tree Physiology, 4:401-414.

Savidge, R. A. 1993. Formation of annual rings in trees, p. 343-363. *In* L. Rensing (ed.), Oscillations and Morphogenesis. Marcel Dekker, New York.

Savidge, R. A. 2000. Biochemistry of seasonal cambial growth and wood formation – an overview of the challenges, p. 1-30. *In* R. A. Savidge, J. Barnett and R. Napier (eds.), Cell and Molecular Biology of Wood Formation, BIOS Scientific, Oxford.

Savidge, R. A. 2001. Intrinsic regulation of cambial growth. Journal of Plant Growth Regulation, 20:52-77.

Savidge, R. A. 2003. Tree growth and wood quality, p. 1-29. *In* J. R. Barnett and G. Jeronimidis (eds.), Wood Quality and its Biological Basis. Blackwell and CRC Press, Oxford and Boca Raton, Florida, USA.

Savidge, R. A., and J. L. Farrar. 1984. Cellular adjustments in the vascular cambium leading to spiral grain formation in conifers. Canadian Journal of Botany, 62:2872-2879.

Savidge, R. A., and P. F. Wareing. 1981. Plant-growth regulators and the differentiation of vascular elements, p. 192-235. *In* J. R. Barnett (ed.), Xylem Cell Development. Castle House, Tunbridge Wells, UK.

Schmidt, M. S., and H. A. W. Schneider-Poetsch. 2002. The evolution of gymnosperms redrawn by phytochrome genes: the Gnetaceae appear at the base of the gymnosperms. Journal of Molecular Evolution, 54:715-724.

Schweitzer, H. J. 1963. Der weibliche Zapten von *Pseudovoltzia liebeana* und seine Bedeutung für die Phylogenie der Koniferen. Palaeontographica B, 113:1-29.

Scott, R. A. 1961. Fossil woods associated with uranium on the Colorado Plateau. *In* Short Papers in the geologic and hydrologic sciences. U.S. Geological Survey Professional Paper, 424-B:130-132.

Scott, R. A., E. S. Barghoorn, and U. Prakash. 1962. Wood of *Ginkgo* in the Tertiary of western North America. American Journal of Botany, 49:1095-1101.

Seward, A. C. 1917. Fossil plants, volume III, Pteridospermeae, Cycadofilices, Cordaitales, Cycadophyta. Cambridge University Press, reprinted in 1969 by Hafner Publishing Company, New York and London, 656 p.

Solms-Laubach, and H. Graf Zu. 1891. Fossil botany, English translation by H. E. F. Garnsey, revised by I. B. Balfour. Clarendon, Oxford, 401 p.

Stewart, W. N. 1983. Paleobotany and the evolution of plants. Cambridge University Press, Cambridge, 405 p.

Stopes, M. C. 1915. Catalogue of the Mesozoic plants in the British Museum (Natural History), the Cretaceous flora, Part II – Lower Greensand (Aptian) plants of Britain. British Museum (Natural History), London, 360 p.

Swaine, P. T., and J. F. C. Hegewald. 1882. Information concerning some fossil trees in the United States National Museum. U.S. National Museum Proceedings, 5:1-3.

Timell, T. E. 1983. Origin and evolution of compression wood. Holzforschung, 37:1-10.

Timell, T. E. 1986. Compression wood in gymnosperms. Volume 1, Springer-Verlag, Berlin, Heidelberg, New York, Tokyo, 706 p.

Trendelenburg, A. 1932. Über die Eigenschaften des Rot- oder Druckholzes der Nadelhölzer. Allgemeine Forst-Jagdzeitung, 108:1-14.

Turkel, H. S. 1968. Anatomical studies of the woods in the Chinle flora. Unpublished Ph.D. dissertation, Harvard University, Cambridge, Massachusetts, 37 p..

Vaudois, N., and C. Privé. 1971. Révision des bois fossiles de Cupressaceae. Palaeontographica B, 134:61-86.

Vozenin-Serra, C. 1979. On the presence of Cycadale, *Lyssoxylon* Daugherty, in the Triassic layers of the Basin of Quang-Nam, centers Viêtnam. Palaeontographica B, 169:70-77.

Ward, L. F. 1900. Status of the Mesozoic floras of the United States. U.S. Geological Survey 20th Annual Report, 2:211-748.

Watson, J. 1988. The Cheirolepidiaceae, p. 382–447. *In* C. B. Beck (ed.), Origin and Evolution of Gymnosperms. Columbia University, New York.

Whipple, A. W., and others. 1855. Report of explorations for a railway route, near the thirty-fifth parallel of latitude, from the Mississippi River to the Pacific Ocean. U.S. 33rd Congress, 1st Session, Secretary of War Executive Document, 129(3):1-154.

Witham, H. 1833. The internal structure of fossil vegetables, found in the Carboniferous and Oolitic deposits of Great Britain, described and illustrated. Adam and Charles Black, Edinburgh, 84 p.

Parker, W. G., Ash, S. R., and Irmis, R. B. eds., 2006,
A Century of Research at Petrified Forest National Park: Geology and Paleontology.
Museum of Northern Arizona Bulletin No. 62.

TWO RARE FOSSIL CONES FROM THE UPPER TRIASSIC CHINLE FORMATION IN PETRIFIED FOREST NATIONAL PARK, ARIZONA, AND NEW MEXICO

BRIAN J. AXSMITH[1] AND SIDNEY R. ASH[2]

[1]Department of Biological Sciences, LSCB 124, University of South Alabama, Mobile, Alabama 36688 <baxsmith@jaguar1.usouthal.edu>
[2]Department of Earth and Planetary Sciences, University of New Mexico, Albuquerque, New Mexico 87122 <sidash@aol.com>

ABSTRACT --- Although the Upper Triassic Chinle Formation in the southwestern United States contains a large flora of about 100 species, they are mostly based on foliar and stem material and only eight are based on cones. In this paper, we present the results of our investigation of two additional species of cones collected from the Chinle Formation in Petrified Forest National Park, Arizona, and from equivalent strata in west-central New Mexico. One is a seed cone described as *Araucarites rudicula* sp. nov.; the other is a pollen cone of uncertain affinity which is described as *Creberanthus bealeii* gen. et sp. nov. The identification of a cone with probable araucarian features is significant because it indicates that the Araucariaceae apparently extended into the Carnian stage of the Late Triassic, and is the first evidence of araucarian conifers in the Chinle impression/compression flora. The morphology of the cone *C. bealeii* indicates affinities with the pteridosperms, and that it is probably related to the somewhat similar pollen cone *Pramelreuthia*, which was recently recognized in the Chinle Formation. This fossil is noteworthy because it demonstrates that pteridosperms were a more diverse and significant component of the Chinle flora than previously realized. The cone is also significant because it contains pollen comparable to the dispersed pollen grain *Alisporites opii* Daugherty, which was originally described from the Chinle Formation in Petrified Forest National Park.

Keywords: *Alisporites opii*, Arizona, Chinle Formation, cones, Upper Triassic, Araucariaceae.

INTRODUCTION

PALEOBOTANICAL INVESTIGATIONS of the Chinle Formation, especially in the parts exposed in Petrified Forest National Park, Arizona, have revealed one of the richest and most thoroughly documented Triassic plant assemblages in the world. Representatives of nearly every major vascular plant group, along with many problematic taxa, have been described from the flora (Ash, 1989). Due to the magnitude of this flora, the dominant taxa and/or those of particular phylogenetic, paleoecological, and paleobiogeographical interest were given research priority in the past. Consequently, several potentially significant plant fossils were temporarily set aside pending the discovery of more informative specimens. After nearly four decades of intensive collecting and analysis of the Chinle flora by the junior author, a clearer picture has emerged as to which taxa will probably not be significantly augmented by more satisfactory material, but still merit description. Two such forms are presented here, because they may have important implications for our understanding of more common components of the Chinle flora.

Both of the new taxa are represented by cones. The first is a coniferous ovulate cone here assigned to a new species of *Araucarites* Presl, 1838. This material provides the first convincing evidence of probable araucarian conifers from the Chinle impression/compression flora. In addition to providing additional evidence for Chinle conifer diversity, this find has potential implications for the interpretation and affinities of the famous *Araucarioxylon arizonicum* Knowlton (in Fontaine and Knowlton, 1890), tree trunks preserved in such abundance in Petrified Forest National Park and elsewhere in the southwestern United States (Ash and Creber, 2000). The second described taxon, which is here placed in a new genus and species, is represented by only two fragmentary specimens of a lax cone bearing lateral synangiate organs with *in situ* bisaccate pollen. Although fragmentary, this material is significant because it adds to a growing realization of greater pteridosperm diversity in the Chinle flora than previously recognized (Ash and Litwin, 1996). We also demonstrate that this cone is the probable source of the dispersed pollen species *Alisporites opii* Daugherty, which is the type species of an important Triassic pollen genus and one of the most common Chinle Formation palynomorphs (Daugherty, 1941).

PREVIOUS INVESTIGATIONS

In contrast to foliar and stem remains, fossil cones are quite rare in the Upper Triassic Chinle Formation and equivalent units in the western United States . Accord-

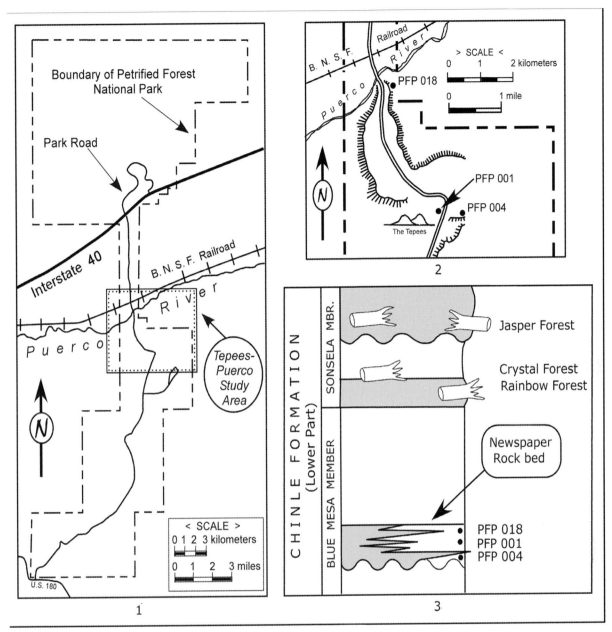

Figure *1*. Maps of Petrified Forest National Park, Arizona and the Tepees-Puerco study area together with a simplified stratigraphic section of the lower part of the Chinle Formation in the area. The positions of the three localities that contained the fossils described here are shown by the large solid dots on the maps and their stratigraphic horizon is indicated on the chart by the same symbol. Information about the localities is contained in the text. Maps adapted from the topographic maps of the park (U.S. Geological Survey) and the chart is adapted from Ash (1987).

ing to a recent compilation by the junior author, of the approximate 100 well-defined species (assigned to 72 genera) of gymnosperms and non-gymnosperms now recognized in these units only eight, excluding the two described here, are represented by more or less complete cones. The previously described cones are one species each of *Equicalastrobus* Grauvogel-Stamm and Ash, 1999 and *Alostrobus* Ash, 1999 and two species each of *Masculostrobus* Seward, 1911 (Ash, 1972, 1999), *Pramelreuthia* Krasser, 1918 (Ash and Litwin, 1996) and *Williamsonia* Carruthers, 1870 (Ash, 1968).

MATERIALS AND METHODS

All but one of the fossils described here were obtained from three localities in the central part of the park in the Tepees – Puerco River study area (Fig. 1). One specimen came from a locality in generally equivalent beds in the Fort Wingate area of west-central New Mexico (Ash, 1973).

The fossils collected in the park occurred in a thick bed of greenish mudstone that is laterally equivalent to the Newspaper Rock bed in the Blue Mesa Member of the

Chinle Formation (Fig. 1). The unit, called "leaf shales" by Stagner (1941), is widely exposed in the Puerco-Tepees area and, as he noted, contains plant fossils at several localities. It has also been termed the "wetland facies" of the Newspaper Rock bed fluvial deposits by Demko (1995) based on his hypothesis that it was deposited during repeated overbank floods on the floodplain of the stream that deposited the Newspaper Rock bed. The bed of mudstone is typically structureless and lacks bedding planes. Plant megafossils found in the deposit include large portions of leaves, small herbaceous stems, and occasional cones and cone parts, all of which are usually preserved as compressions. A few petrified stems are also known from the deposit. Although they are not abundant as plant fossils, the remains of aquatic organisms, such as crayfish, conchostracans, insects, and fish eggs have been found in the same deposit.

Demko (1995) contended that the plant megafossils found in the wetland facies in such abundance represent overbank vegetation (i.e., remains of plants that inhabited the floodplain). However, the plant megafossils typically are irregularly distributed and oriented in the deposit and few if any appear to be preserved in the position of growth. In fact, the general jumbled arrangement of the fossils suggests that most were washed onto the floodplain from elsewhere in a slurry of mud when the stream that deposited the Newspaper Rock bed overflowed its banks. The remains of aquatic organisms listed above that are found in the unit presumably represent organisms that were washed onto the floodplain or inhabited small ponds on the floodplain, although no lacustrine deposits have been recognized in the wetland facies.

The wetland facies is slightly different at locality PFP 018 of this paper than at other localities (e.g., locality PFP 001) because it contains a few thin (1-6 mm in thickness) and irregular clay partings that show abundant small fragments of plants and rare large portions of leaves and cones. The fossils in these partings appear to represent surface litter washed onto and deposited on the floodplain. Since these partings are irregular in distribution and thickness, they most probably represent random rather than seasonal events. Otherwise, the structureless green mudstone at this locality is similar to that found elsewhere and also contains a similar variety of irregularly distributed plant megafossils.

The description of the new *Araucarites* species is based upon only seven articulated cones, five isolated lateral appendages (bract/scales), and a possible isolated seed all collected from locality PFP 018 near the Puerco River. The cones and isolated bract/scales are preserved as stained impressions on thin clay partings in greenish mudstone with varying amounts of thick, coaly organic material, which tends to break up into sub-millimeter sized fragments when re-

moved from the matrix. So far, efforts at isolating cuticles from this material have been unsuccessful. The bract/scales have a tendency to split through the interior tissues revealing the internal vascular strands (Fig. 3.3); however, critical surface details are obscured in these specimens. Fortunately, two isolated bract/scales split along the adaxial surface-matrix interface and, therefore, show the ovule attachment scar. Limited dégagement was required to completely expose some of the cones and bract/scales. The thick carbonaceous residue of the bract/scales and the manner in which they cleave indicates that they most probably were thick, hard, and woody when living.

The new pollen cone described here is known from only two partial cones collected from two localities one of which is adjacent to the small hills called the Tepees in the central part of the park and is designated locality PFP 001. The second locality is about 250 meters east of locality PFP 001 across the main park road and is designated locality PFP 004. Daugherty (1941) first described plant fossils from both of these localities and was followed by several other workers (e.g., Gottesfeld, 1972; Litwin, 1985).

The new pollen cones are preserved as impression/compressions in greenish mudstone. Some parts of the impression are stained red. Dégagement was required to fully expose the lateral synangiate organs, because they occur at different levels within the matrix. The central axes have small amounts of dark organic matter attached. A few of these fragments were removed with needles and macerated in HNO_3 and NH_4OH, but no cuticles were recovered. Some of the synangia are represented by compressed organic material. Using needles, this material was removed from one synangium per pollen organ and macerated in HNO_3 and NH_4OH. A few pollen grains were teased out from the pollen masses with needles to allow for individual examination. The pollen masses and individual grains were mounted in glycerine jelly on glass slides for light microscopic examination.

SYSTEMATIC PALEONTOLOGY

Family ARAUCARIACEAE Henkel and Hochstetter, 1865
Genus ARAUCARITES Presl, 1838 (in Sternberg, 1838)
ARAUCARITES RUDICULA new species
Figures 2-4

Diagnosis.–Cone elongate (at least 6.35 cm long and 1.94 cm wide), lax; lateral appendages (bract/scales) spirally arranged on a narrow (~ 1.5 mm) central axis; individual lateral bract/scales with distinct basal stalk (average 1.6 mm long and 1.0 mm wide) and an expanded, wedge-shaped distal portion (average 8.5 mm long and 8.0 mm wide at widest point near apex), thick and woody with numerous parallel vascular strands, adaxial surface of expanded region with shallow, proximal ovoid depression probably representing ovule attachment area, distally both surfaces with a convex, transverse furrow ~ 2.0 mm below apex, apical extension (area distal to furrow) relatively weakly lignified, rapidly contracting distally to a mucronate tip.

Etymology.–The specific epithet *"rudicula"* is the Latin term for wooden spoon, which refers to the typical appearance of the bract/scales.

Types.–Specimen PEFO 34141A, which includes an articulated cone (Fig. 2.1), is here designated the holotype. The counterpart is specimen PEFO 34141B (Figure 2.2). Paratypes consist of another nearly complete cone PEFO 34142 (Fig. 2.3); several partial articulated cones, including specimens USNM 528904 (Fig. 2.5), PEFO 34143 (Fig. 2.6), PEFO 34144 (Fig. 2.4); and isolated bract/scales, including specimen PEFO 34145 (Fig. 3.2).

Other material examined.–Unfigured cone and isolated lateral appendage material includes specimens PEFO 34146-34150. An isolated seed possibly attributable to *Araucarites rudicula* is specimen PEFO 34145 (Fig. 3.5).

Occurrence.–*Araucarites rudicula* n. sp. is presently known from one site (PFP 018) in the Blue Mesa Member of the Chinle Formation in Petrified Forest National Park, and one site in the Monitor Butte Member of the Chinle Formation in the Fort Wingate area (Fig. 2.5).

Description.–Only two complete or nearly complete cones and four partial articulated specimens of *A. rudicula* are known. The holotype is the best-preserved specimen and is represented by part (Fig. 2.1) and counterpart (Fig. 2.2). It is the only specimen with nearly complete lateral appendages in plan view. This specimen and the other nearly complete cone (Fig. 2.3) are the only specimens revealing much of the main axis. Therefore, it must be emphasized that most of our concept of *A. rudicula* is based on two specimens, and is likely to be expanded or modified if more material is recovered.

Both of the nearly complete cones are isolated with no indication of a peduncle preserved. They are both elongate and narrow. The holotype cone (Fig. 2.1, 2.2) was at least 5.64 cm long and 1.63 cm wide with a narrow axis ~1.5 mm wide. The second relatively complete cone (Fig. 2.3) was at least 6.35 cm long and 1.93 cm wide. The widest specimen is a only slightly wider partial cone (1.94 cm) (Fig. 2.4).

The lateral appendages, which probably represent fused bract/scale complexes like those of extant araucarians (and will be referred to as "bract/scales" throughout this paper), are helically arranged and lax on the cone axis (Fig 2.5). On most specimens, the bract/scales are compressed

at various angles and are, therefore, difficult to interpret morphologically (e.g., Fig. 2.5, 2.6). Several of the bract/scales are covered with coaly residue indicating a thick and woody composition (Fig. 3.1).

The individual bract/scales consist of a proximal stalk-like region averaging 1.6 mm long and 1.0 mm wide (Fig. 2.5, 2.6, 4) and an expanded, wedge-shaped distal portion averaging 8.5 mm long and 8.0 mm wide at the widest point near the apex (Fig. 2.4, 2.5, 3.1, 3.2, 4). The best preserved example (Fig. 3.1) from the mid-region of the holotype cone was probably typical, and was at least 8.0 mm long with a narrow (1.7 mm wide) stalk-like base of uncertain length due to incomplete preservation, and an expanded, wedge-shaped distal portion 6.6 mm long and 7.0 mm wide at the widest point. Bract/scales from the upper parts of the cone, as well as several from partial cones (Fig. 2.5, 2.6) indicate that the stalks could be rather long and narrow (up to 2.5 mm long and 1.6 mm wide). Both surfaces of the expanded portion of the bract/scales possess a convex transverse furrow across the widest part (Fig. 2.4, 3.1, 3.2). The apical extension (i.e. the area distal to the transverse furrow) is up to 2.0 mm long and relatively weakly lignified. On many specimens this area is not preserved at all or is only weakly indicated (Fig. 3.2) giving the false impression that the bract/scale apex is rounded. However, better-preserved specimens indicate that the true appendage apex occurred distally to the furrow. The tip of the apical extension is not well preserved on any of the appendages observed so far, but was probably mucronate based on the broken tip bases sometimes visible (Fig. 3.1). A suggested reconstruction of a complete bract/scale in adaxial view is presented in Figure 4.

In some specimens, such as the holotype, the bract/scales split along the plant surface/matrix interface revealing the abaxial surface. In these specimens, the part has abundant coaly material present (Fig. 2.1, 3.1), whereas the counterpart is mostly represented by an impression (Fig. 2.2). In other specimens, the lateral appendages tend to split through the internal tissues revealing the numerous parallel vascular strands and/or fibers (Fig. 2.4, 3.3). The presence of such multiple vascular strands provides convincing evidence that these cones are of coniferous rather than lycopodalean affinity. Only two isolated appendages are preserved with the adaxial surface visible. On both specimens, a shallow, ovoid depression occurs near the base of the expanded portion of appendage. On the figured specimen (Fig. 3.4), the depression is 2.5 mm long and 1.7 mm wide; on the unfigured specimen it is 3.8 mm long and 1.9 mm wide. This depression is probably the attachment site of a single ovule.

An isolated ovoid seed-like structure 4.0 mm long and 2.25 mm wide is closely associated with an isolated

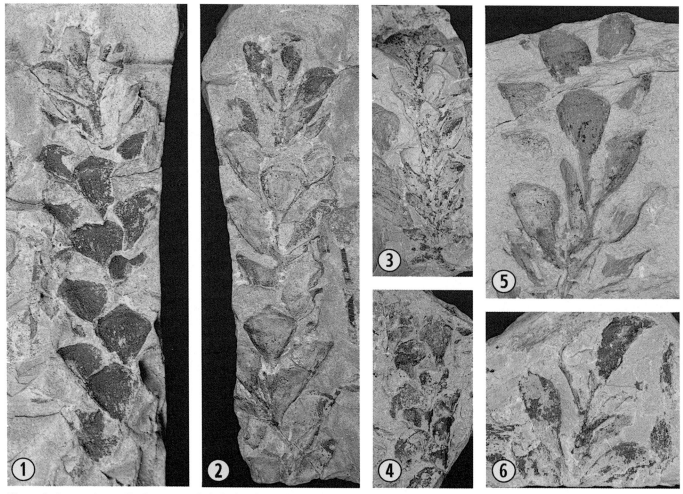

Figure 2. *Araucarites rudicula* sp. nov. *1.* Articulated cone in longitudinal view with adhering organic material. The cone scale marked with an arrow is shown at a higher magnification in Fig. 3.1. Holotype. ×2, PEFO 34141A; *2.* Counterpart of holotype, ×2, PEFO 34141B; *3.* Articulated cone. ×1, PEFO 34142; *4.* Cone with bract/scales in plan view. ×1, PEFO 34144; *5.* Apical region of a specimen from Fort Wingate, NM showing elongate bract/scale bases. ×2, USNM 528904; *6.* Cone apex showing distorted shape of laterally compressed bract/scales. ×2, PEFO 34143.

scale and partial cone (Fig. 3.5). At least one end is flattened (the opposite end is broken off). The seed surface bears many shallow, ovoid depressions about 1.0 mm in diameter. This structure is about the correct size and shape to qualify as the potential seed of *A. rudicula* based on the bract/scale depressions, but this cannot be proved based on one isolated specimen.

Comparisons–Due to the uncertain status of many fossils attributed to *Araucarites*, including unresolved issues regarding the genus name and type material (Buzek et al, 1968; Zijlstra and van Konijnenburg-van Cittert, 2000), comparisons are difficult. For example, reports of *Araucarites* appear sporadically throughout the Late Paleozoic and Early Mesozoic paleobotanical literature of Europe and Asia. Many of these references occur in obscure or difficult to obtain journals, and rarely include detailed descriptions or adequate figures. Fortunately, many of these occurrences are listed in Dobruskina's (1994) review of the Triassic floras of Eurasia, and she indicates that several of these fos-

sils are probably not *Araucarites*. For example, several have been reassigned to *Tomiostrobus* Neuburg, 1936, which is a male lycopod cone. *Araucarites recubariensis* has been transferred to the extinct conifer genus *Voltzia* Brongniart, 1828, and *A. parsoraensis* has been transferred to *Samaropsis* Goeppert, 1864. The Triassic record of *Araucarites* from central and Western Europe is also ambiguous. Isolated bract/scales attributed to *Araucarites* have recently been figured by Kelber and Hansch (1995), but are poorly preserved and provide few points of comparison with the new Chinle species.

The Triassic *Araucarites* record from North America is poor. *Araucarites yorkensis* Wanner and Fontaine (1900), from the New Oxford Formation in Pennsylvania, is represented by one specimen showing only vague triangular impressions. The only other North American Triassic strobilar fossils assigned to the araucarians is *Primaraucaria wielandia* Bock, 1954, which is known from several articulated cones from the Triassic Richmond Basin

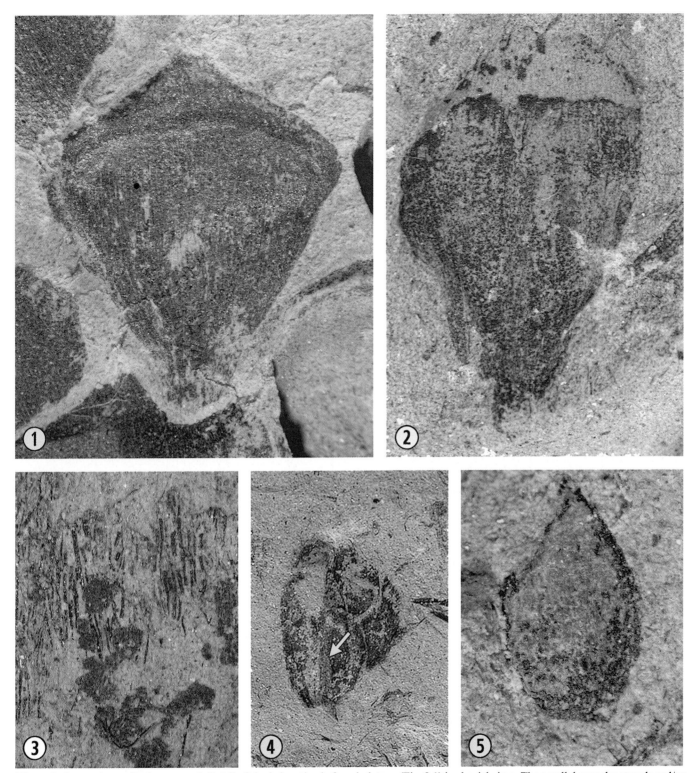

Figure 3. *Araucarites rudicula* sp. nov. *1*. Detail of single bract/scale from holotype (Fig. 2.1) in abaxial view. The parallel vascular strands and/or fibers are clearly visible in this fossil. Note the well-defined transverse furrow and nearly complete mucronate apex. ×8, PEFO 34141A; *2*. Isolated bract/scale with poorly preserved apical extension. ×7, PEFO 34145; *3*. Internal tissues of a bract/scale showing parallel vascular strands and/or fibers. ×20, PEFO 34144; *4*. Isolated bract/scale in slightly oblique adaxial view showing ovule attachment scar (arrow). ×2, PEFO 34144; *5*. Isolated seed associated with *A. rudicula*. ×15, PEFO 34145.

of Virginia. Unfortunately, many of the specimens of *P. wielandia* are now lost (Spamer, 1995). However, Cornet (1986) briefly reconsidered this fossil, and although its true affinities remain uncertain, it is unlikely that *P. wielandia* is

a conifer.

The only description of a Triassic *Araucarites* that includes articulated cones of which we are aware of comes from the classic Scoresby Sound locality of east Greenland

(Harris, 1935). Material of *A. charcoti* Harris, 1935 consists of a single elongate cone 6.0 cm long and 2.5 cm wide, and many isolated bract/scales. Based on figures in Harris (1935, Fig. 44), the bract/scales show considerable variation in shape and size; however, they are all essentially diamond-shaped. Some of the smaller scales are in the size range of *A. rudicula*, but most are nearly twice as large. There is a convex transverse furrow across the broadest part of the bract/scale similar to that of *A. rudicula*, but this occurs close to the middle region instead of at the apex. The area distal to the ridge (the apical extension) is relatively weakly lignified like that of *A. rudicula*; however, in *A. charcoti*, the most distal portion tapers more gradually to an acute tip. Also, the base of the apical extension on *A. charcoti* forms two extensions on each side that point back toward the cone axis. Most of the *A. charcoti* bract/scales taper proximally to a narrow base; however, there is no distinct stalk-like base, as in *A. rudicula*.

Arauracrites rudicula bears a distinct resemblance to cones known as *Compsostrobus neotericus* Delevoryas and Hope, 1973 from nearly coeval deposits of the Pekin Formation of North Carolina. Both cones are elongate with stalked lateral appendages, but *Compsostrobus* is less laxly organized. The lateral appendages of both cones are interpreted as fused bract/scales, and are similar in consisting of a spathulate proximal region and elongate distal portion (Delevoryas and Hope, 1987). However, the "shoulders" (i.e., the edges of the widest portion) of the *Compsostrobus* appendages are more rounded than in *A. rudicula*. The spathulate region of the *Compsostrobus* appendage is interpreted as a cone scale, and the elongate portion as the subtending bract. These structures are intimately fused, and were apparently shed from the cone as a unit. In *Araucarites* the spathulate region is formed by the curved transverse ridge on the lateral appendage, which is unlikely to represent an entire cone scale margin, as it is visible on the adaxial and abaxial sides of the appendage (i.e. it would be obscured on the adaxial side by the subtending bract if it were a cone scale margin). The adaxial surface of the *Compsostrobus* cone scale bears two inverted ovules with elongate micropyles. The ovules have left two distinct scars on the adaxial scale surface in contrast to a single ovule scar of *A. rudicula*. According to Delevoryas and Hope (1973; 1987), the unlobed cone scale of *Compsostrobus*, which bears two inverted ovules, suggested affinities with the Pinaceae. This determination is somewhat strengthened by the associated pollen cones known as *Millerostrobus pekinensis* Taylor et al., 1987, which bear two abaxial pollen sacs per microsporophyll, and bisaccate pollen. Although the similarity of *Compsostrobus* ovulate cones to *A. rudicula* is at first striking, the details of the lateral appendage structure and ovule attachment are dif-

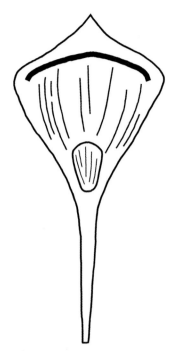

Figure *4*. Reconstruction of an *Araucarites rudicula* sp. nov. bract/scale bearing a single small seed near the base of the distal portion. The transverse furrow is indicated by the broad line in the upper part of the drawing; some of the parallel vascular strands and fibers on the bract/scale and striations on the seed are indicated by narrow longitudinal lines. ×4.

ferent and preclude a close phylogenetic relationship. Furthermore, pollen cones and shoots like those attributed to *Compsostrobus* have not been found to date in the Chinle Formation.

The Jurassic impression/compression record of araucarian conifers is much richer, and a few relevant species from this time are considered in relation to *A. rudicula*. A relatively large number of anatomically preserved araucarian cones from the Jurassic have also been described, but most of these are essentially similar to extant araucarians. Furthermore, the descriptions focus mainly on the anatomical details rather than gross morphology, which makes comparisons with the Triassic fossils impractical. The bract/scales of *A. rudicula* are rather similar, except in size, to those recently attributed to *Araucarites* n. sp. from the Early Jurassic of southeastern Utah (Tidwell and Ash, in press). Although the Utah specimens are generally slightly larger (8-12 mm wide, 11-12 mm long), they have nearly the same morphology; however, each bract/scale bears a much larger (5-6 mm wide, 8 mm long) obovate seed that occupies the lower two thirds of the structure. In addition, the Utah bract/scales lack a distinct basal stalk.

Nearly all of the cones from the Jurassic known from articulated specimens tend to be compact and ovoid, and thus more like those of extant araucarians. Therefore, points of comparison with *A. rudicula* must be based mainly upon the bract/scale morphology. The only species of which we are aware with any particular points of comparison to *A. rudicula* are the similar species *A. phillipsi* Carruthers, 1869 and *A. brodiei* Carruthers, 1869, both of which come from the Middle Jurassic of England. *Araucarites phillipsi* was originally described from the classic Jurassic deposits of Yorkshire. Subsequent studies by Kendall (1949) and Harris (1979) provide more detailed information, including descriptions of the cuticles. The most striking similarity between *A. phillipsi* and *A. rudicula* entails the apical region of the bract/scales, which in both species is strongly truncated to form a short, apical point (i.e. mucronate). Therefore, the widest portion of the fossils in both species occurs close to the apex. The drawings in Kendall (1952) and Harris (1979) also show longitudinal striations that may indicate parallel vascular strands and/or fibers like those of *A. rudicula*. The *A. phillipsi* bract scales are also in the same size range as *A. rudicula*. However, the *A. phillipsi* specimens have a wing-like marginal membrane like that of many other Jurassic-Recent araucarians, and there is no distinct, stalk-like basal portion like that of *A. rudicala*.

Araucarites brodiei was originally from Stonesfield, Oxfordshire and has recently been reconsidered by Cleal and Rees (2003). The bract/scales of this species are similar in shape to those of *A. rudicula*, having the broadest part near the apex. The apex of *A. brodiei* is also weakly lignified and mucronate, and the ovule is oblong and positioned near the base of the bract/scale. However, the bract/scales of *A. brodiei* are more than twice as large as those of *A. rudicula*, and no distinct, stalk-like base is present.

Although there are many additional *Araurcarites* species mentioned in the literature (e. g., Srivastava et al., 2004), those considered here are the only ones of which we are aware that exhibit any particular points of similarity to *A. rudicula*. We submit that the most distinctive feature of *A. rudicula* relative to other conifers with probable araucarian affinities is the distinct stalk-like basal portion of the bract/scales. However, these stalks are apparent only on articulated specimens and appear to be broken off or otherwise not preserved on the isolated bract/scales. Considering that most Triassic records of *Araucarites* are of isolated bract/scales, it cannot be definitively stated that such basal stalks are unique to *A. rudicula*. In fact, Kelber and Hansch (1995, Fig. 249) figured a supposedly aberrant bract/scale from the German Keuper with an elongated basal stalk as in our specimens. Perhaps the presence of basal stalks is a primitive feature lost in all post-Triassic forms.

More detailed comparisons with additional *Araucarites* species will not be practical until specimens of *A. rudicula* with preserved cuticles and attached seeds are found. Clearly, an exhaustive review of the entire genus *Araucarites* based on re-examinations of the actual fossils is also needed, especially the putative Paleozoic and Trias-

sic records, but this is beyond the scope of the present study. Therefore, comparisons with *A. rudicula* must be based for now on the few impression/compression fossils from the Triassic and Jurassic for which reliable, accessible descriptions are available as noted above.

Family Uncertain
CREBERANTHUS gen. nov.

Type species.–*Creberanthus bealeii* sp. nov. by monotypy

Diagnosis.–Cone consisting of a narrow straight axis bearing loosely arranged synangiate organs. Synangiate organs composed of narrow proximal stalk and a distal rectangular synangia containing a single row of several narrow elongate pollen sacs. Pollen sacs containing large, bisaccate grains.

Etymology–The genus is named in honor of Geoffrey Creber for his contributions to our understanding of the Chinle flora and for collecting some of the material described here. The root *"anthus"* refers to the microsporangiate nature of the cone.

Occurrence.–Blue Mesa Member of the Chinle Formation in Petrified Forest National Park.

CREBERANTHUS BEALEII new species
Figures 5-6

Diagnosis.–Cone at least 32.0 mm long and 12.0 mm wide, central axis 1.52 - 2.5 mm wide bearing loosely arranged synangiate organs branching in several planes; individual lateral organs consisting of a narrow, proximal stalk at least 2.2 mm long, and distal synangiate region, synangiate region elongate (typically about 1.5 times higher than long) ranging from ~ 2.5 mm high and 2.0 mm long to 3.0 mm high and 2.5 mm long, with biconvex to nearly straight lateral margins and straight proximal and distal margins, consisting of one row of 7-9 narrow, elongate pollen sacs with well-fused lateral margins; pollen bisaccate, typically 110 μm in diameter, ovoid, sacci large with fine endoreticulations, broadly attached to corpus, distal colpus present.

Etymology.–The species *bealeii* is proposed in honor of Lt. E. F. Beale of the U.S. Army, who explored the region now including Petrified Forest National Park, and unsuccessfully tried to introduce camels as a mode of transportation in the West just before the American Civil War.

Types.–Specimen PEFO 34151, which represents an articulated cone (Figs. 5.1, 5.2, 5.5, 5.6) is here designated as the holotype. *In situ* pollen masses from this specimen (Figs. 6.1, 6.2., 6.4) are mounted on slide PEFO 34151a. A single grain (Fig. 6.3) is mounted on slide PEFO 34151b.

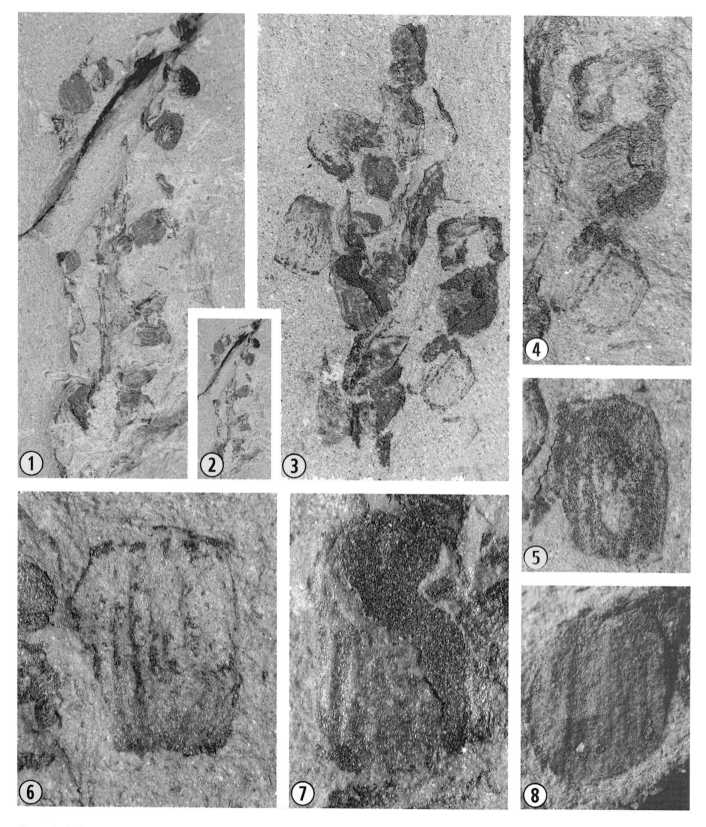

Figure *5. Creberanthus bealeii* sp. nov. pollen organs from the Chinle Formation (Upper Triassic) of Arizona. *1.* Holotype showing central axis and lateral synangia (arrow). ×3, PEFO 34151; *2.* Holotype at actual size. PEFO 34151, ×1; *3.* Paratype with synangia oriented in a possible spiral arrangement. ×6, PEFO 34152; *4.* The synangia under extreme low angle light showing their preservation at different levels in the matrix. ×8, PEFO 34152; *5.* Detail of synangia from upper right of holotype (Fig. 5.1) showing relatively straight lateral margins. ×13, PEFO 34151; *6.* Detail of synangia with little organic material remaining except between several sporangial units. ×18, PEFO 34151; *7.* Detail of synangia showing striations on sporangia. ×21, PEFO 34151; *8.* Detail of synangium from holotype. Note strongly biconvex margins. ×15, PEFO 34151.

Specimen PEFO 34152 (Figs. 5.3, 5.4) is the only additional cone known, and is designated here as a paratype. Pollen masses isolated from this specimen (Fig. 6.4) are mounted on slide PEFO 34152b.

Occurrence.– *Creberanthis bealeii* is presently known from two sites in the Blue Mesa Member of the Chinle Formation in Petrified Forest National Park. Specimen PEFO 34151 comes from locality PFP 004 of this paper and specimen PEFO 34152 comes from locality PFP 001.

Description.–Currently *C. bealeii* is represented by only two lax, articulated cones. It is not clear if the specimens are complete or only parts of larger structures. The holotype (Fig. 5.1) is ~ 32.0 mm long and 12 mm wide, with at least sixteen lateral synangiate organs. The second cone (Fig. 5.3) is ~ 17.0 mm long and 9.0 mm wide, with at least eleven lateral organs. Both cones possess an elongate central axis ~ 1.52 - 2.5 mm wide. Patches of black organic residue adhere to the axis, but no cuticles could be obtained by maceration of this material.

The arrangement of the lateral synangiate organs on the central axis is uncertain, as the stalks are not consistently preserved. On the holotype (Fig. 5.1), three lateral stalk bases are visible lined up on the left side of the axis, which could indicate a pinnate arrangement. However, the synangiate organs seem to occur at different levels of the matrix. Although there is no question that the distal synangia themselves occur at different levels on the paratype (Fig. 5.3), it is difficult to discern on most photographs because the matrix surface appears flat. Therefore, a view of the three synangia from the right side of the cone is shown under extreme incident light (Fig. 5.4), which clearly indicates that the basal synangium in the figure occurs at a lower level in the matrix. Furthermore, the variable orientation of the long axes of the synangiate portion of the lateral organs relative to the central axis on both cones is more consistent with a helical arrangement, but this is uncertain and will only be settled definitively by the discovery of more complete specimens.

The individual lateral organs consisting of a narrow, proximal stalk at least 2.25 mm long and 0.25 mm wide (based on longest preserved section from the holotype), and a distal synangiate region. The stalk expands slightly at the point of attachment to the synangiate region (Fig. 5.5). The synangiate region is recurved relative to the stalk and appears to be directly attached to the stalk apex with no indication of a lamina or any other sterile structure. The individual synangiate regions are elongate (typically about 1.3–1.5 times higher than long) ranging from ~ 2.5 mm high and 2.0 mm long to 3.0 mm high and 2.5 mm long, with biconvex (Figs. 5.8) to nearly parallel lateral margins (Fig. 5.7) and straight proximal and distal margins (Fig. 5.5, 5.6). Each synangiate region appears to consist of a single row of 7–9

narrow, elongate pollen sacs with well-fused lateral margins. The individual sporangia are most visible on the impressions under incident lighting and collectively create a pleated appearance (Fig. 5.5-5.8), which is somewhat obscured on specimens with abundant organic material adhering (Fig. 5.7). Fine longitudinal striations are visible on the impressions of individual sporangia (Fig. 5.7). The dehiscence mode of the individual sporangia could not be determined.

Several masses of *in situ* pollen grains were macerated from the organic matter covering the synangia from both cones. The most intact pollen mass recovered is elongate (at least 1.5 mm long and 0.44 mm wide) and composed of hundreds of tightly packed pollen grains (Fig. 6.1, 6.2), but it is broken off at the base. No overlapping pollen sacs have been found, which supports the interpretation of the synangium as having only a single row of sporangia. The individual pollen grains are large (average 139 µm in diameter based on 20 randomly chosen grains in polar view) with a subcircular to ovoid amb due to the presence of two large, broadly attached sacci with fine endoreticulations (Fig. 6.3). A distinct colpus is sometimes visible on the distal polar surface of the corpus (Fig. 6.2, 6.4, 6.5). The colpus is not always present on isolated grains (Fig. 6.3), but this is probably due to slight over-maceration. These pollen grains are most similar to the dispersed morphospecies *Alisporites opii* Daugherty, 1941; however, the average size of the *in situ* grains is larger (average 100-110 µm vs. 130 µm, respectively). This may not be significant, because Daugherty (1941) did not state how many grains he measured, and several of the *C. bealeii* grains are in the same size range.

Comparisons.–The general morphology of *C. bealeii* invites comparisons with the pollen organs of many so-called "pteridosperms," which are generally thought to represent a paraphyletic and/or polyphyletic assemblage of Paleozoic and Mesozoic seed plants. Nevertheless, we submit that the general morphology of many "pteridosperm" pollen organs is more similar than generally conceded, and should be more seriously considered as a possible synapomorphy in future phylogenetic investigations. *Creberanthus bealeii* is particularly similar to species of the pteridosperm-like pollen organ *Pramelreuthia*, which occurs in the Chinle Formation, and we focus our comparisons on this genus. In fact, the similarity is great enough that we seriously considered describing *C. bealeii* as a new species of *Pramelreuthia*. Our justifications for not doing so are detailed below; however, these plants, and most other Mesozoic pteridosperms, remain poorly enough understood that any determinations should be considered tentative. *Pramelreuthia* is a distinctly pinnately organized pollen organ known from three Late Triassic species. The type species, *P. haberfelneri*, is based on a single specimen from

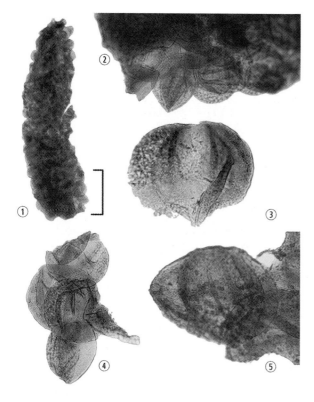

Figure 6. *In situ* pollen of *Creberanthus bealeii* sp. nov. from the Chinle Formation (Upper Triassic) of Arizona. *1.* An *in situ* pollen mass, broken at the bottom. Bracketed area detail appears in next figure. ×37, slide PEFO 34151a; *2.* Detail of pollen grains from the bracketed edge of the pollen mass in Figure 6.1. ×100, slide PEFO 34151a; *3.* A single pollen grain in proximal polar view teased out from an *in situ* pollen mass. ×250, slide PEFO 34151b; *4.* An *in situ* pollen mass. Middle grain in distal polar view showing colpus. ×150, slide PEFO 34152a.; *5.* Detail of pollen grain with obvious colpus. ×250, slide PEFO 34151c.

the classic Luntzerschichten deposits of Austria (Krasser, 1918; Kräusel, 1949). Two additional species, *P. dubielii* Ash and Litwin (1996) and *P. yazzi* Ash and Litwin (1996), are known from abundant material from five widespread localities in the Chinle Formation. One specimen of the small variety of *Pramelreuthia*, *P. yazzi*, occurs at locality PFP 004 of this paper in association with PEFO 34151.

The most obvious similarity between *Creberanthus* and *Pramelreuthia* is the presence of synangiate organs composed of laterally fused sporangia. This feature stands in stark contrast to the free condition of the sporangia in all other Mesozoic pteridosperm organs of which we are aware, including those of the Caytoniales, Corystospermales, and Peltaspermales. The synangiate condition is somewhat like that of several Paleozoic pteridosperms with probable affinities with the Lyginopteridales (e.g. *Crossotheca* Zeiller, 1883) and Medullosales (e.g *Whittleseya* Newberry, 1853) (Taylor, 1988). However, the non-striate bisaccate pollen of *Creberanthus* and *Pramelreuthia* clearly links these organs with other Mesozoic pteridosperm pollen organ taxa.

Well-fused synangia born on narrow stalks are

unique among Mesozoic pteridosperms and indicate a close relationship between *Creberanthus* and *Pramelreuthia*. However, we interpret the differences between the two types of fossils to be great enough to justify erecting the new genus *Creberanthus*. The most obvious difference is the shape of the synangiate organs. In *Pramelreuthia*, the synangiate organ is typically about 1.5 times longer than high, whereas those of *Creberanthus* are typically about 1.5 times higher than long. Furthermore, based on the limited material of *Creberanthus*, the synangiate organ appears to consist of a single row of synangia, whereas those of *Pramelreuthia* are certainly bivalved (Ash and Litwin, 1996). The pollen grains of *Creberanthus* are also distinctive in being much larger (average 110 µm) than those of any *Pramelreuthia* species. Finally, the suggested non-pinnate arrangement of the *Creberanthus* synangiate organs may represent a significant difference from the clearly pinnate structure of *Pramelreuthia*.

The only other Mesozoic pollen organ similar to *C. bealeii* is an unnamed species represented by anatomically preserved material in calcareous nodules from the Chinle Formation (Pigg et al., 1993). Although not well known, this pollen organ is synangiate and produces *Alisporites*-like pollen grains like *C. bealeii*. However, the synangia were probably composed of 10–12 pollen sacs, and the grains measure only 80 µm in diameter. Nevertheless, it remains a possibility that this material represents the same plant as *C. bealeii* in a different preservational mode. More material of both kinds will be needed to resolve this question.

CONCLUSIONS

Although fossils of *A. rudicula* and *C. bealeii* are rare, they may have implications for our understanding of the more common components of the Chinle flora. For example, *A. rudicula* provides the first convincing impression/compression evidence for araucarian conifers in the Chinle Formation. In addition to providing new data on Triassic araucarian morphology and biogeography, this discovery has obvious implications for the possible affinities of the famous *Araucarioxylon arizonicum* logs of Petrified Forest National Park.

Based on the *Araucarioxylon*-type wood anatomy, it has historically been assumed that the *A. arizonicum* logs of Petrified Forest National Park were produced by giant araucarian trees. This belief was reflected in reconstructions depicting the living trees with long, unbranched main trunks, and compact apical crowns like those of most modern *Araucaria* species. Remarkably, until recently, this concept was never tested by detailed observations of the numerous available logs. It was pointed out by Ash (1987) that the limbs of *A. arizonicum* did not occur in whorls as in typical araucarian trees. Ash and Creber (2000) measured and examined many of the larger logs in Petrified Forest National Park, and found that substantial branch scars, and in some cases actual branch bases, occurred almost to ground level. Such a branching pattern, along with the clearly documented presence of a massive taproot, suggests an architecture at variance with that of other fossil and modern araucarians (Ash and Creber, 2000: fig. 3).

The new reconstruction of the *A. arizonicum* tree, along with the absence of definitive araucarian impression/compression remains in the Chinle Formation, appeared to cast doubt on the araucarian affinities of the parent plants. The wood anatomy remained suggestive, but *Araucarioxylon/Dadoxylon*-type wood is known even from non-conifers, such as the glossopterids. The discovery of the *A. rudicula* ovulate cones described here, however, suggests that araucarian conifers were part of the Chinle flora, although it cannot be proven at this time that they are definitively related to the logs. In fact, the rarity of the cones compared to the abundance of logs could be interpreted as evidence against such a relationship. In any event, the possibility that the logs are of araucarian affinity does not cast doubt on the Ash and Creber (2000) reconstruction of the trees, as it is based on observations of the fossil logs rather than assumptions of taxonomic affinity.

Coniferous foliage is rare in the Petrified Forest (Ash, 1989) and includes only *Brachyphyllum hegewaldia* Ash, 1973 and *Podozamites arizonicus* Daugherty, 1941. Of the two, *B. hegewaldia* is the only fossil which might be related to the Araucariaceae because Kendall (1949) clearly demonstrated that some of the Jurassic species of *Brachyphyllum* in England appeared to be araucarian (Har-ris, 1979). However, it should be pointed out that *B. hegewaldia* is not very common in the Petrified Forest and is known from a single locality several km from the locality that contained *A. rudicula.* Thus, there is no strong evidence that the two fossils are in any way related.

The *C. bealeii* pollen organs are, like the conifer cones, extremely rare components of the Chinle impression/compression flora. However, the *in situ* pollen is essentially identical to *Alisporites opii*, which Daugherty (1941, p.98) claimed is the most common dispersed palynomorph in the Chinle Formation. Assuming *C. bealeii* was the sole source of this pollen, the parent plant must have been a more important component of the flora than indicated by the macrofossil record. This fossil, along with the two species of *Pramelreuthia* (Ash and Litwin, 1996) and the unnamed permineralized synangium (Pigg et al., 1993), reveal that pteridosperms were a more diverse and significant component of the Chinle flora than previously believed.

ACKNOWLEDGMENTS

We are grateful to Dr. G. Creber for helping collect some of the material described here. The assistance of the superintendents of Petrified Forest National Park who authorized us to collect in the park, and the encouragement and assistance provided by members of the staff, is acknowledged with thanks. Petrified Forest Museum Association provided financial assistance with fieldwork. Aspects of this material are based on work supported by the National Science Foundation under grant EAR-0105476 to B. Axsmith. Sonja Axsmith provided invaluable assistance with the figures.

REFERENCES

Ash, S. R. 1968. A new species of *Williamsonia* from the Upper Triassic Chinle Formation of New Mexico. Linnean Society (London) Journal (Botany), 61:113-120.

Ash, S. R. 1972. Late Triassic plants from the Chinle Formation in northeastern Arizona. Palaeontology, 15:598-618.

Ash, S. R. 1973. Two new Late Triassic plants from the Petrified Forest of Arizona. Journal of Paleontology, 47:46-53.

Ash, S. R. 1987. Petrified Forest National Park, Arizona, p. 405-410. *In* S. S. Beus (ed.), Centennial Field Guide, Volume 2, Rocky Mountain Section of the Geological Society of America: Geological Society of America.

Ash, S. R. 1989. A catalog of Upper Triassic plant megafossils of the western United States through 1988, p. 189-222. *In* S. G. Lucas and A. P. Hunt (eds.), Dawn of the Age of Dinosaurs in the American Southwest: New Mexico Museum of Natural History, Albuquerque.

Ash, S. R. 1999. An Upper Triassic upland flora from north-central New Mexico, U.S.A. Review of Palaeobotany and Palynology, 105:183-199.

Ash, S. R. and G. Creber. 2000. The Late Triassic *Araucarioxylon arizonicum* trees of the Petrified Forest National Park, Arizona, USA. Palaeontology, 43:15-28.

Ash, S. R. and R. J. Litwin. 1996. New species of the pinnate microsporophyll *Pramelreuthia* from the Upper Triassic of the southwestern United States. American Journal of Botany, 83:1091-1099.

Bock, W. S. 1954. *Primaraucaria*, a new araucarian genus from the Virginia Triassic. Journal of Paleontology, 28:32-42.

Brongniart, A. 1828. Essai d'une flora du grès bigarre. Annales Sci. Nat. 1st Series, 15:435-460.

Buzek, C., F. Holy and Z. Kvacek. 1968. Die Gattung *Doliostrobus* Marion und ihr Vorkommen im Nordböhmischen Tertiär. Palaeontographica B, 123:153-172.

Carruthers, W. 1869. On some undescribed coniferous fruits from the secondary rocks of Britain. Geological Magazine, 6:1-7.

Carruthers, W. 1870. On fossil cycadean stems from the secondary rocks of Britain. Linnaean Society London Transactions, 26:675-708.

Cleal, C. J. and P. M. Rees. 2003. The Middle Jurassic flora from Stonesfield, Oxfordshire, UK. Palaeontology, 46:739-801.

Cornet, B. 1986. The leaf venation and reproductive structures of a Late Triassic angiosperm, *Sanmiguelia lewisii*. Evolutionary Theory, 7:231-309.

Daugherty, L. H. 1941. The Upper Triassic flora of Arizona. Carnegie Institution of Washington Publication 526, 108 p.

Delevoryas, T. and Hope, R. 1973. Fertile coniferophyte remains from the Late Triassic, Deep River Basin, North Carolina. American Journal of Botany, 60:810-818.

Delevoryas, T. and Hope, R. 1987. Further observations on the Late

Triassic conifers *Compsostrobus neotericus* and *Voltzia andrewsii*. Review of Paleobotany and Palynology, 51:59-64.

Demko, T. M. 1995. Taphonomy of fossil plants in Petrified Forest National Park, Arizona, p. 37-52, In Fossils of Arizona - vol. III, Proceedings. Southwest Paleontological Society and Mesa Southwest Museum, Mesa, Arizona.

Dobruskina, I. A. 1994. Triassic floras of Eurasia. Osterreichische Akademie der Wissenschaften Schriftenreihe der Erdwissenschaftlichen Kommission, 10:1-422.

Fontaine, W. M. and Knowlton, F. H. 1890. Notes on Triassic plants from New Mexico: U.S. National Museum Proceedings, 13:281-285.

Goeppert, H. R. 1864. Die fossile Flora der permischen Formation. Palaeontographica 12:1-224.

Gottesfeld, A. S. 1972. Palynology of the Chinle Formation. Museum of Northern Arizona Bulletin, 47 (supplement):13-18.

Grauvogel-Stamm, L. and Ash, S. R. 1999. "*Lycostrobus*" *chinleana*, an equisetalean cone from the Upper Triassic of the southwestern United States and its phylogenetic implications. American Journal of Botany, 86:1391-1405.

Harris, T. M. 1935. The fossil flora of Scoresby Sound, East Greenland, Part 4, Ginkgoales, Coniferales, Lycopodiales and isolated fructifications. Meddelelser om Grönland, 112(1):1-176.

Harris, T. M.. 1979. The Yorkshire Jurassic flora, V, Coniferales. British Museum (Natural History), London, 166 p.

Henkel, J. B. and Hochstetter, W. 1865. Synopsis der Nadelhölzer. J. G. Cottasche Buchhandlung, Stuttgart, 446 p.

Kelber, K.-P., and Hansch, W. 1995. Keuperflanzen. Die Enträtselung einer über 200 Million Jahre alten Flora. Museo, 11:1-157.

Kendall, M. W. 1949. A Jurassic member of the Araucariaceae. Annals of Botany, new series, 13:151-161.

Kendall, M. W. 1952. Some conifers from the Jurassic of England. Annals and Magazine of Natural History, series 12, 2:299-307.

Krasser, F. 1918. Studien über die fertile Region der Cycadophyten aus den Lunzer Schichten, Mikrosporophylle und männliche. Zapfen. Kaiserliche Akademie der Wissenschaften Wien Denkschriften, 94:489-554.

Kräusel, R. 1949. Koniferen und andere Gymnospermen aus der Trias von Lunz, Nieder Österreich. Palaeontographica B, 89:35-82.

Litwin, R. J. 1985. Fertile organs and in situ spores of ferns from the Late Triassic Chinle Formation of Arizona and New Mexico, with discussions of associated dispersed spores. Review of Palaeobotany and Palynology, 42:101-146.

Neuburg, M. F. 1936. On the stratigraphy of the coal-bearing deposits of the Kuznetsk Basin. Izvestia Akademia Nauk S. S. S. R. Seriya Geologiski, 4:469-510. In Russian.

Newberry, J. S. 1853. Fossil plants from the Ohio coal basin. Annals of Science, 1:106-108.

Pigg, K., W. C. Davis and S. R. Ash. 1993. A new permineralized Upper Triassic flora from Petrified Forest National Park, Arizona: A preliminary report, p. 410-413. In S. G. Lucas and M. Morales (eds.), The nonmarine Triassic. New Mexico Museum of Natural History and Science, Bulletin 3.

Seward, A. C. 1911. The Jurassic flora of Sutherland. Royal Society Edinburgh Transaction, 47:643-709

Spamer, E. E. 1995. The surviving component of the Wilhelm Bock collection of fossils (invertebrates, vertebrates, and plants) held at the Academy of Natural Sciences of Philadelphia. Notulae Naturae, 473:1-16.

Srivastava, A. K., S. R. Manik, G. V. Patil, and R. R. Gawande. 2004. The genus *Araucarites* from the Upper Gondwana succession (Early Cretaceous) of Bairam-Belkher area, district Amravati, Maharashtra and district Betul, Madhya Pradesh. Palaeobotanist, 53:91-95.

Stagner, H. R. 1941. Geology of the fossil leaf beds of the Petrified Forest National Monument, p. 9-21. In L. H. Daugherty, The Upper Triassic flora of Arizona. Carnegie Institution of Washington Publication 526.

Sternberg, K. von. 1820-1838. Versuch einer geognostisch-botanischen Darstellung der Flora der Vorwelt. 1(1): 1820, Leipzig, Prag, 24 pp.; 1(2): 1822, Leipzig, Prag, 33 pp.; 1(3): 1823, Regensburg, 39+1 pp.; 1(4): 1825, Regensburg, 48+XLII pp. + Index; 2 (5-6): 1833, Prag, 80 pp.; 2 (7-8): 1838, Prag, pp. 81-200.

Taylor, T. N. 1988. Pollen and pollen organs of fossil gymnosperms; Phylogeny and reproductive biology, p. 177-217. In C. B. Beck (ed.), Origin and evolution of gymnosperms. Columbia University Press, New York.

Taylor, T. N., Delevoryas, T. and Hope, R. C. 1987. Pollen cones from the Late Triassic of North America and implications on conifer evolution. Review of Palaeobotany and Palynology, 53:141-149.

Tidwell, W. D., and Ash, S. R. in press. Preliminary report on the Early Jurassic flora at the St. George Dinosaur discovery Site at Johnson Farm, St. George, Utah. New Mexico Museum of Natural History and Science Bulletin.

Wanner, A. and W. M. Fontaine. 1900. Triassic flora of York County, Pennsylvania, p. 233-255. In L. F. Ward (with the cooperation of W. M. Fontaine, A. Wanner, and F. H. Knowlton). Status of the Mesozoic floras of the United States. First Paper: the older Mesozoic. U.S. Geological Survey Annual Report, 20, pt. 2.

Zeiller, R. 1883. Fructifications de fougères de terrain houiller. Annales sciences naturalle, Botanique, 6th series, 16:177-207.

Zijlstra, G. and J. H.A. van Konijnenburg-van Cittert. 2000. Proposal to conserve the name *Araucarites* C. Presl (Fossil Gymnospermae, Coniferales, Araucariaceae) against *Araucarites* Endl. (Fossil Gymnospermae, Coniferales). Taxon, 49:279-280.

Parker, W. G., Ash, S. R. and Irmis, R. B., eds., 2006,
A Century of Research at Petrified Forest National Park: Geology and Paleontology.
Museum of Northern Arizona Bulletin No. 62.

A RARE BIPINNATE MICROSPOROPHYLL ATTRIBUTABLE TO THE CYCADALES, FROM THE LATE TRIASSIC CHINLE FORMATION, PETRIFIED FOREST NATIONAL PARK, ARIZONA.

JOAN WATSON[1] AND SIDNEY R. ASH[2]

[1]Palaeobotany Laboratory, Williamson Building, University of Manchester, M13 9PL,UK <mbesszjw@man.ac.uk>,

[2]Department of Earth and Planetary Sciences, University of New Mexico, Albuquerque, New Mexico 87120, USA <sidash@aol.com>

ABSTRACT ---A single specimen collected in the Petrified Forest National Park, Arizona, from the Upper Triassic Chinle Formation, is the first bipinnate male sporophyll to be attributed to the order Cycadales. The sporophyll has a broad stalk, four sub-opposite pairs of first order pinnae and an apical pinna, all bearing short pinnules around their margins. Cuticle characters include: typically cycadalean epidermal cells; three types of trichomes, un-branched, branched, short conical; a haplocheilic stoma; monosulcate pollen. Putative pollen-sacs are compared with similar features in extant cycads which support the attribution. *Androcycas* gen. nov. is erected to accommodate the microsporangiate sporophyll as *Androcycas santuccii* sp. nov.

Keywords: Triassic, Petrified Forest, Chinle Formation, Cycadales, microsporophyll

INTRODUCTION

CYCADS ARE gymnospermous seed-plants with widespread but disjunct distribution in tropical, sub-tropical and warm temperate climates (see Jones, 2002, p. 8 for map). They are often referred to as 'living fossils' for several good reasons, especially their production of primitive, motile male gametes (multi-flagellated spermatozoa), a feature shared only with *Ginkgo biloba* amongst seed-plants. The Cycadales are of great antiquity, with their origins in the Paleozoic, and are fundamentally little changed since the Mesozoic, having reached the zenith of their evolution by the Jurassic or early Cretaceous (Pant, 1987, 2002). Living cycads were still quite poorly understood when Chamberlain (1919; 1935) undertook his outstanding pioneering work on the group. There are now eleven extant genera recognized including about 290 species placed in three families, the Cycadaceae (with only *Cycas*), Zamiaceae (with *Ceratozamia, Chigua, Dioon, Encephalartos, Lepidozamia, Macrozamia, Microcycas* and *Zamia*) and Stangeriaceae (with *Bowenia* and *Stangeria*) (Hill, 1998-2004; Jones, 2002; Whitelock, 2002).

All cycad species have separate female and male plants (dioecious) with spiral flushes of pinnate foliage-leaves alternating with flushes of scale-leaves around the apex of the stem. The sexes are distinguishable only by their cones with either naked ovules or pollen-sacs. Both sexes of cones are compact and terminal in all cycads except for the female plant of *Cycas* in which leaf-like megasporophylls (Fig. 3.2) are produced in the phyllotactic spiral, forming a pseudocone (Fig. 3.1). In time the apex of the stem continues to grow, reverting to production of foliage and scale leaves until the next reproductive phase (Pant and Mehra, 1962, p. 89).

Figures 1.1 and 1.2 show the part and counterpart respectively of a highly distinctive and unusual, if not unique, pinnate microsporophyll. The gross morphology shows a strong resemblance to megasporophylls of the *Cycas*-type (Fig. 3.2) and the specimen was recently figured (Watson and Cusack 2005, fig. 78E), as the probable sterile distal part of such a megasporophyll. However, subsequent detailed study by light (LM) and scanning electron microscopy (SEM) has unexpectedly shown this suggestion to be incorrect. The new information presented here indicates that the specimen is a bipinnate microsporophyll, bearing monosulcate pollen along with other cycadalean features. Pinnate cycad megasporophylls are quite well-known from the fossil record (Watson and Cusack, 2005), but as far as we can ascertain, this is the first evidence of a pinnate male structure attributable to the Cycadales. All other known cycadalean microsporangiate reproductive structures, both fossil and extant, including those of *Cycas*, are compact cones with blade-like microsporophylls bearing pollen-sacs on the abaxial surface (Norstog and Nicholls, 1997: 71). Male cones of extant cycads are extensively illustrated by Jones (2002), Whitelock (2002), and Hill (1998-2004). Fossil male cones of putative cycadalean affinity have been described from the Permian onwards (Zhu and Du, 1981) but reports are few in number compared with records for female structures (Pant, 1987; Gao and Thomas, 1989; Norstog and Nicholls, 1997; Jones, 2002). Most recently, Klavins et al. (2003) have presented a detailed study of a cycad male cone, from the Middle Triassic of Antarctica, which is the first record of a microsporangiate cone with internal anatomy preserved.

Because the new Upper Triassic specimen presented here resembles none of the cones, of any age, hitherto described, it is necessary to erect a new genus, in which to accommodate it as a new species.

MATERIAL

The new taxon is known only from a single specimen split into part (PEFO 34158; Fig. 1.1) and counterpart (PEFO

34158A; Fig. 1.2), deposited in the collections at Petrified Forest National Park, Arizona. The specimen was collected across the main park road about 300 meters east of the small hills called The Tepees in the central part of the Petrified Forest. The site has been assigned locality number PFP 004 in the collection records of Petrified Forest National Park. Qualified investigators may obtain its exact location from the Chief of Resource Management, Petrified Forest National Park.

The horizon is in a bed, about 20 meters thick, of greenish-grey, generally massive structureless mudstone in what is currently called the Newspaper Rock bed of the Blue Mesa Member of the Late Triassic Chinle Formation (Parker, this volume). The mudstone unit in the Newspaper Rock bed which contained the fossil has been the source of most of the foliar and cone material previously described from the Park (Ash, 1987). For many years the mudstone unit was included in the lower part of the Petrified Forest Member of the Chinle Formation and later assigned to the Monitor Butte Member (Demko et al., 1998). More recently it has been referred to the Blue Mesa Member (Woody, 2003; this volume). Demko (1995) has suggested that the mudstone unit was deposited in an overbank wetland area adjacent to the high-sinuosity channel in which the sandstone facies of the Newspaper Rock bed was deposited.

METHODS

The macro-photographs in Fig. 1 were taken using a Canon 20D digital camera, with the specimen fully immersed in colourless paraffin (kerosene) in order to increase the contrast between the sample and the matrix. This produced results superior to the use of cross-polarised light on a dry specimen. The photo-micrographs were taken using the same camera attached to a Leitz Dialux microscope and the scanning electron micrographs were recorded digitally using a Jeol SEM.

Specimen PEFO 34158 is preserved as a compression with its inner tissues densely coalified and strongly resistant to oxidative maceration by conventional techniques. The necessary extended use of Schulze's solution, combined with the cleated nature of the carbonaceous material, causes the cuticle to disintegrate and dissolve and fails to yield usable preparations. However, with the use of modified techniques (Watson and Cusack, 2005) it has been possible to obtain and figure both SEM mounts and LM slides, regrettably with lack of clarity regarding their original, precise position on the hand specimen.

SEM preparations for studying surface features were obtained by a simple technique using nail varnish painted over the area to be sampled. This efficiently holds the cleats together, during mechanical removal and the subsequent dissolving of attached matrix in hydrofluoric acid. The resulting cleaned, un-macerated sample is then attached to a stub using double-sided tape (for permanent mounting) or nail varnish if the sample is to be removed (with acetone) and turned over for further study (see Watson and Cusack, 2005 for details). Figs 2.1 and 4.1 show samples prepared by this method and mounted with nail varnish.

Isolated cuticle preparations for light microscopy (Figs 2.3, 2.7, 5.1-4) were much less successful. However, none of the gentler agents, such as sodium hypochlorite or nitric acid alone, was effective in isolating the cuticle and we had to resort to the use of Schulze's solution. Unfortunately, the only surviving pieces of cuticle were minute scraps (Fig. 5) recovered with a one-haired paintbrush for mounting on slides under cover slips.

SYSTEMATIC PALEONTOLOGY

Order CYCADALES
Genus ANDROCYCAS new genus

Diagnosis.–Microsporangiate reproductive organ with pinnate, laminar microsporophylls. Proximal region of sporophyll forming flat, wide stalk; lamina widening distally, divided into lateral and apical pinnae bearing pollen-sacs containing monosulcate pollen.

Etymology.– The Greek andros (male) and the Greek cycas were combined to form a name that emphasizes the similarity of the fossil to the living cycad genus *Cycas*.

Discussion.–The few genera available for fossil cycad male cones all refer to compact cones or simple sporophylls, with various different pollen types (van Konijnenburg-van Cittert, 1971). *Androstrobus* Schimper (1870), the genus most commonly used for Mesozoic male cones (Harris, 1964; Watson and Cusack, 2005), includes species with monosulcate pollen, some clearly bearing a resemblance to extant cycad cones, others poorly distinguished. *Delemaya* Klavins, Taylor, Krings et Taylor (2003), recently established for the structurally preserved type species, *Delamaya*

Figure 1. 1-8, *Androcycas santuccii* sp. nov. *1, 2*, holotype at natural size; *1.* half of specimen designated as the part, with abaxial surface attached to matrix, PEFO 34158; *2.* half of specimen designated as the counterpart, with adaxial surface attached to matrix, PEFO 34158A; *3.* Inflected lateral pinnae on right of specimen in Fig. 1.1 showing absence of pinnules basally, x5; *4.* Apical pinna showing backward-pointing pinnules with terminal spines; traces of surface striations visible along left- hand pinnules, x5; *5.* Spinose pinnules from proximal margin, where sporophyll widens to left (see Fig. 1.2), x5; *6.* Exposed matrix on surface of counterpart showing adaxial surface ridges and grooves, x5; *7.* Close-up view of pinnules with terminal spines visible, x15; *8.* Exposed matrix on surface of part showing numerous detached hairs from the tomentose abaxial surface, x30; *9.* Close-up showing several branched hairs amongst the majority of un-branched hairs, x60.

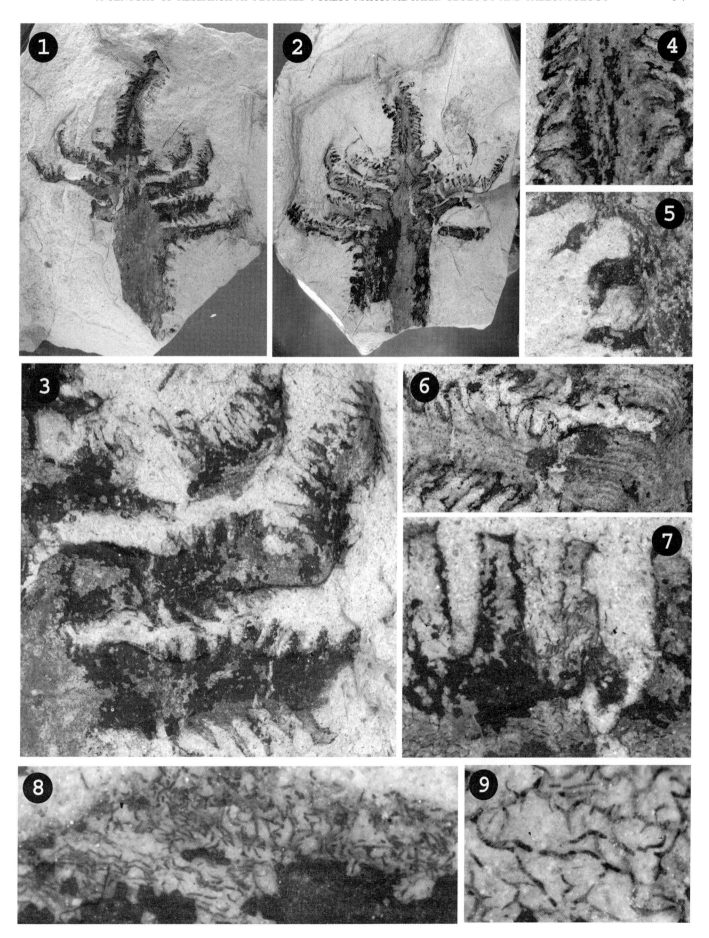

spinulosa Klavins et al. 2003, comprises more or less scale-like sporophylls, helically arranged around a cone axis. Neither of these, nor any other established genus, can accommodate the Chinle specimen described here.

We have thus erected *Androcycas* gen. nov. with a minimal diagnosis, which will allow it, should the need arise, to be adopted for usage in the cautious style of the late Sir Albert Charles Seward (1917) and the late Tom Harris (1961, 1964), which more or less equates to the old paleobotanical use of the organ-genus. Whatever the phylogenetic objections to this sparse approach, it continues to be indispensable for problematical (particularly fragmentary) material (Watson et al., 1999); particularly in offering respite from the proliferation of new genera based on thin evidence.

ANDROCYCAS SANTUCCII new species
Figs. 1, 2, 4-6.

'probable cycad megasporophyll' Watson and Cusack, 2005, p. 126, fig. 78E.

Diagnosis.–Sporophyll at least 8cm long; spreading to at least 7cm wide. Stalk about 2cm wide, parallel-sided, bearing lateral, marginal pinnules typically 2-3mm long and 1.5mm wide, each with 1 or 2 distal spines; sporophyll widening abruptly, approximately half way along length; distal region pinnate, divided into sub-opposite, pinnulate segments, 4-5 attached laterally on each side, single tapering pinna forming apex. Pinnae inflexed; lacking pinnules in basal quarter; pinnules present beyond, spaced 1-1.5mm apart, typically 2-3mm long and 1.5mm wide, with pointed, blunt or square apex bearing 1 or 2 pointed spines. Adaxial surface of sporophyll ridged longitudinally, density of ridges on stalk, about 1.5-2.5 per mm; ridges curving onto surface of pinnae and onto pinnules to form 1-3 fine striations present to pinnule apices. Abaxial surface densely tomentose, trichomes of un-branched and branched types, lengths up to at least 300μm. Cuticle [origin undetermined] with scattered hair bases and stomata; stomatal apparatus haplocheilic; guard cells exposed at surface, surrounded by 6 or 7 unspecialized, straight-walled, subsidiary cells; ordinary epidermal cells in ill-defined, short files, shape square, rectangular or with oblique end walls; cuticle of anticlinal walls of irregular thickness with slightly beaded appearance. Pollen grains ellipsoidal, typically 40μm long; proximal face and sulcus smooth; distal surface finely granulate.

Etymology.–*Androcycas santuccii* sp. nov. is named in honor of Vince Santucci, formerly park paleontologist at the Petrified Forest National Park, who recognised the importance of this unique specimen and drew it to the attention of the junior author.

Holotype.–Specimen PEFO 34158 (part, Fig. 1.1) and PEFO 34158A (counterpart, Fig. 1.2), deposited in the collections at Petrified Forest National Park, Arizona.

DESCRIPTION

General morphology.–The leaf-like nature of *Androcycas santuccii* sp. nov. is evident in Fig. 1.1, 1.2, with four main pairs of sub-opposite, first order pinnae forming the expanded distal region between the tapering apical pinna and the narrower, proximal region which forms a wide, flat, parallel-sided stalk. Unfortunately, the basal part of the stalk, which must include the area of attachment, is not preserved. Small pinnules, 2-3 mm long and about 1.5 mm wide, present along one margin of the stalk (Fig. 1.2), are enlarged in Fig. 1.5 to show their apical spines. They are similar in size and shape to the second order pinnules which form most of the margins of the main pinna segments (Fig. 1.1-1.4, 1.6, 1.7) but are absent, or poorly developed, in the slightly swollen basal part of the pinna (Fig. 1.3, 1.6). The pinnules appear to be rather variable in shape, some clearly defined, others less well so. Of those presenting good evidence of shape, some appear pointed with a single apical spine (Fig. 1.4, lower left) whilst others are clearly square-ended with two or three terminal spines (Fig. 1.7). Some of the differences are almost certainly preservational effects upon pinnules which are folded or damaged in life. Other damage might be caused by the distinct tendency for the substance of the pinnules to separate into different parts when the specimen was split along the bedding plane. This has resulted in well-defined coaly rims on one surface (Fig. 1.4, 1.6, 1.7) and the central parts of the pinnule on the other (Fig. 1.3).

It is fortuitous that the coalified remains adhere in random patches to one or other of the two halves, thus exposing informative areas of matrix on the corresponding opposite side. It was not immediately obvious how the adaxial and abaxial surfaces could be distinguished and our conclusions are based mainly on the features visible in the exposed matrix, compared to similar features known in other fossil and living cycads. We suggest that the half in Fig. 1.1 (the part) is attached to the matrix by the abaxial surface and that the counterpart (Fig. 1.2) is attached by the adaxial surface.

Adaxial surface.–The exposed matrix of the counterpart (Fig. 1.2) is marked by impressions of a series of grooves and ridges disposed longitudinally along the stalk and central pinnate region. Laterally, they curve outwards and run longitudinally to the apex of each pinna (Fig.1.6), and also curve onto the pinnules (Fig. 1.4) reducing in number to two or three which end at the spinose apex. We are unable to ascertain whether the ridges might relate to compression of veins, or other resistant tissues such as fibres, because the exposed coaly adaxial surface of the part (Fig. 1.1) is singularly uninformative on the

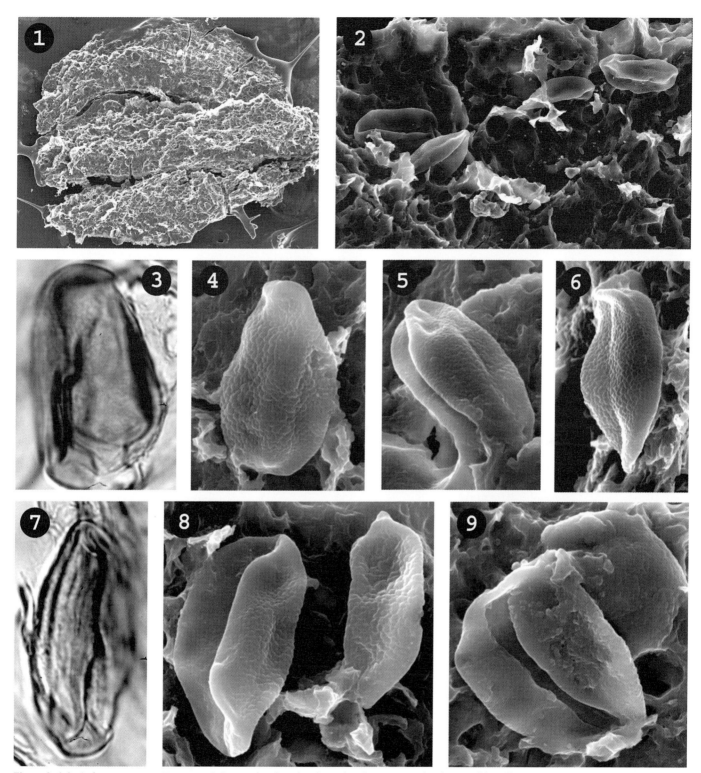

Figure 2. 1-9, *Androcycas santuccii* sp. nov. *1*. Preparation from basal margin of counterpart showing possible pollen-sacs, x60; *2*. Part of specimen in Fig. 1.1 showing four embedded pollen grains, x500; *3-9*. Pollen grains, all x1500. *3, 7*. Grains in LM with sulcus and granular sculpture of exine visible; *4-6, 8*. Grains in SEM showing sculpture on distal surface; *9*. Grain with sulcus comparable to *Cycas revoluta* grain in Fig. 3.4.

matter. The petrified male cone *Delemaya spinulosa* Klavins et al. 2003 from the Middle Triassic of Antarctica, also has longitudinal adaxial ridges (Klavins et al., 2003: figs 2A, 4B) which continue onto the prominent apical projections of the scales. There is clearly no connection with either vascular tissue or fibres in *D. spinulosa*. In the light of this similarity it

seems likely that the striations of *A. santuccii* are also on the adaxial surface of the sporophyll.

Abaxial surface.–The exposed matrix of the part of *A. santuccii* (Fig. 1.7, 1.8, 1.9) shows masses of detached epidermal hairs separated from the sporophyll surface which is attached to the counterpart. A profuse covering of epidermal

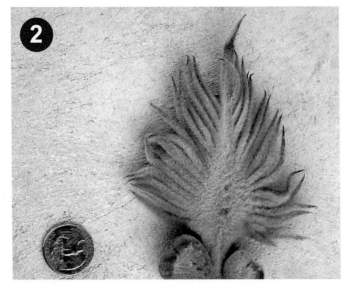

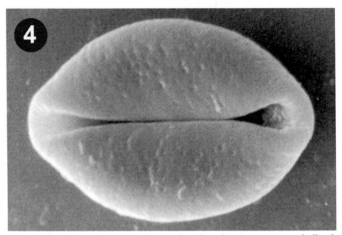

Figure 3. 1-4, *Cycas revoluta*, living cycad. *1*. Pseudocone on female plant growing at The Mirage Hotel, Las Vegas, showing pinnate megasporophylls; *2*. Megasporophyll from same plant showing densely furry abaxial surface and some individual pinnae inflexed or reflexed; *3, 4*. Pollen grains from cone of male plant growing in glasshouses at The Firs Botanical Experimental Grounds, University of Manchester; *3*. Grains showing monosulcate proximal face and finely pitted distal surface, x1000; *4*. Grain with sulcus comparable to *Androcycas* fossil grain in Fig. 2.9, x3000.

hairs on young leaves and cones is a common feature of cycads and Figure 3.2 shows the hairs on the abaxial surface of a *Cycas revoluta* megasporophyll. A dense tomentum on the abaxial surface of the microsporophyll is also characteristic of the male cone of some extant cycad species (Pant and Mehra, 1962, p. 79; Watson and Cusack, 2005, fig. 84D, I, J); hence our suggestion that the densely hairy surface of *A. santuccii* is abaxial.

The trichomes in *A. santuccii* are of three types, long un-branched, long branched (seen on the matrix), and short conical (seen on the cuticle). The most prolific are the long un-branched hairs (Figs 1.8; 4.3) with fewer branched hairs amongst them (Fig. 1.9). Detached hairs of *A. santuccii* in the matrix measure up to 300μm in length but this is probably a conservative figure, because the basal portion of most hairs remains attached to the coaly surface. *In situ* hairs and hair bases on the abaxial surface were exposed in an un-macerated SEM preparation (Fig. 4.1) taken from the apical pinna on the part specimen. This coaly piece was detached after it

was coated in nail varnish, cleaned in HF and mounted on a stub. In effect this achieves the same result as the classic 'transfer technique' (Walton, 1923; Banks, 1970, p. 10) for turning over plants preserved as compressions, but on a very small scale. The hairs seen in this preparation are only about 50μm, with many of them lacking well-defined tips (Fig. 4.2), though the hair in Fig. 4.3 is an exception, being incomplete at its base. Because the hairy abaxial surface was freed from the matrix by dissolving the latter in HF, we conclude that the long parts of the hairs were detached sometime during the preservation process and not mechanically damaged by splitting after collection. This might be the case with the majority of the hairs visible on the exposed matrix (Fig. 1.8, 1.9). The much shorter hairs in Fig. 5.2 are discussed below.

Pollen-sacs.–In extant cycads the pollen-sacs (microsporangia) are borne abaxially and there is some evidence for a marginal abaxial position in *A. santuccii*. The sample in Fig. 2.1 is one of our un-macerated preparations held together with nail varnish. The obvious division into three appears to us to be

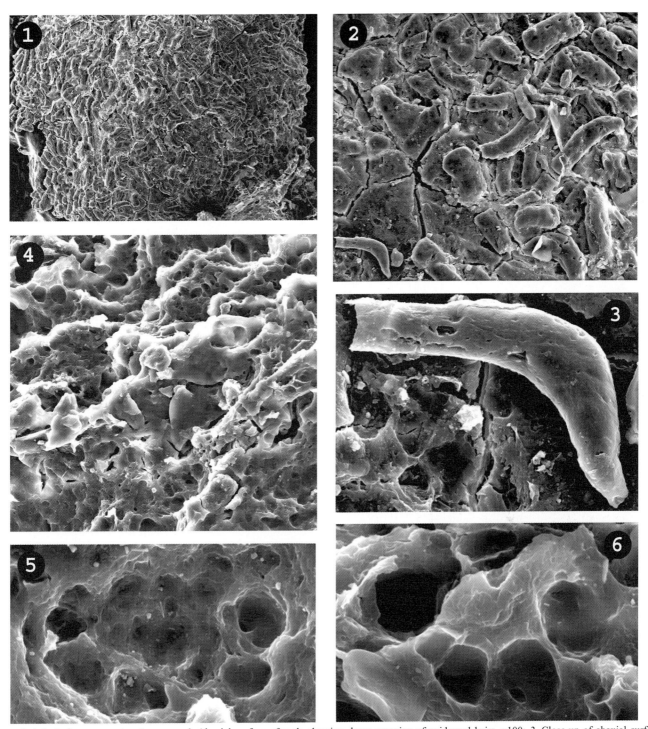

Figure 4. 1-6, *Androcycas santuccii* sp. nov. *1*. Abaxial surface of scale showing dense covering of epidermal hairs, x100; *2*. Close-up of abaxial surface showing individual hairs and hair bases, x400; *3*. Single un-branched epidermal hair, x2000; *4*. Closer view of un-macerated SEM preparation in Fig. 2.1, possibly showing inside view of pollen-sac; see text for discussion, x400; *5*, *6*. Typical circular groups of cells from same preparation, possibly surrounding basal cell of trichome; group in Fig. 6 can be seen at top left of Fig. 4, x1500.

a natural feature with well-defined edges, rather than cracks or cleats, and we are inclined to suggest that they are the remnants of a trio of disrupted pollen-sacs. The sample was taken as a generous piece from the lower left of the counterpart (Fig. 1.2) and cleaned in HF, in the hope of exposing and investigating the lateral pinnules on the stalk. Most of the coaly sample disintegrated in HF, producing minute fragments of cuticle and unrecognisable debris, leaving the sample in Fig. 2.1 as the only sizeable piece, still attached to the nail varnish. Viewed in the SEM it is immediately clear that the effect of the HF treatment, rather than exposing a clean adaxial surface, has been to produce a view of an internal tissue composed of small cells (Fig. 4.4, 4.5, 4.6), probably with quite thick walls. The coalified nature of this sample prevents a clear view of the cell arrangement, except that in places they

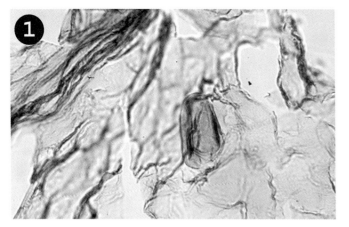

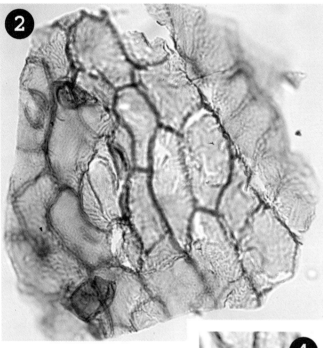

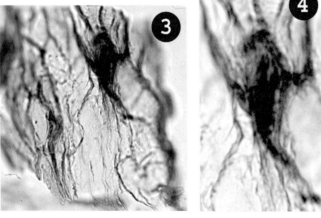

Figure 5. 1-4, *Androcycas santuccii* sp. nov. 1-4. Scraps of thin, delicate cuticle in LM, possibly pollen-sac walls. *1*. Cuticle with pollen grain seen in Fig. 2.3, x500; *2*. Largest piece of cuticle isolated showing two hair bases and ordinary epidermal cells of typical cycadalean type, x500; *3*. Scrap of cuticle with one or two stomata present (see also Fig. 6); dark shadow at top left margin is part of the pollen grain seen in Fig. 2.7, x500; *4*. Enlarged and re-focussed stomatal apparatus showing haplocheilic features (see text for discussion), x1000.

are seen to be disposed in rings (Fig. 4.5, 4.6), around an obscure central structure. This is certainly not a stoma and the possibility of it being a trichome base is discussed below.

A striking feature of this preparation is the presence of numerous, scattered, monosulcate pollen grains (Fig. 2.2), some of them quite deeply embedded, presumably present from before the time of the sporophyll's demise. It seems possible, even likely, that these grains are lying amongst the cellular remains of the inner layer of disrupted pollen-sacs. If this is so, it would seem that the microsporangium was a sessile rather than a stalked structure. The group of three side-by-side, putative sacs (Fig. 2.1) is about 1mm across and a little over 1mm long, a size which matches the distal end of pinnules where they might have been located on the abaxial surface.

Pollen grains.—The typically cycadalean ellipsoidal, monosulcate pollen grains (Figs 2.2-2.9; 6) are all obviously similar in original shape, size and exine sculpture, though with differences resulting from the effects of compression. The grain in Fig. 2.9 shows the longitudinal sulcus in an open condition and also displays the lack of sculpture on the proximal face. Many grains are folded along the line of the sulcus, giving a lateral view (Fig. 2.5, 2.6, 2.8) which shows the granular sculpture on the distal surface. Fig. 2.4 shows a grain presenting the full distal face. All the SEM views are of grains attached to the sample in Fig. 2.1. The two grains seen in the LM in Figs 2.3, 2.7; 5.1; 6 are attached to the tiny scraps of thin cuticle described below and match the grains seen in the SEM.

Cuticle and stomata.—Failure to obtain satisfactory cuticle preparations has been the most problematic aspect of this study, with Figs 5 and 6 indicating the continuing lack of success. Three pieces were isolated for study by light microscopy (Fig. 5.1, 5.2, 5.3) each measuring less than 200mm across. They were retrieved with a one-haired paintbrush from the sludgy residue produced in an attempt at a maceration of pinnules from the apical pinna of the counterpart. Unfortunately, the original position on the sporophyll of these pieces of epidermis still remains a matter of conjecture. Nevertheless, the cuticular evidence is sufficient for several features to be picked out as distinctly cycadalean.

The epidermal cells in Fig. 5.2, 5.3, with their variation in shape, oblique end walls, and arrangement in short files, have a typical form which is well-known in many fossil cycads. Two short trichomes are associated with these cells, the upper one apparently intact with a short, pointed apical cell. They are much more widely spaced than the profusion of hairs in the matrix would suggest and this paucity of hair-bases indicates that this cuticle is probably not from the main abaxial lamina of the sporophyll.

The one stomatal apparatus which has been positively identified is seen in Fig. 5.3, 5.4. It is clearly haplocheilic with 5 or 6 unspecialised subsidiary cells, which is typically cycadalean, but the poorly developed guard cells suggest that it might not have been fully functional. It is probably not from the main surface of the sporophyll.

COMPARISONS

In the absence of any known fossil cone-scales with similar morphology to *A. santuccii* we have indicated the closest comparable features we can find in living cycads. The main sources of detailed information on extant cycad epidermis and cuticle are the works of Pant et al. from the 1960s. Harris (1964) has described several Jurassic male cones with cuticle details. Watson and Cusack (2005) have used LM and SEM illustrations of leaf and cone cuticles for comparisons between Lower Cretaceous and extant cycad species.

Large trichomes.–Epidermal hairs on the leaves of living cycads are known in considerable detail from studies by Stevenson (1981). All have two cells, a basal cell and a longer apical cell (branched or un-branched) and various examples of sporangial hairs have been figured by Pant (2002, pp. 82, 213; repeated from Pant and Nautiyal 1963). The long hairs in the matrix of *A. santuccii* are closely similar to many of these modern examples. Amongst fossil cycads details of hairs are much less well-known, though hair bases are common. *Becklesia anomala*, an English Wealden cycad is unusual in having multicellular trichome bases on the leaves (Watson and Cusack, 2005, figs 8D, 9L, K), with groups of cells which are reminiscent of the circular groups in Fig. 4.5, 4.6. In seeking cuticular features comparable to those of *A. santuccii* we found several closely similar examples in the work of Pant et al. (1962, 1963; Pant, 1973) on recent sporangia. *Dioon edule*, for example, provides three matches.

Sporangial epidermis.–The cycad pollen-sac is often 5-6 layers thick (Pant and Mehra, 1962, p. 82, fig. 40; Pant, 1973, p. 103) with an outermost layer termed the exothecium (= epidermis), a lining called the tapetum, and a middle zone of thin-walled cells sandwiched between them (Pant and Mehra, 1962, p. 81; Pant, 1976, p. 104). The exothecium generally has cells of different size and shape at the apex, middle and base of the sporangium (Pant and Nautiyal, 1963, p. 314, table 10).

The thick-walled cells in Fig. 4.4-4.6 resemble thick-walled exothecium from the sporangium apex of *Dioon edule* (Pant and Nautiyal, 1963, p. 311, fig. 24H) and are also similar to basal sporangial cells of *Microcycas calocoma* (Pant and Nautiyal, 1963, 313, fig.26F). The rings of cells in this layer (Fig. 4.5, 4.6) resemble several examples of prominent hair bases encircled by distinctive cells, given by Pant and Nautiyal (1963), including their text-figs 10B, D (*Encephalartos*) and 21A (*Stangeria*), but these are in leaf epidermis. The central structure in Fig. 4.6 certainly looks very much like a trichome base.

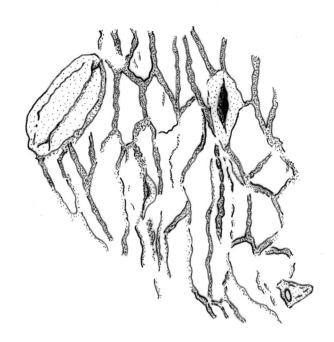

Figure 6. *Androcycas santuccii* sp. nov. *Camera lucida* drawing of cuticle in Fig. 5.3, showing a poorly developed stomatal apparatus (top right) clearly of a haplocheilic, cycad-like construction; a possible laterally squashed stoma (approximate center); ordinary epidermal cells of typically cycadalean form; a short, pointed trichome (lower right); monosulcate pollen grain (top left, also seen in Fig.2.7), x1000.

The cells in Fig. 5.2 are of the typical cycad type seen and discussed for many examples of fossil and extant leaves (Pant and Mehra, 1962; Harris, 1964; Pant, 1973; Watson and Cusack, 2005). But in particular they look very similar to cells figured by Pant and Nautiyal (1963, text-fig. 24J) from the middle region of a *Dioon edule* sporangium.

Sporangial trichomes.–The short, pointed trichomes in Fig. 5.2 are similar to short hairs and hair bases figured by Pant and Nautiyal (1962, figs 24H, 25E) on the surface of the microsporangium in *Dioon edule* and *Ceratozamia mexicana*. They also found trichomes on the sporangia of *Encephalartos* sp. and *Zamia floridiana*.

Sporangial stomata.–stomata have been recorded by Pant and Nautiyal (1963) on the sporangium in *Bowenia, Ceratozamia, Encephalartos, Macrozamia, Microcycas, Stangeria* and *Zamia*, but not in *Cycas* or *Dioon* (Pant and Mehra, 1962, p. 83). A sporangial stoma of *Bowenia serrulata* figured by Pant and Nautiyal (1963, fig. 28B) is closely similar to that of *A. santuccii*, with narrow exposed guard cells and narrow polar subsidiary cells.

In view of the list of similarities to sporangial features in extant species we think that the three cuticle preparations of *A. santuccii* (Fig. 5) are from the outer layer (exothecium) of the exposed wall of a pollen-sac.

Monosulcate pollen.–The pollen of all extant cycads (Fig. 3.3, 3.4) is monosulcate. Comparison of *A. santuccii* pollen in Fig. 2.8, 2.9 with *Cycas revoluta* pollen in Fig. 3.3, 3.4 shows the close similarity, with smooth proximal and sculptured distal faces in both.

Cycads previously described in the Triassic Chinle flora comprise only 8 species of assorted stems, foliage leaves and scale leaves (Ash, 1985, 1991, 2001). The leaves of *Nilssonia lewisii* Ash (2001) and *Pseudoctenis stewartii* Ash (2001) have stomata similar to those of *A. santuccii*, with simple, narrow, exposed guard cells, and undistinguished subsidiary cells. In having a prominent raised ring of subsidiary cells, the stoma of *Aricycas paulae* Ash (1991, p. 128, fig. 15) are not at all similar to *Androcycas* stoma, but they are, however, similar to the ambiguous rings of cells shown here in Fig. 4.5, 4.6. Two types of un-branched trichomes are present on the leaf of *P. stewartii*, with a short, sac-like type being considerably more numerous than other long narrow hairs (Ash, 2001, p. 20, figs 22, 25.). However, given the indifferent preservation of all the cuticles in question it is not yet possible to suggest which, if any, of the known leaf species *A. santucci* might belong to.

DISCUSSION

We are confident of the cycadalean attribution of this specimen, with strong evidence from extant cycads reinforcing our placing of the specimen in the order Cycadales. However, we are aware that we have not proved beyond doubt that it is male rather than part of a female sporophyll of *Cycas*-type. Because it has not been possible to produce indisputable evidence of *in situ* pollen sacs or their contents, the possibility that the pollen was introduced has to be considered. We have more or less discounted the possibility of the numerous pollen grains having been deposited by wind because they are clearly attached to an inner tissue of the sporophyll (Fig. 2.2). It is unlikely that this was accessible in life and was almost certainly exposed as a result of acid treatment. Insect activity is a stronger possibility as all modern cycads are now known to be insect pollinated (Norstog and Nicholls, 1997, p. 147), by beetles in particular. Because the type of cuticle in Fig. 5 is to

be found, as tiny fragments, in almost all the macerations, our assertion that it derives from a vast number of pollen-sacs widespread around the sporophyll seems to us strengthened. Beetle elytra are known from the Chinle Formation and evidence for beetle, and other arthropod, herbivory has been described from several Chinle plant species (Ash, 1997, 1999) and also from coprolites (Ash, 2000). Indeed, insect pollination of cycads must have been well established by the Triassic. Thus it seems most likely that the mature pollen grains on the sample in Fig. 2.1 point to a pollen-filled sac disrupted by feeding insects, rather than deposition by insects visiting a female cone.

Studies relating to the probable Paleozoic pteridosperm ancestry and origin of cycads abound (e.g. Mamay, 1969, 1976; Delevoryas, 1982; Gao and Thomas, 1989; Leary, 1990), almost entirely based on evidence from ovule-bearing structures. Pant (1987) has presented a comprehensive, illustrated review of all the evidence and stated that the "absence of intermediate types of male fructification between the two groups [pteridosperms and cycads] is another difficulty but this may not pose any serious problem since the microsporophyll of the cycads are admittedly homologous to their megasporophylls. Our main difficulty lies in the transitional synthetic forms which can be regarded as ancestral". *Androcycas santuccii* seems to be just such an intermediate type that Pant was anticipating.

ACKNOWLEDGMENTS

The constructive criticisms of Barry Thomas (Aberystwyth, Wales) who reviewed this paper are acknowledged with thanks. We are grateful to Vincent Santucci, for turning this fossil over to us to study; to former Superintendent Gary Cummins, who authorized us to conduct field research in Petrified Forest National Park; and his staff for assisting our work there. The financial support of the research reported here by the Petrified Forest Museum Association is appreciated.

REFERENCES

Ash, S. R. 1985. A short thick cycad stem from the Upper Triassic of Petrified Forest National Park, Arizona, and vicinity. Museum of Northern Arizona Bulletin, 54:17-32.

Ash, S. R. 1987. Petrified Forest National Park, Arizona, *In* Beus, S. S. (ed.), Centennial Field Guide, Vol. 2, Rocky Mountain Section of the Geological Society of America. Geological Society of America, Boulder, p. 405-410.

Ash, S. R. 1991. A new pinnate cycad leaf from the Upper Triassic Chinle Formation of Arizona. Botanical Gazette, 152:123-131.

Ash, S. R. 1997. Evidence of arthropod-plant interactions in the Upper Triassic of the southwestern United States. Lethaia, 29:237-248.

Ash, S. R. 1999. An Upper Triassic upland flora from north-central New Mexico, U. S. A. Review of Palaeobotany and Palynology, 105:183-199.

Ash, S. R. 2000. Evidence of oribatid mite herbivory in the stem of a Late Triassic tree fern from Arizona. Journal of Paleontology, 74(6):1065-1071.

Ash, S. R. 2001. New cycadophytes from the Upper Triassic Chinle Formation of the southwestern United States. PaleoBios, 21:15-28.

Banks, H. P. 1970. Evolution and Plants of the Past. Wadsworth Publishing Company, Inc., Belmont, California, 170 p.

Chamberlain, C. J. 1919. The Living Cycads. University of Chicago Press, Chicago, 172 p.

Chamberlain, C. J. 1935. Gymnosperms. Structure and Evolution. University of Chicago Press, Chicago, 484 p.

Delevoryas, T. 1982. Perspectives on the origin of cycads and cycadeoids. Review of Palaeobotany and Palynology, 37:115-132.

Demko, T. M. 1995. Taphonomy of fossil plants in Petrified Forest National Park, Arizona, p. 37-52. *In* Fossils of Arizona, Volume III, Southwest Paleontological Society and Southwest Museum, Mesa, Arizona.

Demko, T. M., R. F. Dubiel, and J. T. Parrish. 1998. Plant taphonomy in incised valleys: implications for interpreting paleoclimate from fossil plants. Geology, 26:1119-1122.

Gao, Z., and B. A. Thomas. 1989. A review of fossil cycad megasporo-phylls, with new evidence of *Crossozamia* Pomel and its associated leaves from the Lower Permian of Taiyuan, China. Review of Palaeobotany and Palynology, 60:205-223.

Harris, T. M. 1961. The Fossil Cycads. Palaeontology, 4:313-323.

Harris, T. M. 1964. The Yorkshire Jurassic flora, II. Caytoniales, Cycadales, Pteridosperms. British Museum (Natural History), London, 191 p.

Hill, K. D. 1998-2004. The Cycad Pages. Royal Botanic Garden Sydney. http://plantnet.rbgsyd.gov.au/PlantNet/cycad/index.html.

Jones, D. L. 2002. Cycads of the World. Second Edition. Reed New Holland, Sydney, Australia, 456 p.

Klavins, S. D., E. L. Taylor, M. Krings, and T. N. Taylor. 2003. Gymnosperms from the Middle Triassic of Antarctica: the first structurally preserved cycad pollen cone. International Journal of Plant Sciences, 164:1007-1020.

Leary, R. L. 1990. Possible early Pennsylvanian ancestor of the Cycadales. Science, 249:1152-1154.

Mamay, S. H. 1969. Cycads: fossil evidence of Late Paleozoic origin. Science, 164:295-296.

Mamay, S. H. 1976. Paleozoic origin of the cycads. U.S. Geological Survey Professional Paper, 934:1-48.

Norstog, K. J., and T. J. Nicholls. 1997. The Biology of the Cycads. Cornell University Press, Ithaca, 363 p.

Pant, D. D. 1973. *Cycas* and the Cycadales. Central Book Depot, Allahabad, 255 p.

Pant, D. D. 1987. The fossil history and phylogeny of the Cycadales. Geophytology, 17:125-162.

Pant, D. D. 2002. Gymnosperms, *Cycas* and Cycadales. BSIP Monograph No. 4, Birbal Sahni Institute of Palaeobotany, Lucknow, India, 386 p.

Pant, D. D., and B. Mehra. 1962. Studies in Gymnospermous Plants. Cycas. Central Book Depot, Allahabad, 179 p.

Pant, D. D., and D. D. Nautiyal. 1963. Cuticle and epidermis of recent Cycadales. Leaves, sporangia and seeds. Senckenbergiana Biologica, 44:257-347.

Schimper, W. P. 1870. Traité de paléontologie végétale ou la flore du monde primitif. Vol. II. Baillière, Paris, 522 p.

Seward, A. C. 1917. Fossil Plants. A Text-Book for Students of Botany and Geology. III, Pteridospermeae, Cycadofilices, Cordaitales, Cycadophyta. University Press, Cambridge, 656 p.

Stevenson, D. W. 1981. Observations on ptyxis, phenology, and trichomes in the Cycadales and their systematic implications. American Journal of Botany, 68:1104-1114.

Walton, J. 1923. On a new method of investigating fossil plant impressions or incrustations. Annals of Botany, 37:379-391.

Van Konijnenburg-Van Cittert, J. H. A. 1971. *In situ* gymnosperm pollen from the Middle Jurassic of Yorkshire. Acta Botanica Neerlandica, 20:1-96.

Watson, J., and H. A. Cusack. 2005. Cycadales of the English Wealden. Monograph of the Palaeontographical Society, London. 189 p. (Publication No. 622, issued as Vol. 158 for 2004)

Watson, J., S. J. Lydon, and N. A. Harrison. 1999. Consideration of the genus *Ginkgoites* Seward and a redescription of two species from the Lower Cretaceous of Germany. Cretaceous Research, 20:719-734.

Whitelock, L. M. 2002. The Cycads. Timber Press, Portland, Oregon, 374 p.

Woody, D. T. 2003. Revised geological assessment of the Sonsela Member, Chinle Formation, Petrified Forest National Park, Arizona. Unpublished M.S. thesis, Northern Arizona University, Flagstaff, Arizona.

Zhu, J., and X. Du. 1981. [A new cycad - *Primocycas chinenis* gen. et sp. nov. discovery from the Lower Permian in Shanxi, China and its significance.] Acta Botanica Sinica, 23:401-404. [In Chinese; English abstract].

Parker, W. G., Ash, S. R., and Irmis, R. B., eds., 2006.
A Century of Research at Petrified Forest National Park: Geology and Paleontology.
Museum of Northern Arizona Bulletin No. 62.

LATE TRIASSIC CHARCOAL AND CHARCOAL-LIKE PLANT FOSSILS FROM PETRIFIED FOREST NATIONAL PARK, ARIZONA

TIMOTHY P. JONES[1] AND SIDNEY R. ASH[2]

[1]School of Earth, Ocean and Planetary Sciences, Cardiff University, Cardiff, Wales, UK   CF10 3Y <JonesTP@Cardiff.ac.uk>

[2]Department of Earth and Planetary Sciences, University of New Mexico, Albuquerque, New Mexico   87131 <sidash@aol.com>

ABSTRACT–Charcoal-like plant fossils, the majority of which appear to be wildfire derived, occur at several different horizons in the lower part of the Chinle Formation of Late Triassic age in Petrified Forest National Park. The most common of these charcoal-like plant fossils are small fragments of black woody material up to 1 cm long that are found in situ in the formation. Less commonly, similar small fragments are present on the surface of the formation at two localities where they were left behind as a lag deposit after the enclosing matrix had been removed by erosional processes. Also, charcoal-like material occurs in some of the charred logs and stumps found in the formation. Although there is some small doubt about the taphonomy of some of the material, it is possible that the unusual appearance and low reflectance values of this 'problematic' material, may have resulted from later post-burial mineralization of charcoal. The quantitative reflectance values of most of the in situ and reworked fragments ranges from 2.08-3.12% indicating moderate temperature paleowildfires. In contrast, the reflectance results for a charred stump in the Blue Mesa Stump Field of 2.60-2.80% suggests low-temperature in-situ smoldering. Because the phenomenon of smoldering stumps is commonly seen in modern wildfires this locality may represent the remains of an ancient burnt forest.

Keywords: fossil charcoal, Chinle Formation, Upper Triassic, Petrified Forest National Park, reflected light microscopy, wildfires.

INTRODUCTION

SINCE TOM Harris (1958) wrote a paper entitled 'Forest fire in the Mesozoic', and revitalized a subject, as he put it, "warmly put forward and warmly opposed a century ago", a stream of workers have investigated the occurrence and significance of charcoal-like material in the fossil record. The work produced by these investigators generally supports the hypothesis that most charcoal-like fossils are in fact genuine fossil charcoal, and represented the product of ancient wildfires (Schopf, 1975; Scott, 1989). The process of wildfire charcoalification has been described as 'instant fossilization'; however, several researchers have documented 'problematic' fossil charcoal, often coming from the Permo-Triassic (Jones, 1991). Today, interest mostly lies in the occurrence or relative abundance of charcoal in the fossil record to reconstruct paleoenvironments, understanding the ecological role of ancient fires, interpreting charcoal and vertebrate assemblages, and also possible applications for paleoatmospheric reconstructions.

A technique that has an important role in the study of fossil charcoal is the standard coal petrology method of reflected light microscopy, where the material is embedded in resin and polished. This technique provides limited two-dimensional plant anatomical information, and an assessment of whether previously-stratified cell walls are homogenized, an important characteristic of charcoal (McGinnes et al., 1971). Quantitative reflectance has also found a role, once it was established that there was a correlation between intensity of reflectance and temperature of charcoal formation (Jones et

al., 1991), theoretically allowing an estimation of ancient fire temperatures. Researchers could then speculate, for example, whether their fossil material might represent the product of a high-temperature blaze, such as a modern crown fire in a conifer forest, or the low-temperature smoldering of forest litter. However, this speculation is complicated by a number of confounding factors, especially atmospheric oxygen levels, which are liable to influence the nature of the ancient wildfires.

It is well established that there is abundant fossil charcoal in Carboniferous, Jurassic and Cretaceous rocks, and this is reflected in the scientific literature. In contrast, there is a very limited literature on Permo-Triassic fossil charcoal. Some authors have discussed the paucity of charcoal over this period in general terms, for example Scott (2000) notes the 'fewer records' of late Paleozoic and early Mesozoic material. Furthermore, the few papers that do mention Permo-Triassic charcoal tend to concentrate on Permian material. For example, Uhl et al. (2004) record charcoal from a range of depositional settings from the Rotliegend Saar-Nahe Basin in southwest Germany. The Lower Rotliegend (approximately Late Carboniferous) charcoal was found in a range of different sediment types with a wildfire ignition attributed to lightning. In the Upper Rotliegend (approximately Early Permian) charcoal has only been recovered from volcanically-influenced (tuffs or tuffites) deposits. Further, from the size of the material described it may have been entrained in a pyroclastic flow, and thus charred by heat from that flow and not wildfire activity. Uhl et al. (2004) attribute this distribution to an Upper Permian environment with low atmospheric oxygen, sparse vegetation cover, and mechanical breakdown of the macroscopic charcoal fragments under arid conditions. Uhl and Kerp (2003) found charcoal in plant fossil-bearing deposits from the Central European Zechstein (Upper Permian). This material is allochthonous as indicated by the rounded shape of the fragments. Uhl and Kerp (2003) note that "Until now, virtually nothing is known about the fire ecology of the Late Paleozoic, conifer-dominated, upland vegetation".

Fossil charcoal is a common component of coal; usually described as the macerals fusinite and semifusinite, within the inertinite group. This occurrence is unsurprising given the regular wildfires that burn in a variety of coal-forming environments (Ahlgren, 1974; Cohen, 1974; Moore, 1978; Racine et al., 1985; Sanford et al., 1985). A major fire event in a late Permian coal has been identified by Glasspool (2000). Petrographic and mesofossil analyses of a layer dominated by semifusinite in the Lower Whybrow coal in New South Wales, showed that the fire effected both the vegetation and the mineral content of the coal following the fire. Semifusinite is characterized by generally lower reflectance of polished surfaces when compared with fusinite, thus suggesting low fire formation temperatures (Jones et al., 1991). A reconstruction of the Permian fire event suggests a smoldering low-temperature burn, and Glasspool (2000) speculates that fires could have been an integral part of many Gondwana coal-forming ecosystems. It is useful to observe that in circumstances favorable to the preservation of fossil plant material, such as coal, fossil charcoal is often an important component.

Two Permo-Triassic localities with vertebrate and charcoal assemblages have been intensely researched. The Lower Permian Geraldine Bonebed of Archer County Texas, USA, consists of an assemblage of articulated tetrapod skeletons, remains of other vertebrate taxa, plant compression fossils and fossil charcoal (Sander, 1987). This assemblage has been interpreted as a single mass death event that resulted from a forest fire that drove the animals into a pond where they perished. It is assumed that the vegetation must have been of sufficient density and the fire of sufficient intensity to have forced the animals into taking such a course. The Upper Triassic Snyder quarry is located in north-central New Mexico, and has an assemblage of vertebrate fossils with "substantial" amounts of fossil charcoal (Zeigler, 2003). Evidence suggests minimal transport and rapid burial of the bonebed. Quantitative reflectance of the charcoal fragments, 1.2% - 2.1% suggests a moderate wildfire temperature in the range 300-450°C. The scenarios for both localities appear similar, with natural wildfires leading to animals seeking refuge in water, drowning, and their remains being preserved due to rapid burial with the fossil charcoal from the fire.

The occurrence and paleobotany of Late Triassic charcoal in Petrified Forest National Park, Arizona has been reported by Jones et al., 2002. This work builds on that paper, in particular looking at the reflected light microscopy of that material, and the paleoecological and taphonomic implications from those results.

Schuneman and Uhle (2003) have also examined material from the Petrified Forest, undertaking an organic geochemical analysis to identify pyrogenic Polycyclic Aromatics Hydrocarbons (PAHs). Their research is based on the PAH database published by Yunker et al., (2002), and in particular concentrates on the ratios of 6 PAHs found in modern wood charcoal and bituminous coal. The work of Schuneman and Uhle (2003) concludes that the relative abundances of the pyrogenic PAHs in modern, Carboniferous and Triassic charcoal could reflect differences in atmospheric oxygen levels. However they do concede that their conclusions are founded on a small PAH database (Yunker et al., 2002) and uncertainties exist about the formation origins and later taphonomic history of the Petrified Forest Triassic 'charcoal'.

Paleoatmospheric reconstructions of the Permo-Triassic indicate low atmospheric oxygen and high carbon dioxide (Beerling et al., 2002). Although different reconstruction methods have produced different absolute values, the overall atmospheric composition is not seriously disputed. For example, Berner and Canfield (1989) suggest that from a high of ~35% oxygen during the Carboniferous, levels could have fallen to ~15% oxygen in the Triassic. Milo (2004) suggests the lower level of 12% oxygen for the Permo-Triassic boundary. Carbon dioxide, on the other hand, is believed to have increased, possibly as much as 9-fold from the early Permian to middle/late Triassic (Montanez et al., 2000a, 2000b), with an Early Permian peak of 2,000-2,500 ppmV. Milo (2004) suggests a CO_2 level of 2,000 ppmV at the Permo-Triassic boundary. Reconstructed variations in the atmospheric O_2/CO_2 (%) mixing ratio (Beerling et al., 2002, their figure 6) suggest values for the Carboniferous-Permian boundary of ~500 (lowest estimate) to ~1,500 (highest estimate), Permian-Triassic ~50 (lowest estimate) to ~500 (highest estimate), Triassic-Jurassic ~50 (lowest estimate) to ~300 (highest estimate). It is noted that the error margins in the Beering et al. model indicate that theoretically the Paleozoic oxygen maximum could occur at any point from the Tournaisian to the Guadalupian, while the oxygen minimum could occur from mid-Triassic to mid-Jurassic. However, given the paucity of charcoal in the Permo-Triassic, it is reasonable to take the mid-range modeled values when considering possible relationships between charcoal production and paleoatmospheric oxygen levels.

The locality numbers used in this article are the numbers now assigned to the charcoal localities in the records of the Petrified Forest National Park. Where appropriate they are cross referenced with locality numbers used in previous publications. Qualified investigators may obtain their exact locations from the Chief of Resource Management, Petrified Forest National Park.

MATERIALS AND METHODS

The charcoal fragments were found in two main forms, in-situ and lying loose on the surface, depending upon the locality. Locality PFP 098 (= locality 1 of Jones et al., 2002), an arroyo called Dry Wash cutting through what is

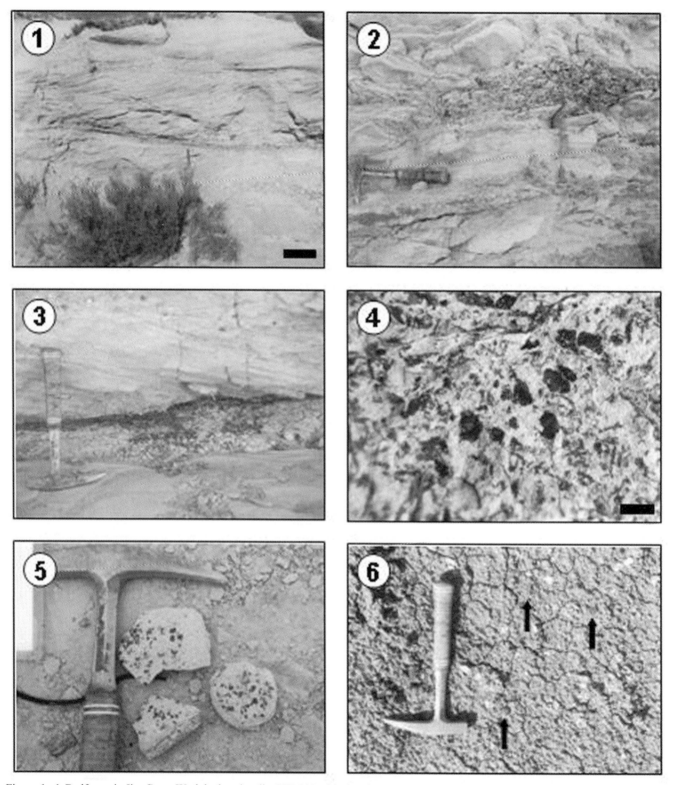

Figure 1. 1. Bedforms in Jim Camp Wash beds at locality PFP 098 with abundant charcoal concentrated at the base. Charcoal plant fossils were found in a number of these bedforms along Dry Wash. Scale bar = 50 cm; 2. Detail of the concentrations of charcoal fragments towards the base of the large bedforms in the Jim Camp Wash beds in Dry Wash near locality PFP 098; 3. Approximately 1 meter long plant compression fossil, believed to represent a single log exposed in the wall of Dry Wash. The plant material is preserved as vitrinite; however it was too degraded to obtain reliable reflectance data from embedded and polished surfaces; 4. Detail of the black fragments of charcoal in the pale beige clastic matrix of the Jim Camp Wash beds at locality PFP 098 in Dry Wash. Scale bar = 1 cm; 5. Samples of charcoal collected in the field from locality PFP 098. These fragments were manually extracted from the matrix, embedded, polished, and examined under reflected light microscopy; 6. Surface exposure at locality PFP 025 near the Tepees. The dark grey 'charcoal' is poorly seen (arrows) against the background of the grey mudstone. The small white crystals are gypsum, which was a common association with the exposed 'charcoal-like' fossils.

Figure 2. The stump in the Blue Mesa Stump Field (locality PFP 066) that was the source of some of the charcoal discussed here. Blue Mesa is just below the horizon and a second stump is indicated by the arrow.

now considered to be a local sandstone bed in the Jim Camp Wash beds of the Sonsela Member (Parker, this volume), has an abundance of *in situ* charcoal fragments concentrated in the bases of large bedforms (Fig. 1-1 and 1-2). Proximal to the charcoal, large compression fossils of isolated logs were found preserved as vitrinite (Fig. 1-3). The charcoal fragments recovered from this locality were still in the clastic matrix (Fig. 1-4 and 1-5). This sandstone is poorly cemented, and it was easy to manually extract the fossil plant fragments with a sharp scalpel. The fossil material is also highly friable, and shows signs of white oxidation on a number of the specimens.

The fragments recovered from locality PFP 025 (= locality 2 of Jones et al., 2002) were lying loose on the surface of a dark green mudstone (Fig. 1-6) in the Newspaper Rock bed in the Tepees area, and are much more robust than the locality PFP 098 material. That this material was derived from the green mudstone is indicated by the fact that it was only found on the surface of this lithology, and had not undergone any modern transport or rounding. As described by Jones et al. (2002), the robustness of the locality PFP 025 material is due to mineral material infilling the open cellular structure of the charcoal (Jones et al., 2002, Plate IIId). The paleobotany of the fragments reveals that they are all composed of wood derived from pycnoxylic wood previously identified from the Upper Triassic of Arizona.

Locality PFP 066 is east of the Tepees in the Blue Mesa Stump Field and contains *in situ* fossil tree stumps (Fig. 2). Anatomically, the material consisted of pycnoxylic wood

generally comparable to that of the *Araucarioxylon arizonicum* tree. The stump field lithology is very similar to that at locality PFP 025 in the Tepees area; however, the stump field is slightly higher in the stratigraphic column in the upper part of the Blue Mesa Member of the Chinle Formation (Parker, this volume). Some of the fossilized stumps at locality PFP 066 have been mapped and the results reported and discussed by Ash and Creber (1992). A detailed account of the stratigraphy and geological history of localities PFP 098 and PFP 025 is given in Jones et al. (2002) and that of locality PFP 066 is given in Ash and Creber (1992).

The embedding of the charcoal fragments in epoxy resin for polishing and reflected light microscopy proved to be highly problematic and time-consuming. This was not unexpected as difficulties have been encountered with previous Permo-Triassic material from other localities (Jones, 1991). The embedding of fossil and modern charcoal is somewhat difficult (Jones and Rowe, 1991 and chapters therein), with problems such as difficulty impregnating resin into the body of the charcoal fragments, the trapping of air pockets, fragments floating on the resin surface, charcoal 'plucking' from the resin during polishing, and mineral scratches on the polished face. Jones and Rowe (1999) suggest a number of potential solutions, including; vacuum-impregnation of the resin, low viscosity resins, painting the fragments with superglue prior to resin embedding, and 'painting' the polishing face with resin at regular intervals during the polishing to minimize 'plucking'. The Petrified Forest material described in this paper needed several

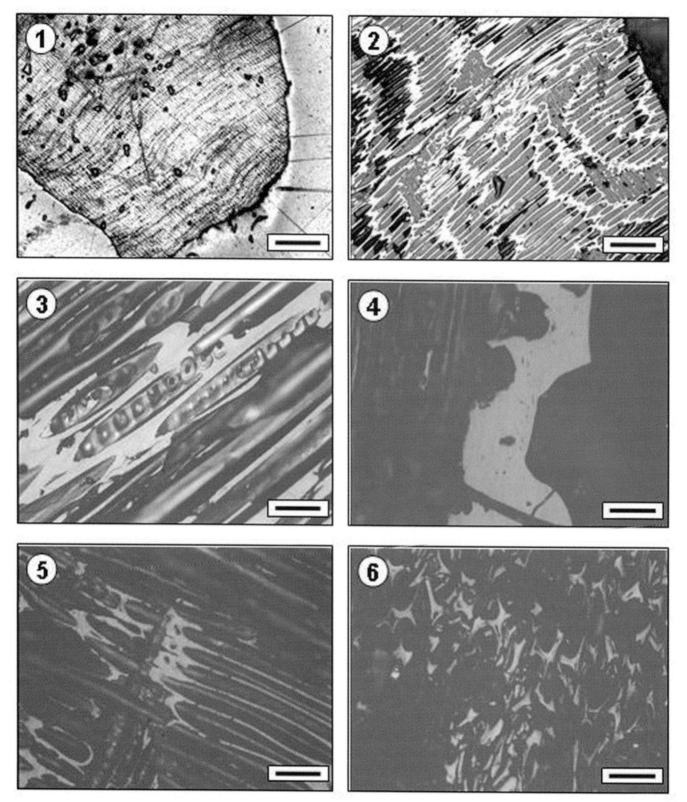

Figure 3. Photomicrographs of charcoal from Petrified Forest National Park, Arizona. *1*. Embedded and polished 'charcoal' fragment. Locality PFP 025. Scale bar = 350 mm; *2*. Embedded and polished charcoal fragment in which there is high contrast between the high reflectance charcoal and the embedding resin seen in the top right corner. Locality PFP 098. Scale bar = 100 mm; *3*. Poorly visible uniseriate pitting. The embedded and polished material has limited palaeobotany applications. Locality PFP 098. Scale bar = 50 mm; *4*. Low reflecting cell wall. The polished face cuts obliquely through the plant's cell wall with the result that a good area is available for taking quantitative reflectance values. The cell wall is also homogenized, a critical parameter used to recognize charcoal. Locality PFP 098. Scale bar = 30 mm; *5*. Extremely thin cell walls, highly problematic for obtaining quantitative reflected light readings. Poorly visible cross-field anatomy. Locality PFP 098. Scale bar = 30 mm; *6*. "Bogenstruktur", a mass of tiny fragmented pieces of charcoal. A commonly observed feature of fossil charcoal it is believed to represent fragile and brittle fossil material that has been mechanically crushed during burial. Locality PFP 098. Scale bar = 33 mm.

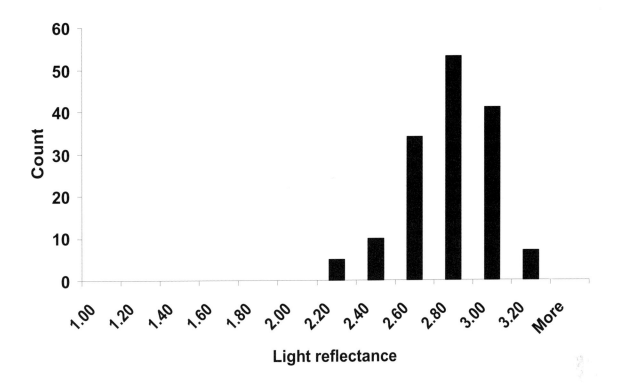

Figure *4*. Charcoal from locality PFP 098 in the Jim Camp Wash beds in Dry Wash. Histogram of 150 reading of reflectance under oil of a polished surface. Minimum = 2.08%, maximum = 3.12%, mean 2.68%, std. error = 0.019, std. dev. = 0.229.

coats of 'painted' Epotek 301 resin during polishing to prevent 'plucking'. Despite efforts, a proportion of the material selected from localities PFP 025 and PFP 098 could not be satisfactorily embedded and polished, and attempts to do so were eventually abandoned. Some vitrinite from the compressed logs at locality PFP 098 was also embedded and polished, with the intention of obtaining comparable vitrinite reflectance values; unfortunately it was concluded that the material was too degraded to give reliable results.

The polished block surfaces were examined using a LEICA DMR reflected light microscope. The observations and measurements were made under oil (SG 1.5) using x100 (observation only), x40 and x20 lenses. Percentage reflectance was measured using LEICA QWIN image analysis software, a light source filtered to 546 nm, and the system was calibrated with McCrone specular reflectance standards; GGG (R_{oil} 1.726), YAG (R_{oil} 0.917), and silica glass (R_{oil} 0.038). The number of measurements was governed by the amount of material exposed on the polished face, and the quality and dimensions of the exposed material.

REFLECTED LIGHT MICROSCOPY RESULTS

A low resolution reflected light image of a fragment of 'charcoal' from locality PFP 025, embedded in resin and polished, is shown in Fig. 3-1. The macroscopic rounded shape is apparent, as is the preservation of wood anatomy. A num-ber of large scratches can been be seen as black lines across the image, these scratches were avoided when selecting points for reflectance measurement. Despite these scratches, overall, the quality of the polished surface was good. It is impossible to accurately gauge the quantitative reflectance of the fossil material from the images, due to light level compensations made by the camera to obtain good pictures. However, an indication is given by comparing the grey tones of the exposed fossil with the embedding resin; the fossil material is only just brighter (higher reflecting) than the surrounding resin. Fig. 3-2 shows a low-resolution image of an embedded and polished charcoal fragment from locality PFP 098. Again there is good preservation of wood anatomy, however in this example, there is a strong contrast between the high-reflectance (white) plant cell walls and the dark grey (almost black) embedding resin exposed in the top right-hand corner of the image. This indicates the much higher reflectance of the material from locality PFP 098, when compared with the locality PFP 025 material.

The amount of anatomical information that can be obtained from the embedded and polished material is limited. Fig. 3-3 shows uniseriate bordered pits. Fig. 3-4 shows homogenized cell walls, an important characteristic of fossil charcoal. Fig. 3-5 shows three-dimensional preservation of very thin cell walls, with 'checking' and crossfield pitting. Under scanning electron microscopy, the surface of the 'charcoal' fragments covered in fine fragments, or 'bogenstruktur', was described by Jones et al. (2002) for the locality PFP 025 mate-

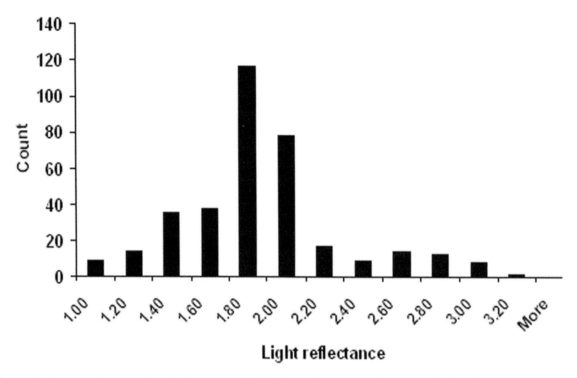

Figure 5. Charcoal (?) from the Newspaper Rock bed at locality PFP 025 in the Tepees area. Histogram of 350 reading of reflectance under oil of a polished surface. Minimum = 0.78%, maximum = 3.12%, mean 1.78%, std. error = 0.029, std. dev. = 0.409.

rial. This can be seen in Fig. 3-6, where a collection of tiny isolated cell wall fragments can be seen against the grey background of the embedding resin. It is problematic to obtain reliable quantitative reflectance values for such small cell wall fragments; however, results were obtained that indicated relatively low reflectance values. A simple, qualitative method to validate those results is to compare the RL percentages obtained with those obtained from larger fragments where the grey-level contrast between the fossil material and embedding resin is comparable; for example with Fig. 3-4.

The histograms for percentage reflectance under oil (R_{oil}) are shown for the three suites of material in Figs 4, 5 and 6.

DISCUSSION

The obvious question, which is still to be definitively answered, is whether or not all the fossil material collected in the Petrified Forest Park is true charcoal, the end product of ancient fires. The material from locality PFP 098, in the Jim Camp Wash beds in Dry Wash, is almost certainly genuine wildfire charcoal, as it possessed all the macroscopic and microscopic characteristics defined by previous researchers to recognize fossil charcoal (Scott, 1989). The material from locality PFP 025, in the Newspaper Rock bed near the Tepees, possesses many of the required characteristics, but not all of them. Macroscopically, the material is highly robust, most fossil charcoal can be crushed by finger pressure, and

this material cannot be crushed. The highly robust nature of the material was probably critical to it remaining intact on the exposed surface, as more delicate material would be rapidly destroyed. Instead of the usual black luster seen in fossil charcoal, the Tepees material has a dark grey sheen. The robust nature and grey sheen are almost certainly due to the 'mineralized' nature of the fossils, as recognized by the in-filled cells when viewed under SEM (Jones et al., 2002).

In addition to their appearance, there is a clear difference in the qualitative reflectance of these two fossil suites (Fig. 4, 5). The reflectance data (Fig. 4) supports the view that the material from the Jim Camp Wash beds is charcoal. The values falling in the range 2.08-3.12% would suggest fire formation temperatures around 400-500°C, based on the experimental work of Jones et al. (1991). This fire temperature range is slightly higher than the 300-450°C proposed by Zeigler (2003), but the difference is probably not that significant. The loose Newspaper Rock bed material has a much broader range of reflectances (Fig. 5), from 0.78 – 3.12%. The lower reflectance values would correspond to a fire temperature just above 200°C, so theoretically the material could still be charcoal. If the material is charcoal, we speculate that the lower reflectance values might be related to the mineralization that the fossils have undergone; however this does not; as yet, offer a mechanism of how the reflectance might be lowered. The taphonomy would require that the mineral matter not only in-filled open cellular spaces, but also impregnated the cell wall material itself.

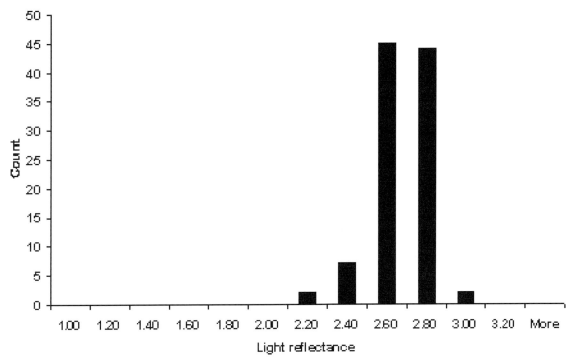

Figure 6. Charcoal from a stump at locality PFP 066 in the Blue Mesa Stump Field; coalified (charcoalified) stump. Histogram of 100 reading of reflectance under oil of a polished surface. Minimum = 2.17%, maximum = 2.94%, mean 2.57%, std. error = 0.014, std. dev. = 0.142.

The reflectance values of the material collected from the 'charred stump' at locality PFP 066 in the Blue Mesa Stump Field (Fig. 6) appear at face value to be less problematic. The stump mean reflectance value at 2.57% is fractionally below that of the Jim Camp Wash beds charcoal at 2.68%; however, importantly the bulk of the material falls in the range 2.60-2.80%, with little higher reflecting material. This agrees with the scenario of a Triassic *in-situ* stump smoldering at low to moderate temperatures; a well-established phenomenon in modern forest fires. What is not explained is how the charred stump charcoal appears to have avoided the mineralization that affected the other loose Tepee material at locality PFP 025. Further work is required, in particular sampling many more stumps, to determine if the fossil forest reported by Ash and Creber (1992) is in fact a burnt fossil forest.

For reconstructions of fire history in ancient ecosystems, one of the crucial parameters is the paleoatmospheric oxygen levels. It is well established by simple experiments and anecdotal evidence about accidents in medical oxygen tents, that fires are more likely to ignite, and burn fiercer and hotter in elevated atmospheric oxygen conditions. At first consideration, it is reasonable to assume that given adequate fuel supplies a Carboniferous fire with 35% atmospheric oxygen would be more likely to ignite, and burn fiercer and hotter than a Triassic fire with 15% atmospheric oxygen: thus there is an abundance of Carboniferous charcoal and paucity of Triassic charcoal in the fossil record. But it is not that simple, because charcoal is produced under conditions where oxygen is limited

(Rabash and Langford, 1968); thus it might be that a moderate Triassic fire could produce more charcoal than a fierce Carboniferous blaze that completely combusted the majority of the available fuel.

Could it therefore be that the more important question was not the relative amounts of charcoal produced, for example, during the Triassic or Carboniferous, but instead how much of that charcoal was deposited in a setting where it was preserved in the fossil record? Certainly the Permo-Triassic fossil assemblages of vertebrate fossil and charcoal (Sander, 1987; Zeigler, 2003) support the notion that if the charcoal is very rapidly buried in appropriate sediment types, then it will be preserved. The taphonomy of charcoal thus becomes of crucial importance, and notions on the 'inertness' of charcoal once buried need to be reconsidered. It is well-known that charcoal will withstand weeks in powerful oxidizing agents such as concentrated nitric acid, a chemical environment that will rapidly breakdown non-charcoalified plant fossils; however, this probably does not supply a comparable metric for longer-term burial conditions. Carboniferous charcoal samples collected by the senior author 20 years ago, survived in good condition for hundreds of millions of years when encased in rock, but 20 years in a storage cupboard and atmospheric exposure has resulted in clear degradation on the charcoal surfaces; taking the form of a white powdery surface and powdery texture. It is also self-evident that coal, and charcoal in coal, is preserved because the burial conditions are satisfactory for fossil plant preservation. Because we know that fires

CONCLUSIONSoccurredoccurred in the Permo-Triassic, it would be more surprising if these coals did not contain a significant proportion of charcoal. It is also possible that the severity of the fires themselves also contributed towards the preservation of the charcoal. Fires can devastate vegetation cover on soil, and this can result in greatly enhanced rates of erosion; values of 30 times that of normal have been recorded following fires (Swanson, 1981); the fires thus helping to generate their own sediment cover.

CONCLUSIONS

We conclude that the majority of charcoal-like plant fossils collected from the Petrified Forest do represent fossil charcoal, the final product of ancient wildfires. There is little doubt about this assessment for localities PFP 098 (Dry Wash) and PFP 066 (Tepees area); however there is still some small doubt about the genesis of the locality PFP 025 (Blue Mesa Stump Field) material. Having said that, a plausible alternative preservation mechanism that could have produced the locality PFP 025 material has yet to be suggested. We speculate therefore that the slightly unusual macroscopic appearance and low reflectance values, could result from later mineralization of genuine charcoal.

The quantitative reflectance values obtained are not too dissimilar to previous published results, and from comparisons with modern experimental work, indicate moderate temperature wildfires. A slight refinement to this story is seen in the reflectance results for the charred stump, which are slightly lower than the locality PFP 098 results, and have been interpreted as a low-temperature smoldering in-situ stump. This phenomenon of smoldering stumps, often smoldering for considerable periods, is commonly seen in modern wildfires. An implication of this finding is that the stump field that was previously considered (Ash and Creber, 1992) to be the remnants of an ancient forest might now be considered to represent the remains of a burnt ancient forest, a much more unusual occurrence.

It is questionable how much significance can be placed on the apparent lack of fossil charcoal in late Paleozoic and early Mesozoic rocks, in terms of paleoatmospheric oxygen levels. The relationship between charcoal production and atmospheric oxygen would appear to be the subject of contradicting positive- and negative-feedback cycles. For example, it cannot be assumed that the high oxygen Carboniferous should have been a time of regular, fiercely burning wildfires, because the very abundance of oxygen would mean that the fires would be unlikely to leave much charcoal as limited oxygen is a requirement for charcoal formation. On the other hand, the low atmospheric oxygen levels of the Triassic should have experienced fewer and less severe wildfires, but the lower oxygen levels should have resulted in enhanced charcoal production. Thinking in broad generalizations, the putatively more severe fires of high oxygen times, such as the Carboniferous, are likely to have had more severe impacts on the paleoecosystems, when compared with the possibly more moderate fires of low oxygen times such as the Triassic. These impacts could have included fires denuding vegetation cover, resulting in enhanced erosion and sediment production; thus resulting in more favorable conditions for the rapid burial and therefore preservation of charcoal in the fossil record.

ACKNOWLEDGMENTS

The constructive criticisms of Ian Glasspool (Chicago, Illinois) and Walter L. Cressler, III (West Chester, Pennsylvania) who reviewed an earlier version of this paper are acknowledged with thanks. We are grateful to the late Micki Hellickson, who, as Superintendent authorized us to conduct field research in Petrified Forest National Park and to her staff for directly assisting our work there. The financial support of the research reported here by the Petrified Forest Museum Association is appreciated.

REFERENCES

Ahlgren, C. E. 1974. Introduction, p. 1-5. In T. T. Kozlowski and C. E. Ahlgren (eds.), Fire and Ecosystems. Academic Press, New York.

Ash, S. And G. Creber. 1992. Palaeoclimatic interpretation of the wood structures of the trees in the Chinle Formation (Upper Triassic) in the area of Petrified Forest National Park, Arizona, U.S.A. Palaeogeography, Palaeoclimatology, Palaeoecology, 96:299-317.

Beerling, D. J., J. A. Lake, R. A. Berner, L. J. Hickey, D. W. Taylor and D. L. Royer. 2002. Carbon isotope evidence implying high O_2/CO_2 ratios in the Permo-Carboniferous atmosphere. Geochimica et Cosmochimica Acta, 66:3757-3767.

Berner, R. A. and D. E. Canfield. 1989. A new model of atmospheric oxygen over Phanerozoic time. American Journal of Science, 289:59-91.

Cohen, A. D. 1974. Evidence of fires in the ancient Everglades and coastal swamps of southern Florida. Miami Geological Society Memoir, 2:213-218.

Glasspool, I. 2000. A major fire event recorded in the mesofossils and petrology of the Late Permian, lower Whybrow coal seam, Sydney Basin, Australia, p. 357-380. In A. C. Scott, J. Moore and B. Brayshay (eds.), Fire and the Environment. Palaeogeography, Palaeoclimatology, Palaeoecology, 164.

Harris, T..M. 1958. Forest fire in the Mesozoic. Journal of Ecology, 46:447-453.

Jones, T. P. 1991. The nature, origin and recognition of fusain. Unpublished Ph.D. thesis. University of London, 225 p.

Jones. T. P., S. Ash and I. Figueiral. 2002. Late Triassic charcoal from Petrified Forest National Park, Arizona, USA. Palaeogeography, Palaeoclimatology, Palaeoecology, 188:127-139.

Jones, T. P. and N. P. Rowe (eds.). 1999. Fossil plants and spores: modern techniques. Special Publication of the Geological Society of London, 396 p.

Jones, T.P., A. C. Scott and M. Cope. 1991. Reflectance measurements the temperature of formation of modern charcoals Implications for studies of fusain. Bulletin of the Geological Society of France, 162:193-200.

McGinnes, E. A., S. A. Kandeel and P. S. Szopa. 1971. Some structural changes observed in the structure of wood. Wood and Fibre, 3:77-83.

Milo, E. 2004. Vertebrate extinction across the Permian-Triassic boundary in Karoo Basin, South Africa; discussion. Geological Society of America Bulletin, 116:1294.

Montanez, I. P. 2000a. Evolution of the Permian atmosphere pCO (sub 2) and western equatorial Pangean climate; as recorded by paleosol morphic and geochemical proxies. AAPG Bulletin, 84:1881.

Montanez, I. P., N. J. Tabor, D. Ekart and J. Collister. 2000b. Evolution of latest Paleozoic through early Mesozoic atmospheric pCO2 derived from mineral and organic matter proxies in paleosols. Geological Society of America, Abstracts with Programs, 32:524.

Moore, P. D. 1978. Forest fires. Nature, 272:754.

Rabash, D. J. and B. Langford. 1968. Burning of wood in atmospheres of reduced oxygen concentrations. Combustion and Flame, 12:33-40.

Racine, C. H., J. G. Dennis and W. A. Patterson, III. 1985. Tundra fire regimes in the Noatak River Watershed, Alaska: 1956-83. Arctic, 38:194-200.

Sander, P.M. 1987. Taphonomy of the lower Permian Geraldine Bonebed in Archer Couny, Texas. Palaeogeography, Palaeoclimatology, Palaeoecology, 61:221-236.

Sanford, R. L. Jr., J. Saldaarraiage, K. E. Clark, C. Uhl and R. Herrera. 1985. Amazon Rainforest fires. Science, 227:53-55.

Schopf, J. M. 1975. Modes of fossil preservation. Review of Palaeobotany and Palynology, 20:27-53.

Schuneman, P. and M. E. Uhle. 2003. Relating the occurrence and abundance of pyrogenic PAH to modern, Triassic and Carboniferous atmospheric oxygen levels. Geological Society of America, Abstracts with Program, 35:437.

Scott, A. C. 1989. Observations on the nature and origin of fusain. International Journal of Coal Geology, 12:443-475.

Scott, A. C. 2000. The pre-Quaternary history of fire. Palaeogeography, Palaeoclimatology, Palaeoecology, 164:281-329.

Swanson, F. J. 1981. Fire and geomorphic processes, p. 401-420. *In* H. AS. Mooney, T. H. Bonnicksen, N. L. Christensen, J. E. Lotan and W. A. Reiners (eds.), Fire Regimes and Ecosystem Properties. USDA Forest Service General technical report, WO-26.

Uhl, D. and Kerp, H.. 2003. Wildfires in the late Paleozoic of Central Europe; the Zechstein (Upper Permian) of NW Hesse (Germany). Palaeogeography, Palaeoclimatology, Palaeoecology, 199:1-15.

Uhl, D., S. Lausberg, R. Noll and K. R. G. Stapf. 2004. Wildfires in the late Paleozoic of Central Europe; an overview of the Rotliegend (Upper Carboniferous – Lower Permian) of the Saar-Nahe Basin (SW Germany). Palaeogeography, Palaeoclimatology, Palaeoecology, 207:23-35.

Yunker, M. B., R. W. MacDonald, R. Vingarzan, R. H. Mitchell, D. Goyette and S. Sylvester. 2002. PAHs in the Fraser River Basin: a critical appraisal of PAH ratios as indicators of PAH source and composition. Organic Geochemistry, 33:489-515.

Zeigler, K. E. 2003. Taphonomic analysis of the Snyder Quarry; a fire-related Upper Triassic vertebrate fossil assemblage from north-central New Mexico. Bulletin of the New Mexico Museum of Natural History and Science, 24:49-62.

VERTEBRATE PALEONTOLOGY

Parker, W. G., Ash, S. R., and Irmis, R. B., eds., 2006.
A Century of Research at Petrified Forest National Park: Geology and Paleontology.
Museum of Northern Arizona Bulletin No. 62.

A NEW SPECIES OF *TRILOPHOSAURUS* (DIAPSIDA: ARCHOSAUROMORPHA) FROM THE SONSELA MEMBER (CHINLE FORMATION) OF PETRIFIED FOREST NATIONAL PARK, ARIZONA

B. D. MUELLER[1]* AND WILLIAM G. PARKER[2]

[1]Museum of Texas Tech University, Box 43191, Lubbock, Texas 79409 <bill.mueller@ttu.edu>
[2]Division of Resource Management, Petrified Forest National Park, Box 2217, Petrified Forest, Arizona 86028 <William_Parker@nps.gov>
* Corresponding author

ABSTRACT — We describe a new trilophosaurid, *Trilophosaurus dornorum* sp. nov., from the Upper Triassic (Late Carnian – Early Norian) Sonsela Member of the Chinle Formation in the Petrified Forest National Park, Arizona. Referred specimens of the new taxon are also known from the Cooper Canyon Formation (Norian) of west Texas. This large, robust trilophosaurid possesses distinct cingula on the transversely expanded, tricuspid teeth. Despite earlier reports to the contrary, this is the first well-preserved material of *Trilophosaurus* from Petrified Forest National Park. The discovery of the new taxon increases the known diversity of the trilophosaurids.

Keywords: **Triassic, Petrified Forest, Chinle Formation, Dockum Group, Archosauromorpha, *Trilophosaurus***

INTRODUCTION

TRILOPHOSAURIDS ARE one of the earliest studied Triassic vertebrate groups from the southwestern U. S. A., with the genus *Trilophosaurus* erected by Case (1928a) for the type species, *Trilophosaurus buettneri*. The holotype, a dentary (UMMP 2338), was collected from the Tecovas Formation (Triassic: Carnian) at Walker's Tank in Crosby County, Texas, and was the only specimen referred to the species by Case (1928b). Gregory's (1945) detailed osteology of *Trilophosaurus* was based on specimens from a large collection of *Trilophosaurus* made by the Work Projects Administration in the 1930s under the supervision of Grayson Meade and deposited at the Texas Memorial Museum. This collection came from two localities near Otis Chalk in Howard County, Texas. The collection at the Texas Memorial Museum contains a large amount of cranial and postcranial material from numerous individuals. This collection is the subject of more recent studies by Parks (1969), Elder (1978), Demar and Bolt (1981), and Merck (1995, 1997). Demar and Bolt (1981) divided the teeth of *Trilophosaurus* into three types: anterior teeth (Type A), transversely expanded teeth (Type T), and the posterior tooth (Type P). Trilophosaurids have also been reported as part of faunas described by Murry (1982, 1986), Kirby (1989, 1991, 1993), Long and Murry (1995), Heckert (2001, 2004), Irmis (2005), and Parker (2005b). Lucas et al. (1993) described *T. buettneri* as part of the diverse fauna from a number of localities in the Otis Chalk area, including the Work Projects Administration quarries.

Murry (1987) described a new trilophosaurid from Arizona, *Trilophosaurus jacobsi*, based on several maxillary and mandible fragments from the *Placerias* quarry southwest of St. Johns, Arizona. *Trilophosaurus jacobsi* was later assigned to a new genus *Chinleogomphius* by Sues and Olsen

(1993), because they thought it possibly represented a procolophonid. Heckert et al. (2003) reported a cache of *Trilophosaurus* specimens discovered in Borden County, Texas, during the early 1990s that they identified as *T. jacobsi* (Heckert et al., 2001; Heckert et al., 2004; Spielmann et al., 2004). Their examination of these specimens led to their conclusion that *T. jacobsi* was not a procolophonid and did belong to the genus *Trilophosaurus*.

A detailed examination of the trilophosaurids was initiated with the discovery by one of us (BDM) of a near complete left and right dentary of *T. jacobsi* in 1999 at MOTT VPL 3869. The first trilophosaurid specimen was collected from this locality in 1993. Numerous trilophosaurid specimens have been collected from this and other Museum of Texas Tech localities over the past decade. In 2003, R. Irmis and J. Shuman discovered a trilophosaurid specimen (PEFO 31165) in the Petrified Forest National Park of Arizona. The Museum of Texas Tech trilophosaurid study and the discovery of the Petrified Forest specimen lead to the examination of the trilophosaurid taxon described here.

Abbreviations.—MNA, Museum of Northern Arizona; MOTT, Museum of Texas Tech University; MOTT VPL, Museum of Texas Tech Vertebrate Paleontology locality; PEFO, Petrified Forest; PFNP, Petrified Forest National Park; PFV, Petrified Forest vertebrate locality; TMM, Texas Memorial Museum; TTU, Texas Tech University; UMMP, University of Michigan Museum of Paleontology; W.P.A., Work Projects Administration.

GEOLOGIC SETTING

The Chinle Formation in Petrified Forest National Park can be divided into five distinct members. From oldest to youngest, these are the Mesa Redondo, Blue Mesa, Sonsela, Petri-

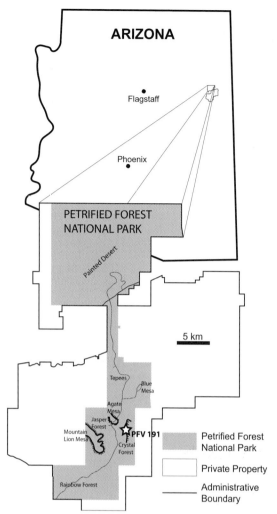

Figure *1*. Index map showing PFV 191 in Petrified Forest National Park, Arizona.

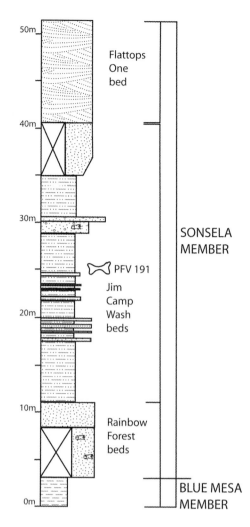

Figure *2*. Stratigraphic section of the Chinle Formation at PFV 191. Modified from Woody (2003).

fied Forest, and Owl Rock Members (Woody, 2003, this volume; Parker and Irmis, 2005). The Blue Mesa and Sonsela Members originally were considered basal units of the Petrified Forest Member (lower Petrified Forest Member of Billingsley, 1985); however, recent stratigraphic work has shown them to be lithologically distinct (Heckert and Lucas, 2002; Woody, 2003, this volume).

The Petrified Forest specimen (PEFO 31165) was collected from the Flag Canyon locality (PFV 191), approximately 1 mile NNE of Crystal Forest at the base of a long, north-south trending escarpment (Fig. 1). PEFO 31165 occurred as float from a series of low, gray, sandy mudstone hills approximately 15 meters beneath the capping sandstone (Fig. 2). Other vertebrate fossils from the locality include a crocodylomorph femur and vertebrae of an indeterminate "rauisuchid".

The capping sandstone can be traced northwards where it roofs Agate Mesa (Fig. 1) and represents the Flattops One bed (Woody, 2003, this volume). PFV 191 is within the Jim Camp Wash beds of the Sonsela Member and is located approximately 20 meters above the top of the Blue Mesa Mem-

ber (Woody, 2003). The exact age of these beds cannot be currently unequivocally constrained, but the presence of the aetosaur *Paratypothorax* and the phytosaur *Pseudopalatus* at lower horizons in the nearby Crystal Forest (PFV 173) and Mountain Lion Mesa (PFV 295), respectively, suggests a Norian age (Lucas, 1998).

The Upper Triassic Dockum Group of West Texas is divided into four formations. From oldest to youngest they are: Santa Rosa Formation; Tecovas Formation; Trujillo Formation; and Cooper Canyon Formation (Lehman and Chatterjee, 2005). The Museum of Texas Tech specimens came from three localities: MOTT VPL 3624, MOTT VPL 3869, and MOTT VPL 3878. All three localities are located south of Post in Garza County, Texas, in the Cooper Canyon Formation (Norian) of the Dockum Group. Detailed locality information and Global Positioning System coordinates are on file with the Paleontology Division at the MOTT.

At MOTT VPL 3869, the trilophosaurid fossils occur in mudstone deposits representing an overbank flood-plain facies (Lehman and Chatterjee, 2005). The majority of the trilophosaurid specimens come from a mudstone less than one meter above a carbonate granule conglomerate that is approximately eight meters above the base of the Cooper Canyon Formation. This zone contains abundant, well preserved fossils of small vertebrates.

The sediments at MOTT VPL 3624 (the Post Quarry) represent a flood deposit in an overbank flood-plain facies (Lehman and Chatterjee, 2005). This locality has produced a varied fauna from small temnospondyl amphibians to large "rauisuchids" and "poposaurids".

The fossils at MOTT VPL 3878 come from mudstones of an overbank flood-plain facies overlying a thin lenticular sandstone deposit (BDM pers. obs.). This locality occurs in the upper portion of the Cooper Canyon Formation, approximately 50 meters above the Post Quarry. This locality differs from the other two MOTT localities in that fossils at this locality are sparse and primarily consist of phytosaur and aetosaur remains. All three of the localities are considered Norian in age (Lehman and Chatterjee, 2005).

SYSTEMATIC PALEONTOLOGY

DIAPSIDA Osborn, 1903
ARCHOSAUROMORPHA von Huene, 1946 sensu
Benton, 1985
TRILOPHOSAURIDAE Romer, 1956
TRILOPHOSAURUS Case, 1928a

Type Species.—*Trilophosaurus buettneri* Case, 1928a

Other species.—*Trilophosaurus jacobsi* Murry, 1987; *Trilophosaurus dornorum* sp. nov.

Distribution.—Upper Triassic; Late Carnian to Late Norian; Arizona, New Mexico, and Texas.

TRILOPHOSAURUS DORNORUM new species
Fig. 3-5

Trilophosaurus sp. Irmis 2005, p. 70.
Trilophosaurus sp. Parker, 2005a, p. 50.
Trilophosaurus sp. Parker and Irmis, 2005, p. 48.
Trilophosaurus sp. Parker, 2005b, p. 44-45.

Holotype.—PEFO 31165, partial left maxillary with teeth and partial left dentary with teeth.

Referred Material.—MOTT VPL 3624: TTU-P09497 (isolated tooth). MOTT VPL 3869: TTU-P10413 (partial right maxilla), TTU-P10582 (partial right maxilla), TTU-P10583 (partial left maxilla), TTU-P10586 (right and left dentary fragments). MOTT VPL 3878: TTU-P10447 (partial maxilla).

Etymology.—To honor PEFO Chief of Resource Management Karen Dorn, under whom the paleontology program of

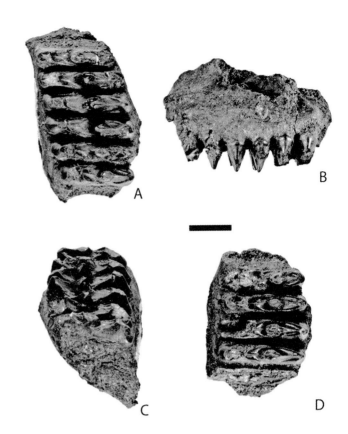

Figure 3. Maxillary and dentary sections of PEFO 31165, the holotype of *Trilophosaurus dornorum* sp. nov. *A-C*. Maxillary section in *A*, occlusal, *B*, lateral view and *C*, oblique views; *D*. Dentary section in occlusal view. Scale bar = 1 cm.

the park has been revitalized; and Chuck Dorn, a PEFO Law Enforcement ranger, for his ongoing protection of fossil resources.

Diagnosis.—Medial and lingual cusps are similar in size and the medial cusp is offset labially. Cingula form deep grooves on larger specimens. Anterior and posterior cingula connecting both labial and lingual cusps to medial cusp, three to three and one-half maxillary teeth posterior to lateral process of maxilla. Maxilla and dentaries more robust in structure than *T. buettneri* and *T. jacobsi*.

Type locality and horizon.—PFV 191, Petrified Forest National Park, Arizona. Global Positioning System coordinates are on record with the park. Jim Camp Wash beds, Sonsela Member of the Chinle Formation.

Age.—Late Triassic (Late Carnian – Early Norian).

Description.—The holotype jaw fragments (Fig. 3) were found as float on some small mudstone mounds at the base of an escarpment. No additional trilophosaur specimens have been collected from that locality. The two fragments, a partial maxilla and a partial dentary, are from the left side of the skull and belong to a large, robust trilophosaurid. TTU-P09497 and TTU-P10447 from the Cooper Canyon Formation are similar in size and are almost twice the size of the largest *Trilophosaurus* specimens from Otis Chalk. The specimens

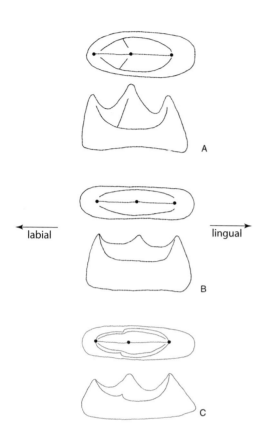

labial ← → lingual

Figure 4. Diagram illustrating the cingula and cusp structure on the teeth of three species of *Trilophosaurus*. A. *T. jacobsi*; B. *T. buettneri*; C. *T. dornorum*. Figures are not to scale.

from MOTT VPL 3869 vary in size. As in the other trilophosaurids examined, the Type A teeth and the Type P tooth differ from the Type T teeth, with the Type A and P teeth being subround to round in the occlusal view. The tricuspid, transversely expanded, Type T teeth vary slightly throughout the tooth row with the primary characters being consistant.

Compared to other species of *Trilophosaurus*, the teeth of *T. dornorum* are very distinct. The Type T teeth are transversely expanded, possess three cusps, and have a sharp occlusal ridge connecting the cusps along the crown of the tooth (Figs. 3, 4). There are cingula on both the anterior and posterior facets of the teeth. Anterior and posterior cingula connect the labial cusp to the medial cusp and anterior and posterior cingula connect the lingual cusp to the medial cusp (Fig. 4). In *T. dornorum*, the cingula usually connect on the labial portion of the medial cusp. The medial cusp is offset labially and equal in size to the lingual cusp. The facets formed by the cingula and the crest of the tooth are often concave.

The teeth are oriented at a slight angle to the line of the tooth row and perpendicular to the sagittal plane of the

skull. The maxilla and dentary are more robust than those of *T. buettneri* or *T. jacobsi*. The maxillae of *T. dornorum* are dorsoventrally shorter than comparable elements of *T. buettneri* and *T. jacobsi*. The maxilla of *T. dornorum* possesses only three to three and one-half teeth posterior to the lateral process of the maxilla (Fig. 5). The posterior tooth of the maxilla is round to sub-round in occlusal view.

DISCUSSION

The holotype and referred specimens of *T. dornorum* were compared to 37 dentary or maxilla specimens of *Trilophosaurus* from the two Otis Chalk localities in the collection of the Texas Memorial Museum, the holotype and seven referred specimens of *T. jacobsi* from the Museum of Northern Arizona, the holotype of *T. buettneri* from the University of Michigan Museum of Paleontology, 62 dentary or maxilla specimens of trilophosaurids in the Museum of Texas Tech collection, and photographs of other trilophosaurid specimens. The analysis of all these trilophosaurid specimens is the subject of a more detailed manuscript that is in progress by BDM.

We concur with Heckert (2004) that all of the specimens from the Otis Chalk localities represent a single species of *Trilophosaurus*. The Otis Chalk *Trilophosaurus* specimens are very uniform in their morphological characteristics and the difference in sizes of the specimens does not affect the characters of the jaws and teeth. All Type T teeth examined exhibited three cusps that are similar in size, with equally spaced cusps, and cingula connecting the lingual and labial cusps (Fig. 4). The maxillae, when a complete posterior portion of the tooth row is preserved, possess five teeth posterior to the lateral process of the maxilla (Fig. 5).

Trilophosaurus dornorum is differentiated from the *T. buettneri* by several characters. Firstly, in *T. dornorum* the cingula connect the labial and lingual cusps to the medial cusp. Secondly, the maxilla of *T. dornorum* possesses three to three and one-half teeth posterior to the lateral process of the maxilla. Furthermore, *Trilophosaurus dornorum* is a more robust taxon than *T. buettneri*. The largest dentaries and maxillae of *T. dornorum* have teeth up to 21 mm in width compared to only 13 mm for the dentaries and maxillae of the largest Otis Chalk specimens of *Trilophosaurus*. In *T. dornorum* the maxilla is not as tall dorsoventrally as in comparable specimens of the Otis Chalk *Trilophosaurus*. Whereas we feel that the robustness of this taxon is significant, we realize that this, by itself, is not sufficient for taxonomic differentiation and rely on other characters to diagnose *T. dornorum*.

Eight specimens of *T. jacobsi* from the MNA were examined in detail and compared to the specimens of *T. dornorum*. Murry (1987, p. 774) described the teeth of *T. jacobsi* as "posterior teeth tricuspid, crowns of teeth forming sharp asymmetrical pyramids, well-developed medial and typi-

Figure 5. Photograph and diagram comparing the posterior maxilla configuration in occlusal view. *A. Trilophosaurus buettneri* (TMM 31025-140); *B. Trilophosaurus dornorum* (referred specimen TTU-P10413). LP, lateral process of maxilla. Scale bar = 1 cm.

cally with lateral cingula joining each cusp." Examination of the holotype and referred specimens of *T. jacobsi* confirmed that adequately preserved specimens possess cingula that connect the labial and lingual cusps of the tooth. The holotype, MNA V3192, is broken; however, the angle of the cingula is consistent with the structure of the best preserved tooth (MNA V9494) that clearly exhibits cingula connecting the labial and lingual cusps. Whereas MNA V9495 appears to have cingula connecting the lingual and labial cusps to the medial cusp, microscopic analysis of the cingula shows that this is an artifact of preservation. The tooth is worn and abraded, giving the false impression of cingula connecting to the medial cusp.

The medial cusp of *T. jacobsi* is more prominent than the lateral cusps, whereas in *T. dornorum* the medial cusp is equal in size to the lingual cusp. This character is consistent with the sample of trilophosaurids collected from MOTT VPL 3869 and identified as *T. jacobsi*. The medial cusp is slightly larger and more bulbous than the lateral cusps and, when abraded or worn, specimens 'appear' to have cingula connecting the labial and lingual cusps to the medial cusp. On

unworn teeth, the cingula clearly traverse from the labial to the lingual cusps. The teeth of *T. jacobsi* from MOTT VPL 3869 are taller relative to tooth width than the teeth of *T. dornorum*. Heckert et al. (2003) and Heckert (2004) described the character of the tooth height being greater than the tooth width for specimens they identified as *T. jacobsi*. One of these specimens, a fragmentary tooth from the Upper Kalgary locality, NMMNH L1430, identified by Heckert (2004, p. 95, fig. 77 E–F) as *T. jacobsi*, appears to be referable to *T. dornorum* but the identification cannot be confirmed without direct examination of the specimen. Heckert described this as the only locality where *T. buettneri* and *T. jacobsi* are both found together; however, *Trilophosaurus buettneri*, *T. jacobsi*, and *T. dornorum* are all now known to occur at MOTT VPL 3869.

The transversely expanded teeth of *T. dornorum* are arranged in the jaw perpendicular to the sagittal plane of the skull. This arrangement is typical for *Trilophosaurus*. The teeth are oriented in the jaws at more of an angle than in *T. buettneri* but less than in *T. jacobsi*.

Trilophosaurids more robust than *T. buettneri* have been previously described. Long and Murry (1995) described a femur (TMM 31025-265) and humeri (TMM 31025-66) from Otis Chalk and three tibia and a pelvis with sacrum from the *Placerias* Quarry in Arizona. They referred this material to "a robust trilophosaurid." There is no association or reason to suggest this material belongs to *T. dornorum*. It merely supports the hypothesis that trilophosaurid taxa more robust than *T. buettneri* existed, and *Trilophosaurus dornorum* represents one such taxon.

The specimens of *T. dornorum* were compared to the published descriptions, diagrams, and photographs of several taxa exhibiting similar characters. *Teraterpeton hrynewichorum* has an edentulous premaxilla but the teeth do not compare with the dentition of *Trilophosaurus* (Sues, 2003). *Variodens inopinatus* possesses posterior tricuspid teeth (Robinson, 1957); however, they differ from those of *T. dornorum* in that the central cusp is larger than the lateral cusps. *Tricuspisaurus thomasi* also possesses tricuspid teeth (Robinson, 1957; Fraser, 1986); however, the teeth are not all tricuspid and their orientation in the jaw varies. These two characters differ from those of *Trilophosaurus*.

The evidence for the distribution and diversity of the trilophosaurids is greater than has previously been thought. *Trilophosaurus* is now known from more than 28 localities in the southwestern U.S.A. (Long and Murry, 1995; Heckert, 2001, 2004; Heckert et al, 2003; BDM pers. obs.). A variety of trilophosaurid specimens have recently been collected by the Museum of Texas Tech University including *T. buettneri*, *T. jacobsi*, *T. dornorum* sp. nov., and two unnamed trilophosaurid taxa. The increase in diversity and distribution of trilophosaurids is greater than has been previously reported due to the discovery of localities such as MOTT VPL 3869 and PFV 191. MOTT VPL 3869 contains extremely well preserved fossils of many smaller vertebrates from the Triassic including procolophonids, sphenodontians, a protorosaur, trilophosaurids, a tritheledontid, small archosaurs including a sphenosuchid, and small ornithodirians along with fossils of larger metoposaurids, dicynodonts, phytosaurs, stagonolepidids, poposaurids, and rauisuchids (BDM, pers. obs.). The *Trilophosaurus* specimen collected at PFV 191 is the first unambiguous occurrence of *Trilophosaurus* in Petrified Forest National Park. The discovery of new localities like PFV 191 and MOTT VPL 3869, where the smaller vertebrates are well preserved, continues to expand our knowledge of trilophosaurids and the environments they lived in.

ACKNOWLEDGMENTS

We would like to thank Scott Williams (PFNP), Tim Rowe, Lyn Murray, Pamela Owen (TMM), Janet Whitmore Gillette (MNA), Sankar Chatterjee (MOTT), and Gregg Gunnell (UMMP) for access to materials. We would also like to thank Andrew Heckert for providing us with a copy of his unpublished PhD dissertation; Randall Irmis and Jeff Shuman for finding the holotype specimen, and Gretchen Gurtler, Sterling Nesbitt, and Michelle Stocker for assistance in the field. Funding for field work, as part of an ongoing paleontological inventory of Petrified Forest National Park, was provided by the Federal Recreation Act Fee Program and the Petrified Forest Museum Association. Randall Irmis provided a modified version of Figure 1. This is PEFO paleontological contribution no. 9.

REFERENCES

Benton, M. J. 1985. Classification and phylogeny of diapsid reptiles. Zoological Journal of the Linnaean Society, 84:97-164.

Billingsley, G. H. 1985. General stratigraphy of the Petrified Forest National Park, Arizona. Bulletin of the Museum of Northern Arizona, 54: 3–8.

Case, E. C. 1928a. A cotylosaur from the Upper Triassic of western Texas. Journal of the Washington Academy of Science, 18:177–178.

Case, E. C. 1928b. Indications of a cotylosaur and a new form of fish from the Triassic beds of Texas, with remarks on the Shinarump Conglomerate. University of Michigan Museum of Paleontology Contributions, 3:1–14.

Demar, R. and J. R. Bolt. 1981. Dentitional organization and function in a Triassic reptile. Journal of Paleontology 55:967–984.

Elder, R. L. 1978. Paleontology and paleoecology of the Dockum Group, Upper Triassic, Howard County, Texas. M.A. thesis, University of Texas at Austin, Austin, Texas, 205 pp.

Fraser, N. C. 1986. Terrestrial vertebrates at the Triassic-Jurassic boundary in south west Britain. Modern Geology, 10:147–157.

Gregory, J. T. 1945. Osteology and relationships of Trilophosaurus. University of Texas Publication, 4401:273–359.

Heckert, A. B. 2001. The microvertebrate record of the Upper Triassic (Carnian) lower Chinle Group, southwestern U.S.A. and the early evolution of dinosaurs. Unpublished Ph.D. dissertation, University of New Mexico, Albuquerque, New Mexico, 465 pp.

Heckert, A. B. 2004. Late Triassic microvertebrates from the lower Chinle Group (Otischalkian-Adamanian: Carnian), southwestern U.S.A. New Mexico Museum of Natural History & Science Bulletin, 27: 1-170.

Heckert, A. B. and S. G. Lucas. 2002. Lower Chinle Group (Upper Triassic: Carnian) stratigraphy in the Zuni Mountains, West-Central New Mexico, p. 51-72. In A. B. Heckert and S. G. Lucas (eds.), Upper Triassic stratigraphy and paleontology. New Mexico Museum of Natural History and Science Bulletin, 21.

Heckert, A. B., S. G. Lucas, R. Kahle, and K. Zeigler. 2001. New occurrence of Trilophosaurus (Reptilia: Archosauromorpha) from the upper Triassic of West Texas and its biochronological significance, p. 115-122. In Geology of the Llano Estacado: New Mexico Geological Society Guidebook, 52nd Field Conference.

Heckert, A. B., S. G. Lucas, L. F. Rinehart, J. A. Spielmann, and R. Kahle. 2003. Trilophosaurus jacobsi is not a procolophonid: data from a new quarry from the Upper Triassic Chinle Group,

West Texas. Geological Society of America Abstracts with Programs, 34:497.

Heckert, A. B., S. G. Lucas, L. F. Rinehart, J. A. Spielmann, and R. Kahle. 2004. Biostratigraphy and evolution of Trilophosaurus, an unusual archosauromorph from the Upper Triassic Chinle Group, Southwestern USA. Geological Society of America Abstracts with Programs, 36:7.

Huene, F. V. 1946. Die grossen Stämme der Tetrapoden in den geologischen Zeiten. Bilogisches Zentralblatt, 65:268–275.

Irmis, R. B. 2005. The vertebrate fauna of the Upper Triassic Chinle Formation in northern Arizona. Mesa Southwest Museum Bulletin, 9:63-88.

Kirby, R. E. 1989. Late Triassic vertebrate localities of the Owl Rock Member (Chinle Formation) in the Ward Terrace area of northern Arizona, p. 12–28. In S. G. Lucas and A. P. Hunt (eds.), Dawn of the age of dinosaurs in the American Southwest. New Mexico Museum of Natural History, Albuquerque, New Mexico.

Kirby, R. E. 1991. A vertebrate fauna from the Upper Triassic Owl Rock Member of the Chinle Formation in northern Arizona. Unpublished M.S. thesis, Northern Arizona University, Flagstaff, Arizona, 476 pp.

Kirby, R. E. 1993. Relationships of Late Triassic basin evolution and faunal replacement events in the southwestern United States: perspectives from the upper part of the Chinle Formation in northern Arizona, p. 233–242. In S. G. Lucas and M. Morales (eds.), The nonmarine Triassic: New Mexico Museum of Natural History and Science Bulletin, 3, Albuquerque, New Mexico.

Lehman, T. M. and S. Chatterjee. 2005. Depositional setting and vertebrate biostratigraphy of the Triassic Dockum Group of Texas. Journal of Earth System Science, 114:325-351.

Long, R. A. and P. A. Murry. 1995. Late Triassic (Carnian and Norian) tetrapods from the southwestern United States. New Mexico Museum of Natural History and Science Bulletin, 4, 238 pp.

Lucas, S. G. 1998. Global Triassic tetrapod biostratigraphy and biochronology. Palaeogeography, Palaeoclimatology, Palaeoecology, 143:347-384.

Lucas, S. G., A. P. Hunt and R. Kahle. 1993. Late Triassic vertebrates from the Dockum Formation near Otis Chalk, Howard County, Texas. New Mexico Geological Society Guidebook: Carlsbad Region, New Mexico and West Texas 44th Field Conference: 237–244.

Merck, J. W., Jr. 1995. The cranial anatomy of Trilophosaurus buettneri revealed by high-resolution computer aided tomography. Journal of Vertebrate Paleontology, 15(3. Supplement):44A.

Merck, J. W., Jr. 1997. A phylogenetic analysis of the Euryapsid reptiles. Unpublished Ph.D. dissertation, University of Texas at Austin, Austin, Texas, 785 pp.

Murry, P. A. 1982. Biostratigraphy and paleoecology of the Dockum Group (Triassic) of Texas. Unpublished Ph.D. dissertation, Southern Methodist University, Dallas, Texas, 459 pp.

Murry, P. A. 1986. Vertebrate paleontology of the Dockum Group, west Texas and eastern New Mexico, p. 109–137. *In* K. Padian (ed.), The Beginning of the Age of Dinosaurs. Cambridge University Press, Cambridge, Massachusetts.

Murry, P. A. 1987. New reptiles of the Upper Triassic Chinle Formation of Arizona. Journal of Paleontology, 61:773–786.

Osborn, H. F. 1903. The reptilian subclasses Diapsida and Synapsida and the early history of the Diaptosauria. Memoirs of the American Museum of Natural History, 1:449–507.

Parker, W. G. 2005a. Petrified Forest National Park: a roadlog. Mesa Southwest Museum Bulletin, 9:33-51.

Parker, W. G. 2005b. Faunal review of the Upper Triassic Chinle Formation of Arizona. Mesa Southwest Museum Bulletin, 11:34-54.

Parker, W. G. and R. B. Irmis. 2005. Advances in Late Triassic vertebrate paleontology based on new material from Petrified Forest National Park, Arizona. New Mexico Museum of Natural History and Science Bulletin, 29:45-58.

Parks, P. 1969. Cranial anatomy and mastication of the Triassic reptile *Trilophosaurus*. Unpublished M.S. thesis, University of Texas at Austin, Austin, Texas, 89 pp.

Robinson, P. L. 1957. An unusual sauropsid dentition. Journal of the Linnean Society of London, 43:283–292.

Romer, A. S. 1956. Osteology of the reptiles. University of Chicago Press, Chicago, Illinois, 772pp.

Spielmann, J. A., A. B. Heckert, S. G. Lucas, L. F. Rinehart, and A. P. Hunt. 2004. The Late Triassic archosauromorph *Trilophosaurus* is an arboreal climber. Geological Society of America Abstracts with Programs, 36(5):61.

Sues, H.-D. 2003. An unusual new archosauromorph reptile from the Upper Triassic Wolfville Formation of Nova Scotia. Canadian Journal of Earth Sciences, 40:635-649.

Sues, H.-D. and P. E. Olsen. 1993. A new procolophonid and a new tetrapod of uncertain, possibly procolophonian affinities from the Upper Triassic of Virginia. Journal of Vertebrate Paleontology, 13:282–286.

Woody, D. T. 2003. Revised geological assessment of the Sonsela Member, Chinle Formation, Petrified Forest National Park, Arizona. Unpublished M. S. thesis, Northern Arizona University, Flagstaff, Arizona, 207pp.

Parker, W. G., Ash, S. R., and R. B. Irmis, eds., 2006.
A Century of Research at Petrified Forest Natonal Park: Geology and Paleontology.
Museum of Northern Arizona Bulletin No. 62.

A NEW SPECIES OF THE LATE TRIASSIC PHYTOSAUR *PSEUDOPALATUS* (ARCHOSAURIA: PSEUDOSUCHIA) FROM PETRIFIED FOREST NATIONAL PARK, ARIZONA

WILLIAM G. PARKER[1] AND RANDALL B. IRMIS[2]

[1]Division of Resource Management, Petrified Forest National Park, P.O. Box 2217, Petrified Forest, AZ 86028 <William_Parker@nps.gov>
[2]Museum of Paleontology and Department of Integrative Biology, 1101 Valley Life Sciences Building, University of California, Berkeley, CA 94720-4780 <irmis@berkeley.edu>

ABSTRACT—We describe a partial phytosaur skull (PEFO 31207) from the Sonsela Member of the Upper Triassic Chinle Formation of Petrificd Forest National Park, Arizona as a new species of *Pseudopalatus*, *P. jablonskiae* sp. nov. Although the holotype specimen is incomplete, the new taxon is diagnosed by at least one autapomorphy and a unique suite of character-states. A phylogenetic analysis of pseudopalatine phytosaurs recovers *P. jablonskiae* as the most basal species of *Pseudopalatus*. The holotype of *P. jablonskiae* is especially important because it includes a well-preserved braincase; this portion of the skull is not preserved or described in detail for most phytosaur specimens. Additionally, *P. jablonskiae* is of biochronological significance because it is the stratigraphically lowest occurrence of *Pseudopalatus* within the Chinle Formation of Petrified Forest National Park, and provides strong evidence for the overlap of the Adamanian and Revueltian land-vertebrate faunachrons.

Keywords: **Triassic, Petrified Forest, Chinle Formation, Sonsela Member, Archosauria, Phytosauridae,** *Pseudopalatus*

INTRODUCTION

THE PARASUCHIA (=Phytosauria) form a basal clade of pseudosuchian archosaurs known as phytosaurs that are common in Laurasian deposits of Late Triassic age. Phytosaurs bear superficial resemblance to extant crocodylians and have been interpreted as possessing a similar semi-aquatic lifestyle (Gregory, 1962). Phytosaur taxonomy has a confused history; however, recent studies by Doyle and Sues (1995), Long and Murry (1995), and Hungerbühler (2002) have attempted to clarify ingroup relationships and taxonomy. Phytosaur alpha taxonomy has been plagued by descriptions of non-diagnostic fragmentary material, incorrect referral of material, misinterpretation of crushed and deformed specimens, inclusion of non-phytosaur specimens (aetosaurs), lost holotypes, stratophenetic assignment of specimens, and speculations about sexual dimorphism based on rostral characters. Phytosaur taxonomy is based almost exclusively on skull characteristics and early workers have been inconsistent regarding which characters are phylogenetically informative. Furthermore, character variance in the skull due to ontogeny, sexual dimorphism, and individual variation is poorly understood.

Despite the ambiguity surrounding phytosaur systematics, it is clear that this clade, although temporally restricted, was taxonomically diverse. Recent workers (e.g., Hungerbühler, 2002: table 1) recognize at least 14-17 valid species, all found in the Upper Triassic sediments of North America, Europe, and north Africa. Fragmentary material is also known from Madagascar (Gregory, 1969; Burmeister, 2000), Brazil (Kischlat and Lucas, 2003), Turkey (Buffetaut et al., 1988), and Thailand (Buffetaut and Ingavat, 1982).

In nearly all cases where relatively complete cranial material is preserved, co-occurring taxa include both robust and gracile morphs that have been interpreted as separate species. Recently, Zeigler et al. (2002, 2003) have suggested that these two forms in *Pseudopalatus* (*P. pristinus* and *P. buceros*) represent conspecific sexual dimorphs. This idea is not new (e.g., Camp, 1930; Colbert, 1947; Lawler, 1979), and though intriguing, it rests on a number of assumptions that have yet to be tested. We tentatively reject the sexual dimorphism hypothesis until further testing for the reasons outlined by Irmis (2005). In particular, it is difficult to hypothesize dimorphism in *Pseudopalatus* when similar "dimorphic" features have evolved separately several times in phytosaurs (e.g., *Rutiodon*/ *Angistorhinus*, *Leptosuchus*, *Nicrosaurus*, *Mystriosuchus*, and *Redondasaurus*). It is impossible to determine with the current evidence if *P. buceros* and *P. pristinus* are sympatric but separate species, ecological dimorphs, or true sexual dimorphs. We also consider *Pseudopalatus mccauleyi* to represent a valid taxon following Ballew (1989) and Hungerbühler (2002), *contra* Long and Murry (1995) and Zeigler et al. (2002, 2003); this is supported by previous phylogenetic analyses as well as the phylogeny presented in this paper.

In September 2002, a partial phytosaur skull was discovered near Mountain Lion Mesa in Petrified Forest National Park, Arizona at locality PFV 295 (Fig. 1). Parker and Irmis (2004) tentatively referred this specimen to *Pseudopalatus* cf. *mccauleyi* based on the morphology of the squamosals and the opisthotic. Although less than complete, further examination and comparison makes it clear that PEFO 31207 is a unique specimen that represents a new spe-

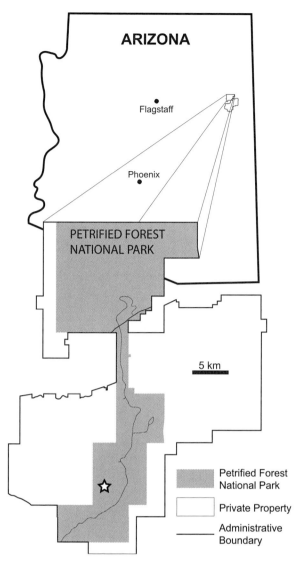

Figure *1*. Map of Petrified Forest National Park and surrounding vicinity. The type locality of *Pseudopalatus jablonskiae* n. sp. is indicated by a star.

cies with important implications for phytosaur systematics and biostratigraphy.

Institutional Abbreviations.—PEFO, Petrified Forest National Park, Arizona; UCMP, University of California Museum of Paleontology, Berkeley, California.

GEOLOGICAL SETTING

Petrified Forest National Park Vertebrate locality (PFV) 295 is in the basal Jim Camp Wash beds of the Sonsela Member of the Chinle Formation (Fig. 2; Heckert and Lucas, 2002; Woody, 2003, this volume). The Chinle Formation in Petrified Forest National Park is divisible into five members: the Mesa Redondo, Blue Mesa, Sonsela, Petrified Forest, and the Owl Rock Members. The Sonsela Member consists of a lithologically distinct package of sandstones and mudrocks that are bounded by upper and lower sandstone beds (Woody, this

volume). The upper sandstone bed was historically assigned to the "Sonsela Sandstone Bed" (Akers et al., 1958; Deacon, 1990) and has recently been correlated to a local bed in PEFO called the Flattops Sandstone #1 of Billingsley (1985) (Heckert and Lucas, 2002; Woody, 2003, this volume). The lower sandstone bed was historically called the Rainbow Forest sandstone (Billingsley, 1985), now the Rainbow Forest beds (Woody, this volume). Sandstone and mudstone beds between these units display characteristic cut and fill architecture and the unit as a whole possesses a high sand content (Woody, 2003, this volume). The medial unit is called the Jim Camp Wash beds (Heckert and Lucas, 2002) and consists of strata that in the southern portion of the park had previously been assigned to the upper Petrified Forest Member (Billingsley, 1985; Long and Murry, 1995) and in the central portion of the park, to the lower Petrified Forest Member (Billingsley, 1985; Long and Murry, 1995). Historically, PFV 295 would have been considered to be low in the upper Petrified Forest Member (Long and Murry, 1995); however, the work of Heckert and Lucas (2002) and Woody (2003) suggests instead that it is low in the Sonsela Member, a few meters above the Rainbow Forest beds. This represents the stratigraphically lowest occurrence of *Pseudopalatus* in PEFO (Parker and Irmis, 2005; Parker, this volume).

The specimen was recovered from a sandy brown-gray mudstone containing pebble-sized mud rip-up clasts 10.75 meters below a thick, cross-bedded brown sandstone that represents the Flattops One bed of Woody (2003) (Fig. 2). The skull is several meters above a whitish-gray cross-bedded sandstone that is correlative with the Rainbow Forest beds (Woody, 2003). Although this sandstone is not directly visible at PFV 295, it floors the valley in this area and is exposed in a large wash to the north (Fig. 2). The conglomeratic nature of the encasing deposits suggests that the specimen was transported before burial.

TAPHONOMY

The skull was discovered palate side up, a common position for recovered phytosaur skulls. The rostrum anterior to the external nares and the ventral portion of the skull are missing. Bone fragments collected as float allowed reconstruction of a portion of the right jugal as well as much of the braincase. The skull was located in a path used by cultural researchers to access sites on the mesa top above the specimen locality and apparently the skull sustained damage from repeated human foot travel. The discoverer, Pat Jablonsky, brought the specimen to the attention of park staff who subsequently excavated it. The specimen displays very little distortion. The skull roof and the external nares has been slightly twisted left laterally and downwards causing some separation along the midline suture. The parietals are slightly depressed

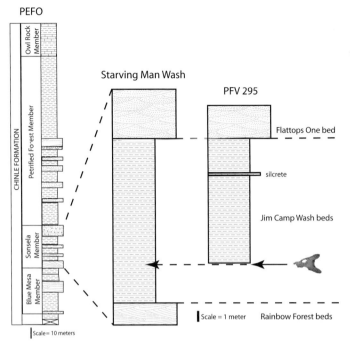

Figure 2. Measured stratigraphic sections showing the level where the holotype of *Pseudopalatus jablonskiae* n. sp. was recovered. These sections are correlated to the regional stratigraphy of the Upper Triassic Chinle Formation in the Petrified Forest National Park area.

relative to the frontals and postorbitals, although this appears to be uniform and may be natural.

SYSTEMATIC PALEONTOLOGY

ARCHOSAURIA Cope, 1869-71 sensu Gauthier, 1986
PSEUDOSUCHIA Zittel, 1887-90 sensu Gauthier, 1986
PARASUCHIA Huxley, 1875 sensu Sereno, 1991
PHYTOSAURIDAE Jaeger, 1828 sensu Doyle and Sues, 1995
PSEUDOPALATINAE Long and Murry, 1995 sensu Hungerbühler, 2002
PSEUDOPALATUS Mehl, 1928

Definition.—All phytosaurs closer to *P. pristinus* Mehl, 1928 and *P. buceros* Cope, 1881 than to *Redondasaurus gregorii* Hunt and Lucas, 1993; *Mystriosuchus planirostris* (von Meyer, 1863); and *Nicrosaurus kapffi* (von Meyer, 1860).

Revised Diagnosis.— Differs from all other phytosaurs in possessing the following synapomorphies: strongly developed medial lamella of postorbito-squamosal bar with the supratemporal fenestra reduced to slit (Hungerbühler, 2002: character 19) and visible in dorsal view; rounded top of the parieto-supraoccipital complex (Hungerbühler, 2002: character 24); dorsal portion of squamosals mediolaterally expanded forming a shelf level with the parietal and pos-

torbital; lamina of the squamosal extends onto the paroccipital process forming the ventrolateral border of the posttemporal fenestra (unknown in *Pseudopalatus jablonskiae* n. sp.) (Hungerbühler, 2002: character 38). Differs from *Redondasaurus* and *Mystriosuchus* in possessing a posttemporal fenestra less than three times wider than high (Hungerbühler, 2002: character 41). Differs from *Redondasaurus* in having a supratemporal fenestra that is visible in dorsal view.

Comments.—There is a long history of alternating names for the clade of archosaurs known as phytosaurs. The earliest available name, Phytosauridae (also Phytosauria), was proposed by Jaeger (1828) (see Hungerbühler, 2002), although Huxley's (1875) name Parasuchia has also been widely used. Sereno (1991) was the first to explicitly phylogenetically define and diagnose this clade. He considered the clade Parasuchia to include the common ancestor and all the descendents of *Angistorhinus, Francosuchus, Mystriosuchus, Nicrosaurus, Parasuchus,* and *Rutiodon.* Doyle and Sues (1995) defined the Phytosauria as the closest common ancestor and all its descendents of *Paleorhinus* and Phytosauridae. They defined the Phytosauridae as the last common ancestor of *Angistorhinus, Mystriosuchus, Nicrosaurus, Pseudopalatus,* and *Rutiodon* and all descendents of their closest common ancestor. With our current understanding of phytosaur phylogenetics, Sereno's Parasuchia has the same content as Doyle and Sues' Phytosauria. Thus, under the rules of phylogenetic taxonomy (de Queiroz and Gauthier, 1992) we use the first phylogenetically defined name, Parasuchia. We recognize that *Parasuchus* (= "*Paleorhinus*") may represent a paraphyletic grade (see Irmis, 2005), in which case Parasuchia and Phytosauria might not have synonymous content.

Hungerbühler (2002) did not explicitly define Pseudopalatinae phylogenetically, but he clearly used it to mean a clade that included *Nicrosaurus, Mystriosuchus, Pseudopalatus,* and *Redondasaurus* (e.g., Hungerbühler, 2002: fig. 11). Therefore, we follow Hungerbühler and define the node-based clade Pseudopalatinae as *Nicrosaurus, Mystriosuchus, Pseudopalatus, Redondasaurus,* and all descendents of their closest common ancestor.

Historically, phytosaur taxonomists have often chosen particular characters they found phylogenetically informative (e. g., rostral morphology) to the exclusion of other characters. This "cherrypicking" of characters based on personal preference has lead to much of the confusion in phytosaur systematics and instability in the alpha taxonomy of the group. Because of this, and also because genus-level clades have no more natural meaning than higher-level clades, we provide a phylogenetic definition for the clade *Pseudopalatus* based on our concept and that of Ballew (1989) and Hungerbühler (2002).

PSEUDOPALATUS JABLONSKIAE new species
(Figs. 3-8, 11)

Pseudopalatus cf. *mccauleyi* Parker and Irmis (2004: p.100A)
Pseudopalatus sp. Parker and Irmis (2005: p.47, fig. 3)

Diagnosis.—*Pseudopalatus jablonskiae* differs from all other phytosaurs in possessing the autapomorphy of a distinct, smooth beveled edge on the antero-medial edge of the postorbital-squamosal bar that forms a supratemporal fossa lateral to the supratemporal fenestra and a unique combination of the following characters: apomorphic characters for the *Pseudopalatus*-clade such as supratemporal fenestra that are slit-like and visible in dorsal view (hidden from dorsal view in *Redondasaurus*), and a transversely broad postorbito-squamosal bar that is heavily sculptured; squamosal tips that are not knob-like as in *P. buceros* and *P. pristinus*; thin, oar-like paroccipital process of the opisthotic that is fused to the internal squamosal process as in *P. buceros* and *P. mccauleyi*; anterior process of the squamosal enters the lateral wall of the braincase as in *M. westphali* and *L. gregorii* (unknown in *Redondasaurus*); differs from all other *Pseudopalatus* species in the lack of a lateral groove or ridge on the squamosal and in possessing squamosals that are strongly anteroposteriorly shortened.

Etymology.—For Pat Jablonsky, discoverer of the type and only known specimen.

Holotype.—PEFO 31207, posterior skull roof and braincase missing the rostrum and palate.

Type Horizon and Locality.— Basal Jim Camp Wash beds, Sonsela Member (*sensu* Woody, this volume), Upper Triassic Chinle Formation. PFV 295, near Mountain Lion Mesa, Petrified Forest National Park, Arizona (Figs. 1-2).

DESCRIPTION

The dorsal surface of the skull is heavily sculptured as in other pseudopalatines making determination of sutures other than the midline extremely difficult. The entire rostrum anterior to the posterior margin of the external nares is missing. Also missing are both quadrates, quadradojugals, maxillae, the left lacrimal, both jugals, and the entire palate. No teeth are preserved. The upper portion of the braincase and the rear of the skull were pieced together from float and are mostly complete and well-preserved. The skull has postnarial lengths of 162 mm (posterior border of external nares to the back of the parietal) and 236 mm (from the posterior border of the nares to the squamosal tips).

Nasal.—The nasals are incomplete, only the portions posterior to the external nares are well-preserved. Despite the heavily ornamented external surface, sutures with the frontals and the prefrontals are discernable (Fig. 3), demonstrating that the nasals rapidly taper medially upon contact with the pre-

frontal as is typical for phytosaurs. What appears to be the suture with the dorsal surface of the lacrimal is also apparent where these two bones form a tri-radiate suture with the prefrontal (Fig. 3). The posterior margin of the external nares is damaged; however, it is apparent that they were situated above the level of the skull roof as is typical for *Pseudopalatus*. The lateral surface below the external nares is preserved but badly damaged and offers no information.

Ventrally, the nasals meet the frontals posteriorly in a broad "U"-shaped suture (Fig. 4). Here, each nasal forms a distinct crescent-shaped platform with the posterior-most projection nestled between the frontal and the prefrontal. The margin with the prefrontal is thickened as is the symphysial area between the nasals, causing the crescent-shaped platform to be noticeably concave dorsally. This platform extends anteriorly to approximately midway between the nasal-frontal suture and the opening for the external nares. A sharp anteromedially directed ridge separates the crescent-shaped platform from a thinner smooth, depressed region of bone that appears to be a posteriorly expanded ventral expression of the external nares. In this region, just anterior to the anteromedial corner of the crescent-shaped platform and the nasal symphysis are two deep pits, the anteriormost being largest (Fig. 4).

Prefrontal.—Both the left and right prefrontals are present. Dorsally, they are heavily ornamented and form the anteromedial margin of the orbits. This margin is slightly raised and forms a distinct "bar" that rims that portion of the orbit (Fig. 3). The ventral prefrontal-lacrimal suture is not clear; thus the ventral extension of this element cannot be determined. As previously mentioned this element is thickened in comparison to the nasals, and thins laterally and ventrally. The ventral surface of the prefrontals is exposed but unremarkable.

Lacrimal.— The right lacrimal is preserved but badly damaged and too incomplete to provide much information, and the left lacrimal is missing. The lacrimal forms the antero-ventral border of the orbit. The orbital 'bar' of the prefrontal extends ventrally onto the lacrimal so that the posterior portion of the element is slightly raised compared to the more anterior portions (Fig. 5a, b). The suture with the postorbital is not discernible; in other phytosaurs it excludes the jugal from the ventral margin of the orbit. The anterior portion of the lacrimal is badly damaged and incomplete; the margin of the antorbital fenestra is not preserved, nor is the suture with the more ventrally situated jugal. There is a round area of missing bone in the area where the lacrimal/nasal suture was probably located (Fig. 5a).

Frontals.—The frontals are heavily sculptured and form the medial margins of the orbits (Fig. 3). The symphysial region is slightly depressed in comparison to the orbit margins, providing a slightly concave surface for this portion of the skull roof. The anterior portion of the dorsal surface slopes ventrally very slightly anteriorly to where the frontals contact the

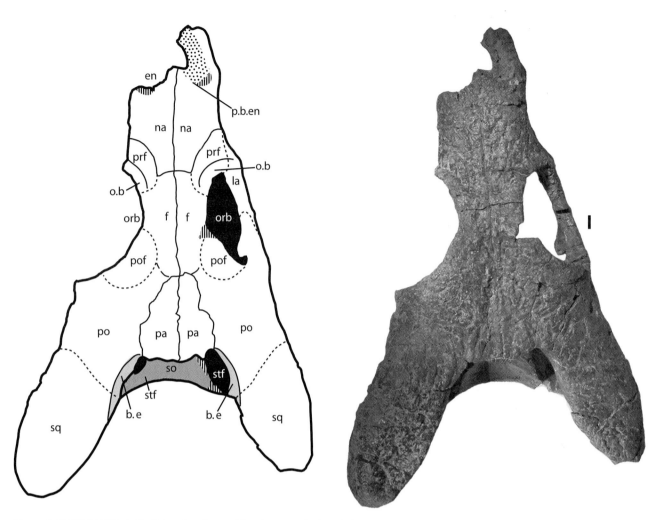

Figure 3. PEFO 31207, skull of *Pseudopalatus jablonskiae* n. sp. in dorsal view. b.e, beveled edge; en, external nares; f, frontal; la, lacrimal; na, nasals; o.b, orbital bar; orb, orbit; p.b., posterior border of...; pa, parietal; po, postorbital; pof, postfrontal; prf, prefrontal; so, supraoccipital; sq, squamosal; stf, supratemporal fenestra. In all figures, dotting pattern represents matrix and cross-hatching pattern represents broken areas. Scale bar = 1cm.

nasals. Consequently, the orbital bar described for the prefrontals does not continue posteriorly onto the frontals.

The ventral surface of the frontals is 'hour-glass' shaped with an anterior projection that meets the nasals in a broad "U"-shaped suture (Fig. 4). Just posterior to this is an elongate depression that fits the dorsal surface of the laterosphenoid. Lateral to this depression are thin sharp ridges that form the ventromedial margin of a large ventral orbital fossa (Fig. 4). This fossa is fairly deep with medial margins that slope ventromedially at approximately 45° and delineate the ventral and dorsal expressions of the orbits.

Postfrontals.—The postfrontals cannot be discerned on the dorsal surface but are presumably similar to those of other phytosaurs in forming the posterodorsal rim of the orbits (Fig. 3). There is no raised orbital 'bar' on the postfrontals. Ventrally, they must form the posteroventral surface of the orbital fossa but the sutures are not visible (Fig. 4).

Postorbital.—The only clear sutures delineating the postorbitals are those meeting the medial border of the pari-

etals (Fig. 3). In most phytosaurs, the postorbital forms much of the posterior and ventral margins of the orbit, and contacts the lacrimal excluding the jugal from participation in the orbital rim (Camp, 1930). Therefore, all of the right postorbital appears to be present, whereas the anterior sub-orbital process is missing from the left postorbital. The dorsal surface is heavily ornamented and the anterior portion of the postorbito-squamosal bar is thickened transversely as is typical for pseudopalatine phytosaurs (Ballew, 1989). The medial expansion of the posterior process of the postorbital results in the narrowing of the dorsal expression of supratemporal fenestra (Fig. 3). Laterally, the postorbital forms the dorsal and anterodorsal margins of the lateral temporal fenestra (Figs. 5a, b).

The contact of the posterior process of the postorbital with the squamosal is unknown because no clear suture can be discerned on the dorsal surface. Camp (1930: fig. 2b) placed the suture between the posterior portion of the supratemporal fenestra and the posterior margin of the lateral temporal fenestra in his reconstruction of "*Machaeroprosopus*

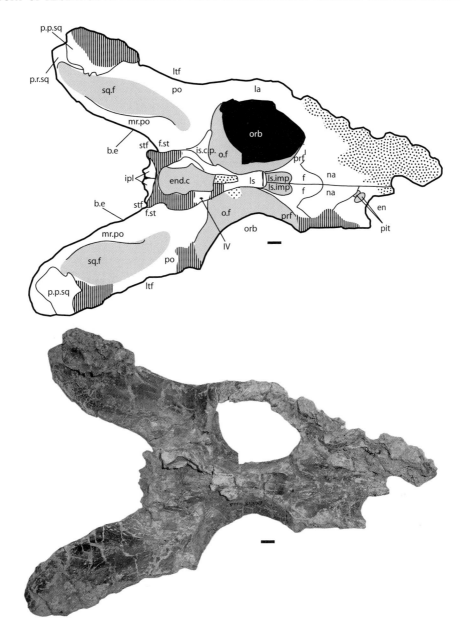

Figure 4. PEFO 31207, skull of *Pseudopalatus jablonskiae* n. sp. in ventral view with a portion of the braincase removed. b.e, beveled edge; en, external nares; end.c, endocranial cavity; f, frontal; f.st, supratemporal fossa; ipl, incipient parietal ledge; la, lacrimal; ls, laterosphenoid; ls.c.p., capitate process of laterosphenoid ; ls.imp, impression of the laterosphenoid; mr.po, medial ridge of the postorbital; na, nasals; o.f, orbital fossa; orb, orbit; p.p., parietal process of…; pa, parietal; po, postorbital; pr.sq, posterior squamosal ridge; prf, prefrontal; sq, squamosal; sq.f, squamosal fossa; stf, supratemporal fenestra. Scale bar = 1cm.

tenuis" (*Pseudopalatus pristinus* of subsequent authors), in agreement with the Mehl's (1928: fig. 1) reconstruction of the holotype of *P. pristinus*. This is also the case for *Mystriosuchus westphali* (Hungerbühler, 2002: fig. 2) and for *Leptosuchus zunii* (= *L. adamanensis*) (Camp, 1930: fig. 9; Long and Murry, 1995). From these reconstructions, it appears that the length of the posterior process of the postorbital is equal to the length of the supratemporal fenestra in dorsal view. Accordingly, phytosaurs with slit-like supratemporal fenestrae have shorter posterior postorbital processes that shorten the total length of the postorbital-squamosal processes.

Ventrally, just lateral to the supratemporal fenestra, there is a thickened, rugose, and ornamented medial ridge that extends anteriorly to form the lateral border of a shallow fossa that is a ventral expression of the supratemporal fenestra (Fig. 4). This ridge is also expressed in the lateral edge of the supratemporal fenestra as a beveled edge partially incised into the dorsal surface of what is presumably the posteromedial portion of the postorbital (Figs. 3, 4, 6). This beveling forms what is essentially a supratemporal fossa on the lateral margin of the supratemporal fenestra. We have not noted this characteristic beveled edge in any other phytosaur and consider it an autapomorphy of *P. jablonskiae*.

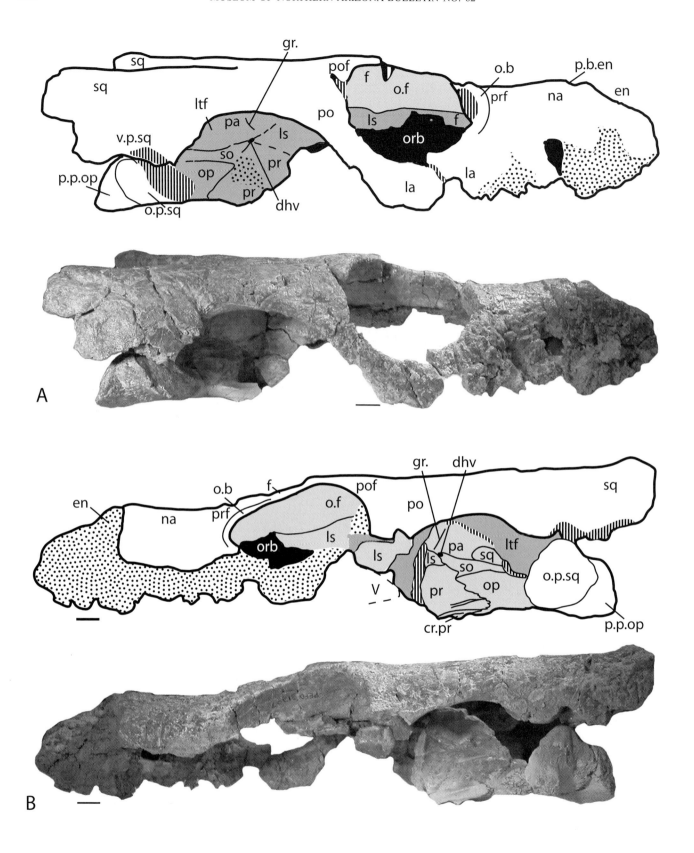

Figure 5. PEFO 31207, skull of *Pseudopalatus jablonskiae* n. sp. *A*. right lateral view and *B*. left lateral view. cr.pr, crista prootica; dhv, dorsal head vein; en, external nares; f, frontal; gr., groove; la, lacrimal; ls, laterosphenoid; ltf, lateral temporal fenestra; na, nasals; o.b, orbital bar; o.f, orbital fossa; o.p., ophisthotic process of…; op, opisthotic; orb, orbit; pa, parietal; p.b., posterior border of…; po, postorbital; pof, postfrontal; prf, prefrontal; pr, prootic; so, supraoccipital; sq, squamosal; v.p., ventral process of….; V, notch for passage of cranial nerve V. Scale bar = 1cm.

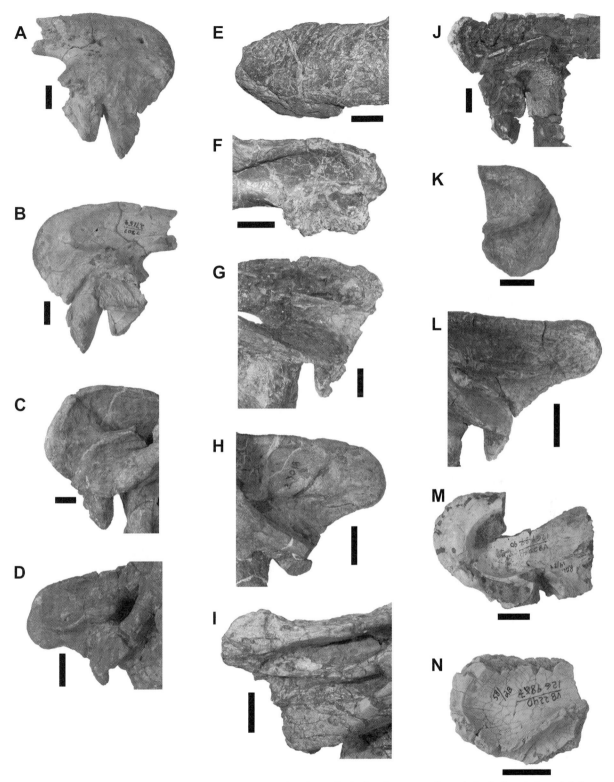

Figure 6. Comparison of squamosals from *Leptosuchus* and *Pseudopalatus* displaying the range of morphological variation. *A*. left squamosal of *Leptosuchus adamanensis* (UCMP 27159) in lateral view; *B*. left squamosal of *Leptosuchus adamanensis* (UCMP 27159) in medial view; *C*. left squamosal of the holotype of *Leptosuchus adamanensis* (UCMP 26699) in medial view; *D*. left squamosal of *Leptosuchus crosbiensis* (UCMP 27181) in medial view; *E*. right squamosal of *Pseudopalatus jablonskiae* n. sp. (PEFO 31207) in dorsal view; *F*. right squamosal of *Pseudopalatus jablonskiae* n. sp. (PEFO 31207) in ventral view; *G*. right squamosal of the holotype of *Pseudopalatus mccauleyi* (UCMP 126999) in ventral view; *H*. right squamosal of *Pseudopalatus pristinus* (holotype of "*Machaeroprosopus*" *tenuis*, UCMP 27018) in ventral view; *I*. left squamosal of *Pseudopalatus buceros* (UCMP 34250) in ventro-medial view; *J*. left squamosal of *Leptosuchus crosbiensis* (UCMP 27182) in medial view; *K*. right squamosal of *Leptosuchus* sp. (UCMP 126737) in medial view; *L*. right squamosal of *Pseudopalatus pristinus* (UCMP 137319) in ventral view; *M*. left squamosal of *Pseudopalatus* sp. (UCMP 126990) in ventral view; *N*. left squamosal of *Pseudopalatus* sp. (UCMP 126987) in ventral view. All scale bars = 2 cm.

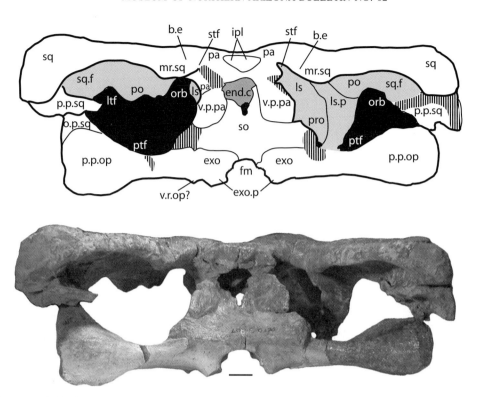

Figure 7. PEFO 31207, skull of *Pseudopalatus jablonskiae* n. sp. in posterior view. b.e, beveled edge; end.c, endocranial cavity; ex.p, exocipital pillar; exo, exoccipital; fm, foramen magnum; ipl, incipient parietal wings; ls, laterosphenoid; ls.c.p., capitate process of laterosphenoid ; m.r.sq, medial ridge of the squamosal; o.p., ophisthotic process of…; orb, orbit; p.p., parietal process of…; pa, parietal; po, postorbital; pr, prootic; ptf, post temporal fenestra; so, supraoccipital; sq, squamosal; sq.f, squamosal fossa; stf, supratemporal fenestra; v.p. ventral process of…; v.r., ventral ramus of… Scale bar = 1cm.

Parietals.—Both parietals are preserved. They have a sculptured dorsal surface, and are slightly depressed relative to the rest of the skull roof, allowing clear identification of their sutures. The supratemporal fenestrae are strongly incised into the posterolateral corner of the parietal, a character found in all pseudopalatines except *Redondasaurus* (Fig. 3; Hunt and Lucas, 1993). Two small posterior projections (incipient parietal ledge) occur along the symphysial surface and the posterior projections of the parietals 'roof' the supraoccipital like in other pseudopalatine phytosaurs (Fig. 4; Ballew, 1989).

Posteriorly, two wedge-shaped processes sharply downturn ventrally to laterally contact the external surface of the supraoccipital (Fig. 7). Internally, these processes form the dorsolateral wall of the braincase contacting the laterosphenoid anteroventrally and an anterior process of the supraoccipital ventrally (Figs. 5a, b). The contact between this process of the supraoccipital and the laterosphenoid prohibits contact between the parietal and the prootic and opisthotic. In *Mystriosuchus westphali*, these wedge-shaped processes are a separate ossification, which Hungerbühler (2002) called a 'supernumerary occipital' bone. Camp (1930) considered these processes to represent tabulars in *Leptosuchus gregorii*, but in *P. jablonskiae* no suture is visible and therefore these elements are most likely part of the parietal as in *Nicrosaurus kapffi* (McGregor, 1906), *Pseudopalatus pristinus* (Mehl, 1928; Ballew, 1989), and *Pseudopalatus mccauleyi* (Ballew, 1989).

Squamosals.—Both squamosals are present and almost complete except for the internal squamosal processes (portions of which are fused to the paroccipital processes of the opisthotics) and the parietal processes of the squamosal (the parieto-squamosal arcade of McGregor (1906) and earlier authors). The squamosals have an approximate length of 70 mm and are transversely broad with a flat medial dorsal surface and rounding laterally to form an almost vertical lateral surface roofing the lateral temporal fenestrae (Fig. 3). The squamosals lack a prominent lateral 'groove' or ridge found in many pseudopalatine squamosals (Figs. 6, 8; Murry and Long, 1989). The squamosal tips are rounded, not pointed as in *P. pristinus* and *P. buceros*, and do not possess the thickened "pinched" knob-like process that is always found in *P. pristinus* and *P. buceros* (Fig. 6; Ballew, 1989). Although the squamosals of *P. jablonskiae* show some similarities to *Leptosuchus*, the broad dorsal surface of the squamosal and the dorsoventrally shortened nature of the squamosal are different from any known specimens of *Leptosuchus*. The squamosals of *P. jablonskiae* are similar to those of *Redondasaurus gregorii* in lacking the knob-like posterior process and a lateral ridge; however, the postorbital/squamosal bar is much wider mediolaterally (52% length to width ratio of process in *R. gregorii* compared to 32% in *P. jablonskiae*) in *Redondasaurus* effectively hiding the supratemporal fenestra in dorsal view (Hunt and Lucas, 1993).

Ballew (1989) described the squamosals of *Pseudopalatus* (especially those of the *P. mccauleyi*) as being anteroposteriorly short in comparison to *Leptosuchus*. The squamosals of *P. jablonskiae* are proportionally even more shortened. The distance from the posterior rim of the external nares to the back of the parietals makes up 68% of the total postnarial length (external nares to the squamosal tips) in *P. jablonskiae* compared to 61% in UCMP 126999 (holotype of *P. mccauleyi*), and 62% in UCMP 34250 (referred to *P. buceros*) and UCMP 27018 (holotype of *M. tenuis*, referred to *P. pristinus*). A referred specimen of *Redondasaurus* (YPM 3300) has a ratio close to 65%. The higher percentages in these taxa is due to a shorter length of the squamosal.

The internal squamosal process is preserved and fused to the paroccipital processes of the opisthotics (Figs. 5b, 7). Ballew (1989) considered fusion of the opisthotic to the squamosal to be a synapomorphy of *P. buceros* and *P. mccauleyi*, exclusive of *P. pristinus*, although this character is often difficult to evaluate in articulated skulls.

BRAINCASE

Much of the dorsal and posterodorsal portions of the braincase are preserved, including much of the otic capsule. Only an isolated basipterygoid process was recovered from the ventral portion of the braincase. An isolated partial braincase of *Pseudopalatus* cf. *pristinus* (PEFO 34042) was used to help determine sutures within the endocranial cavity and in the lateral braincase wall. Because very few descriptions of pseudopalatine braincases exist, both specimens will be described here. When a description specifically refers to PEFO 34042, the specimen will be explicitly mentioned, otherwise all of the following description pertains solely to PEFO 31207 or to both specimens.

Parietal.—The ventral process of the parietal forms the dorsolateral wall of the braincase (Figs. 5b, 9). Both Camp (1930) and Hungerbühler (2002) considered this process to represent a separate ossification; a "tabular" bone in *Leptosuchus gregorii* and a supernumerary bone in *Mystriosuchus westphali*. In *M. westphali* there is a distinct suture that demonstrates that this process does indeed represent an element separate from the parietal. Such a suture is not clear in the holotype of *L. gregorii*. There is no evidence in PEFO 34042 or *P. jablonskiae* to suggest that they have this separate ossification. In *P. jablonskiae*, the posterior portion of the parietal process meets a process of the squamosal that invades the lateral braincase wall (Fig. 5b).

The dorsolateral surface of the ventral projection of the parietal in *P. jablonskiae* is marked by a distinct groove that originates just below the level of the skull roof and continues antero-ventrally to contact the suture with the laterosphenoid, anterior of the opening for the dorsal head vein

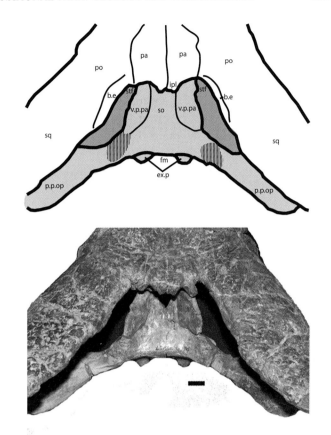

Figure 8. PEFO 31207, skull of *Pseudopalatus jablonskiae* n. sp. in posterodorsal view. b.e, beveled edge; ex.p, exoccipital pillar; fm, foramen magnum; ipl, incipient parietal ledge; p.p., parietal process of...; pa, parietal; po, postorbital; so, supraoccipital; sq, squamosal; stf, supratemporal fenestra; v.p. ventral process of...Scale bar = 1cm.

(Figs. 5a, b). The purpose of this groove is a mystery. It is not an artifact of preparation because the groove is present in the same position on both sides of the skull. It does not represent a suture and is most likely a path for a blood vessel. This structure is not present in PEFO 34042.

Squamosal.—A U-shaped medial process of the squamosal enters the lateral braincase wall dorsal to the anterior supraoccipital process, where it meets the posterior portion of the parietal process (Fig. 5b). As mentioned above, this process also occurs in *L. gregorii* (Camp, 1930) but not in PEFO 34042. Hungerbühler (2002) figures a "squamosal lamella" in the braincase of *M. westphali*; however, it divides the anterior portion of the opisthotic (exoccipital) and does not contact the supernumerary bone (ventral process of the parietal in other forms). The contribution of the squamosal in the lateral wall of the braincase may have systematic value. According to Hungerbühler (2002) this contribution occurs in *Pseudopalatus buceros* and *P. mccauleyi*, but not in *P. pristinus*. It also occurs in *Redondasaurus bermani* but is absent in *R. gregorii*. Thus, the lack of this medial extension of the squamosal in PEFO 34042 along with the presence of a knob-like squamosal suggests that this specimen is referable to *P. pristinus* even though it consists of only a few isolated elements.

Supraoccipital.—In posterodorsal view the supraoccipital is a triangular-shaped element that slopes posteroventrally roofing the foramen magnum (Fig. 8). Dorsally and dorsolaterally the supraoccipital meets the parietals (Fig. 7). There is no evidence for a separate supernumerary bone ("tabular") as described for *Mystriosuchus westphali* and *Leptosuchus gregorii* by Hungerbuhler (2002) and Camp (1930) respectively. Camp (1930) also restricted the supraoccipital to the region just dorsal to the foramen magnum and considered two separate elements, interparietals, to contact the parietals in *L. gregorii*. There is no evidence for these elements in *Pseudopalatus*. Ventrolaterally, the supraoccipital contacts the exoccipitals and forms the dorsal margin of the foramen magnum.

Dorsal and lateral to the ventrolateral corners of the supraoccipital, an anteromedially directed flange is sandwiched between the parietal and squamosal dorsally and the opisthotic and prootic ventrally (Figs. 5b, 9). At its anteriormost extent it meets the laterosphenoid just below the parietal. At this junction is a foramen that probably represents the exit for the vena capitis dorsalis (dorsal head vein). Hungerbühler (2002) identified a similar flange in *Mystriosuchus westphali* as an anterior projection of the squamosal; however, reference to PEFO 34042 demonstrates that in *Pseudopalatus* this flange is a continuation of the supraoccipital (Fig. 11). An autapomorphy of *Mystriosuchus* is a squamosal/prootic contact (Hungerbühler, 2002), a character state that is absent in *Pseudopalatus* and *Leptosuchus* (Camp, 1930).

Internally, the supraoccipital forms almost the entire roof and a portion of the lateral walls of the posterior endocranial cavity. At its anteriormost extent, just posteroventral to the suture with the laterosphenoid, a prominent foramen is present that represents the internal path of the dorsal head vein (Fig. 5b).

Exoccipitals.—The sutures between the exoccipitals and the opisthotics are indistinguishable as in most archosaurs. The exoccipitals form the lateral margins of the foramen magnum and are prevented from meeting dorsally by the supraoccipital (Fig. 7). The ventral portions are not preserved. The preserved dorsal portion, which borders the proximal end of the paroccipital process, is roughly trapezoidal-shaped in ventral view with the medial edge and posteromedial corner meeting the supraoccipital and forming a portion of the lateral wall of the posterior portion of the endocranial cavity just inside the foramen magnum (Figure 12). The anteriormost corner is dorsally excavated, forming the posterodorsal portion of the vestibule of the inner ear. Here, the exoccipital meets the prootic anteriorly and laterally (Fig. 12). In PEFO 31207 the anterior portion of the right vestibule is free of matrix and although the lateral wall is missing, some internal details can be made out. The medial wall is damaged but appears to have not been closed. A similar condition is present

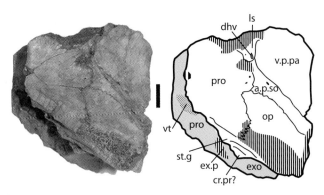

Figure *9*. PEFO 34042, partial braincase of *Pseudopalatus* cf. *pristinus* in left lateral view. a.p. anterior process of…; cr.pr, crista prootica; dhv, dorsal head vein; ex.p, exoccipital pillar; exo, exoccipital; ls, laterosphenoid; op, opisthotic; pa, parietal; pr, prootic; so, supraoccipital; st.g, stapedial groove; v.p. ventral process of…; vt, vestibule of the inner ear. Scale bar = 1 cm.

in PEFO 34042 (Fig. 12). This lack of closure results in an opening at the junction between the prootic, supraoccipital and the exoccipital in the dorsomedial corner of the vestibule (Figs. 11, 12). This resulting foramen would most likely represent the opening for the endolymphatic sac (Camp, 1930). Just dorsal to this foramen is a second opening in the roof of the vestibule, which Camp (1930) labeled as a superior sinus. The posterodorsal corner of the vestibule (part of the exoccipitals) is marked by a pronounced foramen that Camp (1930) identified as the entrance of the posterior semicircular canal (Figs. 11, 12).

Only the dorsal-most portions of the exoccipital pillars are preserved. Just anterior to these within the foramen magnum are two prominent fenestrae that may represent a path for the hypoglosseal nerve (XII) (Figs. 11, 12). Alternatively, it could represent the interior expression of the metotic foramen and the opening for cranial nerves IX, X, and XI. Unfortunately, the ventral portion of the exoccipitals is missing, obfuscating other possible locations for these structures. A perusal of the available literature on pseudosuchian braincases turned up no other taxa with foramina in this position, yet they are present in both *P. jablonskiae* and PEFO 34042.

Because the ventral portion of the exoccipitals is not preserved in both specimens, determination of the morphology and locations of the metotic fissures, the fenestra ovalis is difficult, and a determination of the make-up of the floor of the endocranial canal is not possible. Anterolateral to the exoccipital pillar, the stapedial groove is present. This groove extends posterolaterally from the vestibular wall back to an area approximately halfway along the paroccipital process (Fig. 11). The groove is demarcated by two elongate ridges that are parallel to the orientation of the paroccipital process. The anterior ridge is situated along the suture between the exoccipitals and the prootic. Posterior to the stapedial

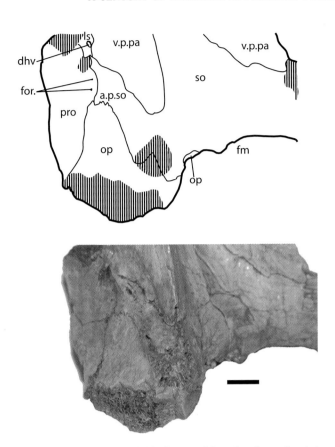

Figure *10*. PEFO 34042, partial braincase of *Pseudopalatus* cf. *pristinus* in left posterolateral view. a.p. anterior process of...; dhv, dorsal head vein; fm, foramen magnum; for., foramina; ls, laterosphenoid; op, opisthotic; pa, parietal; pr, prootic; so, supraoccipital; v.p. ventral process of.... Scale bar = 1cm.

groove is another parallel trough that is directed sharply medially at its distal end where it occurs between the posterior corner of the vestibule and the anterior margin of the exoccipital pillar. This groove intersects the foramen mentioned above that is just within the foramen magnum and likely represents the dorsal-most expression of the metotic fissure (i.e., the jugular groove).

Opisthotics.—In ventral view, the suture between the opisthotic and the supraoccipital is indistinguishable. The opisthotic has an anteriorly directed, triangular shaped process that is bounded by the prootic ventrally and the anterior process of the supraoccipital dorsally (Fig. 5b, 9). The ventral ramus of the opisthotic is not preserved. The majority of the opisthotic consists of the paroccipital process which is directed posterolaterally. The process is "twisted" posteroventrally, thinning medially before expanding into a broad head that articulates with the squamosal anteriorly and laterally (Figs. 7, 11). Ballew (1989) described this morphology as "oar-shaped". The opisthotic process forms the entire ventral margin of the supratemporal fenestra.

The internal process of the squamosal is still firmly fused to the anterolateral face of the distal end of the paroccipital process. In phytosaurs, Ballew (1989) considered this

fusion to be a synapomorphy of *Pseudopalatus mccauleyi* and *P. buceros*. *P. jablonskiae* shares with *P. mccauleyi* this fusion of the paroccipital process with the squamosal, an oar-shaped paroccipital process, and a squamosal tip that is not knob-like (Ballew, 1989). These similarities led Parker and Irmis (2004) to originally refer PEFO 31207 to *P. mccauleyi*.

Epiotics.—In most reptiles the epiotic fuses indistinguishably with the supraoccipital (Currie, 1997). In PEFO 34042 and *P. jablonskiae*, an anterior process of the supraoccipital that is present in the lateral wall of the braincase may represent the epiotic (Figs. 5, 9; Hungerbühler, 2002); however, because there is no clear suture between this process and the main body of the supraoccipital (Fig. 10) we consider it to be an anterior process of the supraoccipital.

Hungerbühler (2002) described a ventrally open, crescent-shaped crest that forms the posterodorsal border of the epiotic in *Mystriosuchus westphali*. Ventral to this crest is the foramen for the vena capitis dorsalis. Whereas this crest and associated foramen is clearly visible in PEFO 34042, in *P. jablonskiae* the vena capitis dorsalis is ventral to a slightly developed ridge that is straight rather than crescentic. In both PEFO 34042 and *P. jablonskiae* this ridge is part of the posterior margin of the wedge-shaped process of the parietal (the supernumerary bone in *M. westphali*) (Figs. 5a, 9). Unfortunately, the area anterior to the vena capitis dorsalis is not well-preserved in either of the PEFO specimens; however, what is preserved appears to represent the posterior portion of the laterosphenoid (Fig. 9). Camp (1930) described this foramen for *Leptosuchus gregorii* piercing the anterodorsolateral surface of the anterior portion of the supraoccipital (= epiotic of other authors) where it meets the "tabular" bone; however, in both of the Petrified Forest specimens there is a clear suture separating the anterior supraoccipital process from the foramen (Figs. 5a, 9).

Prootics.—PEFO 31207 preserves much of both prootics. The anterior portions are damaged and incomplete in places, whereas the posterior portions are preserved in both specimens. A posteriorly tapering process overlaps the anteroventral surface of the opisthotic at the base of the paroccipital process (Fig. 12). Behind this, the prootic forms much of the lateral wall of the braincase (Figs. 5b, 9). The lateral sutures with the opisthotic and anterior portion of the supraoccipital are clear. This suture starts ventral to the opisthotic, just dorsal to the tympanic fossa of the paroccipital process, and continues posterodorsally to an area just ventral to the vena capitis dorsalis. The prootic is separated from the parietal by the union of the anterior supraoccipital process with the laterosphenoid. Ventrally, the prootic includes the medial extent of the stapedial fossa at the base of the paroccipital process, with a straight suture parallel to the paroccipital process that meets the exoccipital posteriorly (Fig. 12). Medially, the prootic forms a

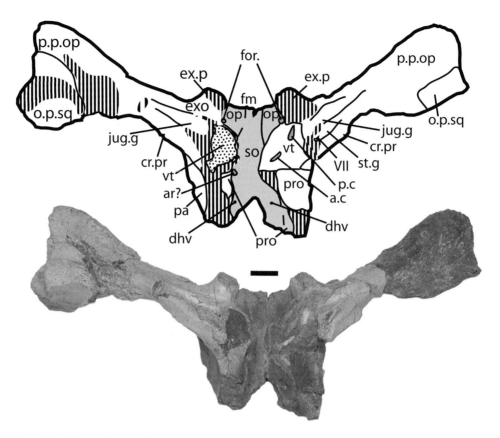

Figure *11*. PEFO 31207, partial braincase of *Pseudopalatus jablonskiae* n. sp. in ventral view. ar, auricular recess; cr.pr, crista prootica; dhv, dorsal head vein; e.s., endolymphatic sac; ex.p, exoccipital pillar; exo, exoccipital; fm, foramen magnum; for., foramina; jug.g., jugular groove; ls, laterosphenoid; o.p., ophisthotic process of…; op, opisthotic; p.c, posterior canal; p.p., parietal process of…; pa, parietal; pr, prootic; s.sin, superior sinus; so, supraoccipital; sq, squamosal, st.g, stapedial groove; vt, vestibule of the inner ear. Scale bar = 1cm.

longitudinal suture with the supraoccipital; the dorsalmost extent of this suture is unclear due to missing bone.

Posteroventrally, the prootic forms the anterolateral and anteromedial margins of the vestibule of the inner ear. Lateral to the anterolateral margin of the vestibule, the prootic forms the anterior portion of the base of the paroccipital process (Fig. 12). Two grooves are present that are parallel with the paroccipital process and are separated by a sharp ridge that although broken proximally appears to have curved to project ventromedially. The posteriormost groove is part of the stapedial groove which meets the vestibule wall laterally. The anteriormost groove ends in a small foramen that probably represents an opening for the facial nerve (VII) (Fig. 11; Camp, 1930). Anterolateral to this is another sharp ridge with an anterolaterally facing crest (Figure 12). This crest originates a short distance from the posteriormost extent of the prootic tongue that overlaps the opisthotic, and progresses anteromedially where it then curves anteriorly before flattening on the lateral prootic wall just dorsal to the point where the prootic divides into dorsal and ventral rami (the prootic foramen or trigeminal notch) (Hungerbühler, 2002). This ridge most likely represents the crista prootica; however, none of the existing phytosaur braincase descriptions (e.g., Camp, 1930; Chatterjee, 1978; or Hungerbühler, 2002) have labeled this struc-

ture or noted the presence of the crista prootica.

The interior surface of the prootic just anterior to the vestibule and along the supraoccipital/prootic suture is a pronounced foramen (Fig. 11). Chatterjee (1978) labeled an opening in a similar position in *Parasuchus* as the endolymphatic sac; however Gower and Nesbitt (in press) considered this opening in the archosaur *Arizonasaurus babbitti* to represent an opening for the auricular recess.

The anterior portions of the prootics are incompletely preserved and damaged in PEFO 31207. Hungerbühler (2002) described a thin, sinuous slit that divided the anterior portion of the braincase into dorsal and ventral portions. In *Mystriosuchus westphali* the slit originates in the prootic, effectively dividing that bone as well. This is similar to the condition found in *Parasuchus* (Chatterjee, 1978) and *Leptosuchus* (Camp, 1930). The posterior portion of this slit is the opening for the trigeminal nerve (V); however, this area can only be inferred for *P. jablonskiae* as it is missing, although the prootics are divided into dorsal and ventral rami suggesting that this slit was present (Fig. 5b). Only the proximal portion of the ventral margin of the dorsal branch is preserved on the right side, whereas on the left side a more medial portion is preserved that is probably part of the laterosphenoid and will be described as part of that bone. Thus, the anterior extent of the prootic

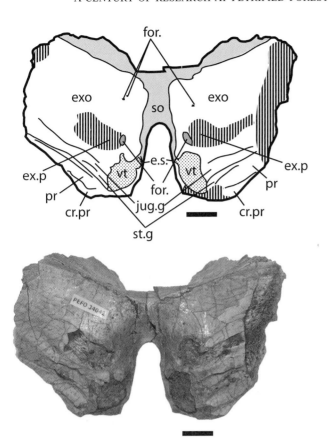

Figure *12*. PEFO 34042, partial braincase of *Pseudopalatus* cf. *pristinus* in ventral view. cr.pr, crista prootica; e.s., endolymphatic sac; ex.p, exoccipital pillar; exo, exoccipital; for., foramen; ls, laterosphenoid; p.c, posterior canal; p.p., parietal process of...; pa, parietal; pr, prootic; s.sin, superior sinus; so, supraoccipital; sq, squamosal, st.g, stapedial groove; typ.g, tympanic groove; vt, vestibule of the inner ear. Scale bar = 1cm.

cannot clearly be determined, but it most likely did not extend much farther anteriorly than the base of the paroccipital process.

Laterosphenoids.—The posterior portion of the laterosphenoid is triangular in shape and points posteriorly, meeting the prootic ventrally, the parietal dorsally and the anterior process of the supraoccipital posteriorly (Figs. 5a, 9). The anteriormost portions are badly damaged, with much of the prootic/laterospenoid suture missing and the laterosphenoid/parietal suture being indeterminable along much of its length. The walls are thin and deep in the otic region, shallowing anteriorly in the sphenoid region where the laterosphenoids meet medially to form a pronounced hour-glass-shaped ridge between the orbits (Fig. 4). A vertically oriented thickened bar (the capitate process of the laterosphenoid) is formed along the lateral wall of the laterosphenoid from the dorsal margin of the trigeminal notch to a portion of the skull roof where the postorbital is located (Fig. 4). On the left side of the braincase where this process meets the forward portion of the trigeminal notch is a small foramen that according to Chatterjee (1978) is the opening for the trochlear nerve (IV) (Fig. 4).

A portion of the interorbital septum is present; it is unclear whether this represents a separate orbitosphenoid bone as in *Mystriosuchus westphali* or just an anterior projection of the laterosphenoid as in *Leptosuchus gregorii*. The anteriormost portion of this bone (medial to the anterior margins of the orbits) is missing; a shallow depression in the skull roof shows that the bone extended to the anterior border of the orbits, was lobate, and transversely expanded (Fig. 4).

Basisphenoid.—As mentioned previously, the ventral portion of the occiput and the entire sphenoid region are missing with the exception of a single right basal tuber of the basisphenoid/basioccipital complex that was collected as float. The process is short, blunt and roughly horn-shaped, being slightly recurved posteriorly. It is indistinguishable from the basal tubera of other phytosaurs.

PHYLOGENETIC ANALYSIS

The phylogenetic relationships of PEFO 31207 were determined using Hungerbühler's (2002) matrix, adding *Pseudopalatus jablonskiae* as an OTU (Appendix 1), and rescoring character 5 (state 2) for *Pseudopalatus buceros*, and characters 32 (state 1) and 42 (state 0) for *Pseudopalatus mccauleyi* after re-examining material from the UCMP collections. The matrix was analyzed using PAUP* version 4.0b10 for Windows. All characters were equally weighted and treated as unordered. A heuristic search resulted in a single most parsimonious tree (Fig. 13) with a length of 108, a consistency index (CI) of .6667, a retention index (RI) of .7000, and a rescaled consistency index (RC) of .4667. Bootstrap values for 1000 replicates were determined for nodes (Fig. 13).

The recovered tree is almost identical to the one figured by Hungerbühler (2002) with five fewer steps. *Pseudopalatus jablonskiae* is the basal sister taxon to the other three species of *Pseudopalatus*. It is important to note that Hungerbühler (2002) did not include *Angistorhinus* or *Leptosuchus* in his analysis. Their inclusion is beyond the scope of this study; based on the analysis presented by Ballew (1989), these taxa would most likely fall out as successive sister taxa to Pseudopalatinae. Although the bootstrap value for the clade containing *P. jablonskiae* plus the other species of *Pseudopalatus* is low (34%), this is most likely a result of missing data in *P. jablonskiae* because the placement of this taxon in *Pseudopalatus* is supported by several synapomorphies (see diagnosis).

DISCUSSION

Although the holotype and only known specimen of *Pseudopalatus jablonskiae* is incomplete, the unique suite of preserved character-states provides a strong case for establishing a new taxon. These include: a squamosal posterior terminus that is not mediolaterally 'pinched' and knob-like (Ballew, 1989); the lack of a lateral ridge of the squamosal; a

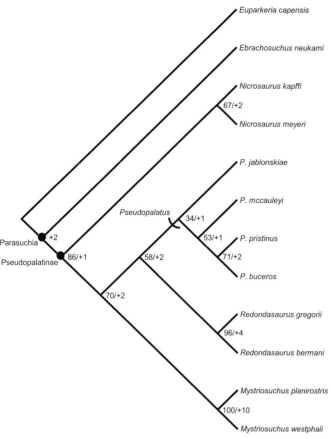

Figure *13*. Single most parsimonious tree showing phylogenetic relationships of *Pseudopalatus jablonskiae*.

post-temporal arcade that is ventrally depressed; supratemporal fenestra that are slit-like but still exposed in dorsal view; a mediolaterally broad postorbito-squamosal bar; a heavily sculptured skull roof; anteroposteriorly foreshortened postorbito-squamosal processes; and the contribution of a medial process of the squamosal to the lateral braincase wall, sandwiched between the anterior projection of the supraoccipital and the ventral flange of the parietal. In addition, the presence of a beveled medial margin of the postorbital forming a distinct supratemporal fossa lateral to the supratemporal fenestra has not been described for any other phytosaur and is an autapomorphy of *P. jablonskiae*. The combination of character-states not only differentiates *P. jablonskiae* from phytosaur taxa such as *"Paleorhinus"*, *Parasuchus*, *Angistorhinus* (= *Rutiodon*), and *Leptosuchus*, they also distinguish this taxon from all other pseudopalatine phytosaurs.

The morphology of the posterior process of the squamosal has been repeatedly utilized in studies by phytosaur systematists and biostratigraphers. This is at least in part because the squamosal is one of the most robust cranial elements that preserves well and is easily identifiable; therefore it is a commonly collected isolated cranial element. Camp (1930) was the first to propose that characteristics of the squamosal are taxonomically relevant for phytosaurs, using them to partially diagnose his proposed new species of

"Machaeroprosopus." Camp argued that a clear progression of change could be seen in phytosaurs from stratigraphically older to stratigraphically younger forms. Unfortunately, because of this hypothesis, Camp (1930) assigned much of his material to taxa based on stratigraphic position rather than possession of discrete character-states. Gregory (1962) also noted variation in squamosal morphology between phytosaur taxa; however, he placed more emphasis on rostral morphology for distinguishing genera, downplaying characters of the squamosal and temporal regions. Long and Ballew (1985) divided the phytosaurs of the Chinle Formation into those with 'primitive' (*"Rutiodon* Group A") and 'advanced' (*"Rutiodon* Group B") temporal regions. Phytosaurs with depressed post-temporal arcades and reduced supratemporal fenestra were considered more derived than those with depressed arcades but with supratemporal fenestrae still fully open dorsally. Ballew (1989) was the first worker to emphasize the usefulness of explicit squamosal characters (e.g., presence of a knob-like squamosal; squamosals vertical) in differentiating taxa, especially in a cladistic framework. She recognized that most of the specimens grouped in *"Rutiodon* Group B" actually belonged to a separate genus, *Pseudopalatus*. Long and Ballew (1985) and Ballew (1989), followed by Long and Murry (1995), demonstrated that isolated squamosals had taxonomic utility. Nevertheless, there has been little published on the potential variation within and among taxa.

To understand the variation in squamosal morphology and their utility in phytosaur taxonomy, we examined collections of North American phytosaur squamosals, both those associated with skulls and isolated specimens. We focus on specimens of *Leptosuchus* and *Pseudopalatus*, because they represent the vast majority of phytosaur specimens from Arizona, and isolated squamosals assigned to these two taxa are commonly used for biostratigraphic correlation in the Upper Triassic strata of the American southwest. Squamosals of *Parasuchus* (=*"Paleorhinus"*) would be difficult to confuse with those of *Pseudopalatus* because they enclose completely dorsally exposed supratemporal fenestrae, and have not been found in the Chinle Formation to date.

In both *Leptosuchus* and *Pseudopalatus*, the posterior process of the squamosal extends past the posterior margin of the braincase and quadrate. It is dorso-ventrally expanded, with a triangular process that extends ventrally and articulates with the paroccipital process of the opisthotic (Fig. 6). A thin ridge originates medially on the posterior-most portion of the squamosal, and enlarges antero-medially to become the parietal process of the squamosal (Figs. 6b-d). This process forms the dorsal margin of the posttemporal fenestra and the postero-ventral margin of the supratemporal fenestra. Just above this ridge on the ventro-medial face of the squamosal is a well developed fossa that borders the supratemporal fenestra (Figs. 6b-d) and probably accommodated the jaw musculature that originates from this area. Both the ridge and fossa vary widely among specimens of phytosaur squamosals. In particular, the posterior extent of these two features is subject to extensive variation in the sample of specimens examined, and does not appear to have any taxonomic utility. For example, in some specimens of *Pseudopalatus*, the ridge and/or the fossa extend to the posterior tip of the squamosal (Fig. 6n), whereas in other specimens they stop well short of the posterior extremities (Fig. 6h, l-m).

The posterior squamosals of *Leptosuchus* species are expanded dorsoventrally to form a broad plate-like process (Figs. 6a-b). Mediolaterally, they are not very thick relative to their height. In all specimens examined, the posterior margin is broadly rounded. In the species *L. adamanensis* and *L. gregorii*, this margin is nearly semicircular and does not extend much beyond the posterior edge of the opisthotic process, whereas it is more angular and extends significantly beyond the opisthotic process in *L. crosbiensis* (Figs. 6d, j), although these characters can vary somewhat with size. In contrast, the dorsal portion of all *Pseudopalatus* squamosals is mediolaterally expanded to form a shelf level with the parietal and postorbital (Fig 6e). This dorsal portion of the squamosal is often moderately to heavily sculptured (Fig 6e). In all *Pseudopalatus* species except *P. jablonskiae* (i.e., *P. pristinus*, *P. buceros*, and *P. mccauleyi*), the medio-lateral expansion of the dorsal portion of the squamosal results in the development of a strong ridge along the dorso-lateral margin of the squamosal, with a corresponding shallow trough ventrally adjacent to it. In *Pseudopalatus pristinus* and *P. buceros*, the dorsal portion of the squamosal extends well beyond the posterior margin of the opisthotic process and is extremely thickened (Fig 6h ,i ,l), resulting in a morphology that Ballew (1989) described as "knob-like". This contrasts with the condition in *P. jablonskiae* (Figs. 4, 6e) and *P. mccauleyi* (Fig. 6g), where the squamosal tips only extend slightly beyond the opisthotic process.

Our examination of phytosaur squamosal morphology reaffirms the utility of the squamosal for taxonomic discrimination. Although some characters display significant individual variation (e.g., posterior extent of the ridge and fossa on the medial squamosal), most characters previously used to differentiate *Leptosuchus* and *Pseudopalatus* squamosals are still valuable in phytosaur systematics. This suggests that when more complete specimens are also known and taxon ranges are well-refined, isolated phytosaur squamosals are useful as biostratigraphic markers, at least at a local to regional level.

CONCLUSIONS

Although the specimen is incomplete, a new partial phytosaur skull (PEFO 31207) from the Sonsela Member of the Upper Triassic Chinle Formation of Petrified Forest National Park, Arizona clearly represents a new taxon, *Pseudopalatus jablonskiae*. This new species is diagnosed by the autapomorphy of a beveled medial edge on the postorbito-squamosal bar as well as a suite of other character-states not observed in phytosaurs. The braincase of *P. jablonskiae* is well preserved; clarifying and augmenting our understanding of pseudopalatine braincase morphology. Including *P. jablonskiae* in a phylogenetic analysis of pseudopalatine phytosaurs recovers it as the basal-most species of *Pseudopalatus*. To clarify future systematic studies, we provide phylogenetic definitions for the clades Pseudopalatinae and *Pseudopalatus*.

This new species of *Pseudopalatus* is not only important because it increases the diversity of known phytosaur taxa from the Chinle Formation. The holotype and only known specimen of *P. jablonskiae* is equally important because it is the stratigraphically lowest occurrence of *Pseudopalatus* within Petrified Forest National Park. The First Appearance Datum of *Pseudopalatus* defines the beginning of the Revueltian land-vertebrate faunachron (Lucas, 1998) and this specimen provides strong evidence for the overlap of the end of the Adamanian lvf and the beginning of the Revueltian lvf in Petrified Forest National Park (Parker and Irmis, 2005). This suggests that at least a portion of the Sonsela Member in Petrified Forest National Park preserves a transitional fauna between the two biostratigraphic units (Woody and Parker, 2004).

ACKNOWLEDGMENTS

Special thanks to Pat Jablonsky who discovered this specimen and helped with the initial excavation. Doug Cunningham (TTUP) and Pete Reser (PEFO) helped prepare the specimen. Scott Williams (PEFO) provided access to curated material and photographed some of the specimens. Patricia Holroyd (UCMP) provided access to collections in her care. Discussions with Axel Hungerbühler helped us realize the uniqueness of this specimen. Thanks to Dave Gower and Sterling Nesbitt for providing their in press manuscript on the braincase of *Arizonasaurus*. Reviews by David Smith and Axel Hungerbühler improved the manuscript. This is PEFO paleontological contribution no. 15 and UCMP contribution no. 1913.

REFERENCES

Akers J. P., Cooley, M. E., and C. A. Repenning 1958. Moenkopi and Chinle Formations of Black Mesa and adjacent areas. New Mexico Geological Society Guidebook, 9:88-94.

Ballew, K. L. 1989. A phylogenetic analysis of Phytosauria (Reptilia: Archosauria) from the late Triassic of the western United States, p. 309-339. *In* S. G. Lucas and A. P. Hunt (eds.), Dawn of the age of dinosaurs in the American Southwest. New Mexico Museum of Natural History, Albuquerque.

Billingsley, G. H. 1985. General stratigraphy of the Petrified Forest National Park, Arizona. Museum of Northern Arizona Bulletin, 54:3-8.

Buffetaut, E., and R. Ingavat. 1982. Phytosaur remains (Reptilia, Thecodontia) from the Upper Triassic of northeastern Thailand. Geobios, 15:7-17.

Buffetaut, E., Martin, M., and O. Monod. 1988. Phytosaur remains from the Cenger Formation of the Lycian Taurus (Western Turkey); stratigraphical implications. Geobios, 21:237-243.

Burmeister, K. C. 2000. Paleogeographic and biostratigraphic implications of new early Mesozoic terrestrial vertebrate fossils from the Poamay site; central Morondava Basin, Madagascar. Unpublished Masters thesis, University of California, Santa Barbara, 109 p.

Camp, C. L. 1930. A study of the phytosaurs with description of new material from western North America. Memoirs of the University of California, 10:1-174.

Chatterjee, S. 1978. A primitive parasuchid (phytosaur) reptile from the Upper Triassic Maleri Formation of India. Palaeontology, 21:83-127.

Colbert, E. H. 1947. Studies of the phytosaurs *Machaeroprosopus* and *Rutiodon.* American Museum of Natural History Bulletin, 88:53-96.

Cope, E. D. 1869-71. Synopsis of the extinct Batrachia, Reptilia, and Aves of North America. Transactions of the American Philosophical Society, New Series, 14:1-252.

Cope, E. D. 1881. *Belodon* in New Mexico. American Naturalist, 15:922-923.

Currie, P. J. 1997. Braincase anatomy, pp. 81-85. *In* Currie, P. J., and K. Padian (eds.), The Encyclopedia of Dinosaurs, Academic Press, San Diego.

Deacon M. W., 1990. Depositional analysis of the Sonsela Sandstone Bed, Chinle Formation, northeast Arizona and northwest New Mexico. Unpublished M. S. thesis, Northern Arizona University, Flagstaff, 127p.

De Queiroz, K., and J. Gauthier. 1992. Phylogenetic taxonomy. Annual Review of Ecology and Systematics, 23:449-480.

Doyle, K. D., and H. -D. Sues. 1995. Phytosaurs (Reptilia: Archosauria) from the Upper Triassic New Oxford Formation of York County, Pennsylvania. Journal of Vertebrate Paleontology, 15:545-543.

Gauthier, J. A. 1986. Saurischian monophyly and the origin of birds. Memoirs, California Academy of Sciences, 8:1-55.

Gower, D. J., and S. J. Nesbitt. In press. The braincase of *Arizonasaurus babbitti* – further evidence for the non-monophyly of Rauisuchia. Journal of Vertebrate Paleontology.

Gregory, J. T. 1962. The genera of phytosaurs. American Journal of Science, 260:652-690.

Gregory, J. T. 1969. Evolution und interkontinentale Beziehungen der Phytosauria (Reptilia). Paläontologische Zeitschrift, 43:37-51.

Heckert, A.B., and S.G. Lucas 2002. Revised Upper Triassic stratigraphy of the Petrified Forest National Park. New Mexico Museum of Natural History and Science Bulletin, 21:1-36.

Hungerbühler, A. 2002. The Late Triassic phytosaur *Mystriosuchus westphali*, with a revision of the genus. Palaeontology, 45:377-418.

Hunt, A. P., and S. G. Lucas. 1993. A new phytosaur (Reptilia: Archosauria) genus from the uppermost Triassic of the western United States and its biochronological significance. New Mexico Museum of Natural History and Science Bulletin, 3:193-196.

Huxley, T. H. 1875. On *Stagonolepis robertsoni*, and on the evolution of the Crocodilia. Quarterly Journal of the Geological Society of London, 31:423-438.

Irmis, R. B. 2005. The vertebrate fauna of the Upper Triassic Chinle Formation in northern Arizona, p. 63-88. *In* S. J. Nesbitt, W.G.

Parker, and R. B. Irmis (eds.), Guidebook to the Triassic formations of the Colorado Plateau in northern Arizona: Geology, Paleontology, and History. Mesa Southwest Museum Bulletin 9.

Jaeger, G. F. 1828. Über die fossilen Reptilien, welche in Würtemberg aufgefunden worden sind. Metzler, Stuttgart, 48 pp., 6 pls.

Lawler, D. A. 1979. Osteological variation in the phytosaur *Rutiodon tenuis* from Ghost Ranch, New Mexico. Unpublished M. A. thesis, University of California, Berkeley. 140 p.

Long, R. A., and K. L. Ballew. 1985. Aetosaur dermal armor from the Late Triassic of southwestern North America, with special reference to material from the Chinle Formation of Petrified Forest National Park. Museum of Northern Arizona Bulletin, 54:45-68.

Long, R. A., and Murry, P. A. 1995. Late Triassic (Carnian and Norian) tetrapods from the southwestern United States. New Mexico Museum of Natural History and Science Bulletin, 4:1-254.

Lucas, S. G. 1998. Global Triassic tetrapod biostratigraphy and biochronology. Palaeogeography, Palaeoclimatology, Palaeoecology, 143:347-384.

Kischlat, E.-E., and S. G. Lucas. 2003. A phytosaur from the Upper Triassic of Brazil. Journal of Vertebrate Paleontology, 23:464-467.

McGregor, J. H. 1906. The Phytosauria, with especial reference to *Mystriosuchus* and *Rhytidodon*. Memoirs of the American Museum of Natural History, 9:27-100.

Mehl, M. G., 1928. *Pseudopalatus pristinus*, a new genus and species of phytosaurs from Arizona. University of Missouri Studies, 3:1-22.

Meyer, H. von. 1860. Briefliche Mittheilung an Prof. Bronn. Neues Jahrbuch für Mineralogie, Geognosie, Geologie und Petrefakten-Kunde, 1860:556-560.

Meyer, H. von. 1863. Der Schädel des *Belodon* aus dem Stubensandstein des oberen Keupers. Palaeontographica, 10:227-246, pls 38-42.

Murry, P. A., and R. A. Long. 1989. Geology and paleontology of the Chinle Formation, Petrified Forest National Park and vicinity, Arizona and a discussion of vertebrate fossils of the southwestern Upper Triassic; pp. 29-64. *In* S. G. Lucas and A. P. Hunt (eds.), Dawn of the age of dinosaurs in the American Southwest. New Mexico Museum of Natural History, Albuquerque.

Parker, W. G., and R. B. Irmis. 2004. A revision of the phytosaur species *Pseudopalatus mccauleyi* (Archosauria: Pseudosuchia), based on two new specimens from Petrified Forest National Park, AZ. Journal of Vertebrate Paleontology, 24(3 Supplement):100A.

Parker, W. G., and R. B. Irmis. 2005. Advances in vertebrate paleontology based on new material from Petrified Forest National Park, Arizona. New Mexico Museum of Natural History and Science Bulletin, 29:45-58.

Sereno, P. C. 1991. Basal archosaurs:phylogenetic relationships and functional implications. Society of Vertebrate Paleontology Memoir, 2:1-53.

Stewart, J. H., Poole, F. G., and R. F. Wilson. 1972. Stratigraphy and origin of the Chinle Formation and related Upper Triassic strata in the Colorado Plateau region: U.S. Geological Survey Professional Paper 690, 336 p.

Woody, D. T. 2003. Revised geological assessment of the Sonsela Member, Chinle Formation, Petrified Forest National Park, Arizona. Unpublished M. S. thesis, Northern Arizona University, Flagstaff.

Woody, D. T., and W. G. Parker. 2004. Evidence for a transitional fauna within the Sonsela Member of the Chinle Formation, Petrified Forest National Park, Arizona. Journal of Vertebrate Paleontology 24 (3 Supplement):132A.

Zeigler, K. E., Lucas, S. G., and A. B. Heckert. 2002. The Late Triassic Canjilon quarry (Upper Chinle Group, New Mexico) phytosaur skulls: evidence of sexual dimorphism in phytosaurs.

New Mexico Museum of Natural History and Science Bulletin, 21:179-188.

Zeigler, K. E., Lucas, S. G., and A. B. Heckert. 2003. Variation in the Late Triassic Canjilon quarry (Upper Chinle Group, New Mexico) phytosaur skulls: evidence of sexual dimorphism. Paläontologische Zeitschrift, 77:341-351.

Zittel, K. A. 1887-90. Handbuch der Palaeontologie. 1. Abteilung: Palaeozoologie, 3. – XII+900 S., 719 Abb.; München & Leipzig.

APPENDIX 1-Character codings for *Pseudopalatus jablonskiae* using the matrix of Hungerbühler (2002).

P. jablonskiae: ?????   ???0?   ???10   ?1?30   20211
20021   100?1   1??1?   ?????   ??

SHORT PAPERS

Note: These papers have not undergone peer-review.

Parker, W. G., Ash, S. R., and Irmis, R. B., eds., 2006.
A Century of Research at Petrified Forest National Park: Geology and Paleontology.
Museum of Northern Arizona Bulletin No. 62.

XYLOTOMIC EVIDENCE FOR TWO NEW CONIFERS AND A GINKGO WITHIN THE LATE TRIASSIC CHINLE FORMATION OF PETRIFIED FOREST NATIONAL PARK, ARIZONA, USA

RODNEY A. SAVIDGE

Forestry and Environmental Management, University of New Brunswick, Fredericton, NB, CANADA E3B 6C2 <savi@unb.ca>

INTRODUCTION

THE NATURE and extent of woody plant paleobiodiversity existing in the Late Triassic in the vicinity of Petrified Forest National Park (PEFO) can be discovered through comprehensive wood anatomical investigations of the petrified logs in the area. Species assignment on the basis of xylotomic features has uncertainty due to variable cellular phenotypes being expressed in response to changing environmental factors; however, some features of woody elements are genetically determined and thus serve for differentiating among species (Savidge, 2001).

Two of the fossils described here were found within the bounds of PEFO, in the Sonsela Member of the Chinle Formation. The third, from a mudstone facies of the Shinarump Member, Chinle Formation, was uncovered during an excavation not far from the PEFO boundary, near Holbrook, Arizona. Ground thin sections (30 μm) of each stem were prepared and examined by light microscopy. By comparing the observations below with Table 2 in Savidge and Ash (this volume), it emerged that all three trees were different from known species in PEFO, also from one another.

SYSTEMATIC PALEONTOLOGY

Family CHEIROLEPIDIACEAE Hirmer and Hörhammer, 1934.
Genus PROTOCUPRESSINOXYLON Eckhold, 1922.

Type species.–*P. arizonica* sp. nov. by monotypy.

PROTOCUPRESSINOXYLON ARIZONICA new species
Figure 1

Etymology.–*arizonica* to indicate the geographical location of the holotype.

Diagnosis.–Pycnoxylic secondary xylem; cross sectional xylem comprising well-organized radial files of mostly angular tracheids, some rounded with intercellular spaces, scattered thin-walled axial parenchyma, uniseriate rays; in radial section, long spaced or contiguous chains of abietinoid uniseriate, rarely biseriate, bordered pits with circular apertures, oblate pits when contiguous, alternately arranged biseriate pitting infrequent, angular pit outlines rare, ray cells thin-walled with ergastic material, cross-field pits (1-4) cupressoid with steeply inclined openings; in tangential section, rays moder-

ately spaced, uniseriate, rarely partially biseriate, mostly thin-walled homocellular, rarely heterocellular, short, 1-10 circular or oblate, rarely elliptically shaped cells per ray, single-celled rays scarce to absent, bordered pits in 'latewood' elements of same diameter and shape as those in radial walls.

Description.–This holotype was found as an isolated segment, ~30 cm long and ~12 cm in diameter, with small diameter (c. 3 mm) pith and conspicuous rings on its transverse surface.

Occurrence.–Monotype, Crystal Forest, Petrified Forest National Park, locality PFP 117, PEFO 35348 (Holotype).

Horizon.– Rainbow Forest beds, Sonsela Member, Chinle Formation.

Discussion.–Wood of *Protocupressinoxylon arizonica* n. sp. (Figs. 1.1-1.9) is very like that of Upper Jurassic *Protocupressinoxylon purbeckensis* Francis (1983), except that the axial parenchyma indicative of Cupressaceae were not seen in the latter. In cross section, *P. arizonica* n. sp. xylem has circumferential rings, each occurring where a few tiers of radially narrow, thicker walled tracheids form a boundary line contrasting with centrifugally adjoining, radially enlarged, thinner walled tracheids, similar to the latewood – earlywood boundary of extant temperate-zone conifer species. Fully circumferential rings have not previously been confirmed in PEFO fossils, but the presence of circumferential rings is of dubious value as a criterion for distinguishing species because onset of cambial dormancy is unquestionably environmentally controlled. Zones of limited radial width consist of tracheids conspicuous by their variable diameter and loss of normal axial polarity, probably responses to cambial wounding as an uncommon development within this fossil, but no resin canals, traumatic or otherwise, were seen.

Family PROTOPINACEAE Kräusel, 1949.
Genus PROTOPICEOXYLON Gothan, 1907.

Type species.– *Protopiceoxylon novus* n. sp. by monotypy.

PROTOPICEOXYLON NOVUS new species
Figure 2

Etymology.–*novus* for its novel anatomy in relation to known PEFO and Upper Triassic woods.

Diagnosis.–Pycnoxylic secondary xylem; in cross section, radial files of angular tracheids and uniseriate rays, also scattered small-diameter vertical resin ducts, no resinous tracheids or

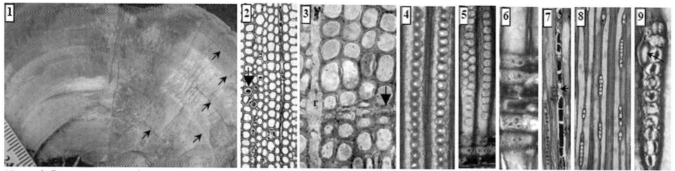

Figure 1. *Protocupressinoxylon arizonica* n. sp. in transverse (1-3), radial (4-7) and tangential (8, 9) sections. *1*. Overview of rings (arrowed), mm scale; *2*. Axial parenchyma (one arrowed); *3*. Ring boundary (arrow) and a ray (r); *4*. Contiguous oblate bordered pits; *5*. Partially biseriate, alternating, abietinoid bordered pits; *6*. Cupressoid cross-field pits; *7*. Axial parenchyma (one arrowed); *8*. Spaced, short homo-cellular rays, oblate, thin-walled cells; *9*. A rarely seen hetero-cellular, partially biseriate ray with a secondary-walled ray cell (arrowed).

axial parenchyma; in radial section, uniseriate contiguous or non-contiguous chains of abietinoid bordered pits, oblate when contiguous, circular apertures, homo- and hetero-cellular rays, thin-walled ray parenchyma with ergastic contents, cross-field pits (1-4) cupressoid with steeply inclined openings, bordered pits in secondary-walled ray cells; in tangential section, bordered pits infrequent, same diameter/shape as in radial walls, short rays often one-celled, distant, no horizontal resin canals.

Description.–This holotype was found as a partially buried trunk with exposed roots and ~0.6 m dia. root collar.

Occurrence.–Monotype, Blue Mesa, Petrified Forest National Park, locality PFP 118, PEFO 35349 (Holotype).

Horizon.– Flattops One bed, Sonsela Member, Chinle Formation.

Discussion.–Features of *Protopiceoxylon novus* n. sp. wood are shown in Figures 2.1 to 2.9. The presence of hetero-cellular rays with ray tracheids and of weakly developed longitudinal resin canals indicates Pinaceae affinity.

Family GINKGOACEAE Engler, 1897.

Type species.– *G. hewardii* n. gen et n. sp. by monotypy

GINKGOXYLPROPINQUUS HEWARDII new genus and species
Figure 3

Etymology.–*Ginkgoxylpropinquus*, indicating the fossil wood's similarity to wood of *Ginkgo biloba* L.; *hewardii*, recognizing the person who discovered the fossil and made it available for research.

Diagnosis.–Pycnoxylic secondary xylem; in cross section, oft-disorganized tracheid radial files, tracheids of varied tangential diameter, axial parenchyma; in radial section, ray cells long, swollen, uniformly thin-walled with ergastic contents, cross-field pits (1-3) cupressoid with openings inclined c. 60°, long uniseriate chains of abietinoid bordered pits separated by weak crassulae, occasionally biseriate chains of non-araucoid pits arranged alternately sometimes oppositely; in tangential section, high frequency uniseriate rays to 16 cells in height, single-celled rays common, 1-2 biseriate cells rarely within uniseriate rays, cells upright of variable width.

Description.–Before excavation, a trunk >20 m in length and ~1 m root collar diameter with attached roots.

Occurrence.–Single specimen, discovered during an exca-

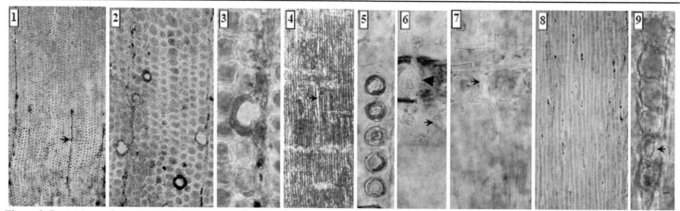

Figure 2. *Protopiceoxylon novus* n. sp. in transverse (1-3), radial (4-7) and tangential (8, 9) section. *1*. Overview of tracheids and uniseriate rays (one arrowed) with ergastic material; *2, 3*. Sporadically distributed, small-diameter vertical resin canals border the rays; *4*. Rays and part of a resin canal (arrow) in radial view; *5*. Non-contiguous abietinoid bordered pits, generally circular apertures; *6*. An hetero-cellular ray with cupressoid cross-field pitting (small arrow) in a thin-walled cell, and a neighbouring thicker-walled cell with a remnant of a bordered pit (large arrow); *7*. Ray cells with thick walls (one arrowed); *8*. Distantly spaced, generally short, uniseriate hetero-cellular rays; *9*. A hetero-cellular ray showing one ray cell with thickened walls (arrow).

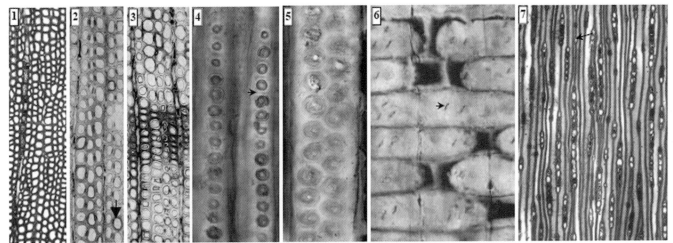

Figure 3. *Ginkgoxylpropinquus hewardii* n. gen. n. sp. in transverse (1-3), radial (4-6) and tangential (7) sections. *1.* Overview of generally disorganized xylem; *2.* Non-inflated axial parenchyma (one arrowed); *3.* The darker radially compressed cells are evidence for a growth interruption; *4.* Uniseriate chains of abietinoid bordered pits, possibly separated by crassulae (arrow); *5.* Biseriate chains of abietinoid bordered pits; *6.* Cupressoid cross-field pits with steeply inclined apertures (one arrowed) in greatly swollen ray cells with ergastic material polarized to their ends; *7.* Closely spaced uniseriate rays among undulating tracheids; single-celled rays (arrow) are common.

vation south of Navajo Boulevard within the city limits of Holbrook, Arizona, PEFO 34356 (Holotype).

Horizon.– Shinarump Member, Chinle Formation.

*Discussion.–*Features of *G. hewardii* n. gen. n. sp. wood are shown in Figures 3.1 to 3.7. Tracheids of varied diameter, disorganized radial files, abundant unicellular rays, swollen ray cells, and cupressoid cross-field pitting support assignment of this tree to Ginkgoaceae. Besides *Ginkgo*, Ginkgoaceae form genera include *Arctobaiera*, *Baiera*, *Baieroxylon*, *Czekanowskia*, *Eretmophyllum*, *Ginkgoidium*, *Ginkgoites*, *Ginkgomyeloxylon*, *Ginkgophyllum*, *Ginkgophyton*, *Ginkgophytoxylon*, *Ginkgoxylon*, *Nehvizdya*, *Proto-ginkgoxylon*, *Sphenobaiera*, *Windwardia* and additional putative genera such as *Pecinocladus* (Scott et al., 1962; Philippe, 1995; Falcon-Lang, 2004). Reliable differentiation among species and genera is complicated by the fact that phenotypic features of *Ginkgo biloba* L. can be highly variable within individual trees. Compared with Lower Permian *Ginkgophytoxylon lucasii* Tidwell et. Munzing (1995) of New Mexico, *G. hewardii* n. gen. n. sp. is distinct by lacking biseriate rays and long chains of biseriate pits, and in having generally short rays and 1-3 cross field pits. *G. hewardii* n. gen. n. sp. wood evidently has axial parenchyma but, if so, they are not conspicuously

inflated. Calcium oxalate crystals were not seen in *G. hewardii* n. gen. n. sp., but under conditions of acidic silicification they would dissolve. It could not be determined if growth interruptions in outer trunk wood of *G. hewardii* n. gen. n. sp. were fully circumferential. Augmenting this report, two ginkgophyte leaves have been found in PEFO (S. R. Ash, pers. com.).

CONCLUSIONS

Anatomical features found in the three investigated fossils indicate that, during Late Triassic times in this region, conifers and ginkgophytes having abietinoid wood co-existed with trees having araucoid secondary xylem.

ACKNOWLEDGMENTS

My thanks are extended to Karen Beppler-Dorn, PEFO Chief of Resource Management, for permitting me to collect samples within PEFO, to William Parker and Sidney Ash for sampling the Holbrook tree, to Joseph Savidge for field assistance, to Ancel Murphy and Calvin Nash for preparing slides, and to NSERCanada for financial support.

REFERENCES

Falcon-Lang, H. J. 2004. A new anatomically preserved ginkgoalean genus from the Upper Cretaceous (Cenomanian) of the Czech Republic. Palaeontology, 47:349-366.

Francis, J. E. 1983. The dominant conifer of the Jurassic Purbeck formation, England. Palaeontology, 26:277-294.

Philippe, M. 1995. Bois fossiles du Jurassique de Franche-Comté (NE France). Palaeontographica B, 236:45-103.

Savidge, R. A. 2001. Intrinsic regulation of cambial growth. Journal of Plant Growth Regulation, 20:52-77.

Scott, R. A., Barghoorn, E. S. and Prakash, U. 1962. Wood of Ginkgo in the Tertiary of western North America. American Journal of Botany, 49, 1095–1101.

Tidwell, W. D. and Munzing, G. E. 1995. Gymnospermous woods from the Lower Permian Hueco formation of south-central New Mexico. New Mexico Museum of Natural History and Science Bulletin, 6:91-100.

Parker, W. G., Ash, S. R., and Irmis, R. B., eds., 2006.
A Century of Research at Petrified Forest National Park: Geology and Paleontology.
Museum of Northern Arizona Bulletin No. 62.

THE FIRST MESOZOIC RECORD OF THE ENIGMATIC FOSSIL *PALAEOXYRIS* FROM NORTH AMERICA; CHINLE FORMATION, PETRIFIED FOREST NATIONAL PARK

BRIAN J. AXSMITH

Department of Biological Sciences, University of South Alabama, LSCB 124, Mobile AL 36688 <baxsmith@jaguar1.usouthal.edu>

THE PROBLEMATIC fossil genus *Palaeoxyris* is represented by about 15 described species of fusiform capsular structures. Specimens of several species are particularly abundant in Pennsylvanian siderite nodules such as those from Mazon Creek, Illinois and many localities in Great Britain. Mesozoic records are rare and extend into the Lower Jurassic or Lower Cretaceous depending on the affinities of *?P. jugleri* (Crookall, 1930; Zidek, 1976). Until now, there have been no reports of *Palaeoxyris* from the Mesozoic of North America.

The affinities of *Palaeoxyris* are uncertain, and speculation on this issue has been ongoing for over 150 years. Based on their common association with fossil plants, and features such as a pedicle-like structure at one end and rhomboidal markings on the surface, they were thought to be some form of plant fruiting structure. However, other workers have noted that the so-called pedicel occurs distally in attached specimens, and the rhomboidal structures are actually artifacts caused by compression of the spiral segments. Furthermore, no specimens have been reported with preserved cuticle showing cellular structure, even when occurring with well-preserved plant compression fossils. Some workers believe that *Palaeoxyris*

is a fossil shark egg case somewhat similar to those of extant heterodontid sharks, as this is the only modern group with spiral egg cases. However, the extinct hybodont sharks have been implicated by some researchers as the most likely producers of *Palaeoxyris* (e.g., Zidek, 1976).

Three impression fossils attributable to *Palaeoxyris* were recently discovered in Petrified Forest National Park by S. R. Ash and provided to the author for study. The fossils were found in the wetland facies associated with the Newspaper Rock bed in the Blue Mesa Member of the Chinle Formation at locality PFP 004 (see Parker, this volume) together with many other fossils including crayfish, clam shrimps, insects, and impressions of leaves, stems, and cones of several types. Presumably, the putative egg capsules and other fossils were deposited on the floodplain when the adjacent stream that formed the Newspaper Sandstone Bed overflowed its banks.

Based on the three available specimens (Figs. 1 - 4), the body of the Chinle *Palaeoxyris* was about 12.5 mm long and 7.5 mm wide at the widest point, and tapered gradually toward each end. The "pedicel" is 4.3 mm wide at the point of

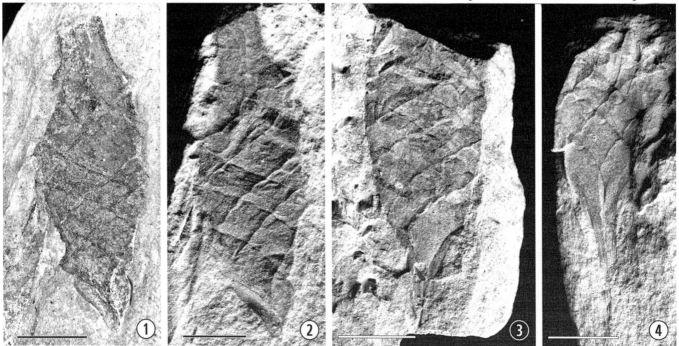

Figure 1. 1-4, *Palaeoxyris* sp. from the Blue Mesa Member of the Chinle Formation in Petrified Forest National Park. Scale bars = 0.5 mm. *1.* Nearly complete specimen showing gross morphology. The "pedicel" is at the top of the image [i.e., pointing up.] PEFO 34350; *2.* Specimen from Fig. 1 under extreme incident light to emphasize the spiral banding pattern. PEFO 3450; *3.* Partial specimen showing banding on body. PEFO 3451; *4.* Partial specimen with well-preserved beak pointing downward. PEFO 3452.

attachment to the body, and extends out at least 13.5 mm before ending at the edge of the matrix on one specimen (Figs, 1 – 2). A partial specimen with a well-preserved beak (Fig. 4) indicates that this structure terminated as a spine-like structure at least 3.0 mm in length. The body is traversed by about 5 spiral bands averaging 1.9 mm in width (Figs. 1 – 3). The bands arise at an angle of about 27 degrees in the middle of the body, but at a steeper angle (~ 56 degrees) near the ends. Compression of the bands on each side of the body produces the characteristic rhomboidal pattern (Figs. 1- 4).

Comparisons with previously described species of *Palaeoxyris* are ongoing. However, it appears that the Chinle form is most similar in size, shape, and banding characteristics to the European Triassic/Lower Jurassic form *P. muensteri* (Crookall, 1930). The lack of any indication of preserved cuticle on the new specimens could be interpreted as further evidence that *Palaeoxyris* is not a plant, as cuticle is common on many Chinle plant fossils. However, the Chinle sample size is very small, and cuticle is sometimes absent from the plants as well. It is also intriguing that hybodont shark remains are known from the Chinle Formation in the park (Murry and Kirby, 2002) as well as elsewhere in Arizona (e.g., Kirby, 1989). Although the Chinle form sheds no new light on the affinities of *Palaeoxyris*, this occurrence is consistent with the hybodont egg case hypothesis. It is also significant in representing the only Mesozoic record of this taxon from North America.

REFERENCES

Crookall, R. 1930. Further morphological studies in *Palaeoxyris*, etc. Geological Survey of Great Britian and Museum of Practical Geology, Summer Program for 1929, 3:8-36.

Kirby, R. E. 1989. Late Triassic vertebrate localities of the Owl Rock Member (Chinle Formation) in the Ward Terrance area of Northern Arizona, p. 12-28. *In* S. G. Lucas and A. P. Hunt (eds.), Dawn of the Age of Dinosaurs in the American Southwest. New Mexico Museum of Natural History, Albuquerque, NM.

Murry, P. A., and R. E. Kirby. 2002. A new hybodont shark from the Chinle and Bull Canyon Formations, Arizona, Utah, and New Mexico. New Mexico Museum of Natural History & Science Bulletin, 21:87-106.

Zydek, J. 1976. A new shark egg capsule from the Pennsylvanian of Oklahoma, and remarks on the chondrichthyan egg capsules in general. Journal of Paleontology, 50:907-915.

Parker, W. G., Ash, S. R., and Irmis, R. B., eds., 2006.
A Century of Research at Petrified Forest National Park: Geology and Paleontology.
Museum of Northern Arizona Bulletin No. 62.

CURATION CORRECTION FOR A FOSSIL FROM THE MIDDLE TRIASSIC MOENKOPI FORMATION OF ARIZONA

WILLIAM G. PARKER

Division of Resource Management, Petrified Forest National Park, P. O. Box 2217, Petrified Forest, AZ 86028 <William_Parker@nps.gov>

ABSTRACT – A partial skull of a temnospondyl amphibian from the Moenkopi Formation of Arizona was catalogued with a Petrified Forest National Park specimen number. This number is preoccupied in the Petrified Forest Museum database and the specimen is not in the PEFO collections, so the assignment of this number to the specimen is invalid.

DISCUSSION

HUNT ET AL. (2000) assigned a partial skull of a temnospondyl amphibian from the Holbrook Member of the Moenkopi Formation to the Trematosauridae. In the description of the specimen, the catalogue number is published as PEFO 5077, signifying that the specimen is reposited in the museum collections at Petrified Forest National Park (PEFO).

Unfortunately, this number is preoccupied in the PEFO collections by vertebrae belonging to a "rauisuchian", and is therefore not available to be assigned to the Moenkopi specimen. Furthermore, the specimen was never accessioned into the PEFO collections, and since the specimen is not from a geological unit or locality within the park boundary, it falls outside of the park museum's scope of collections. For these reasons and as the current location of the specimen itself is unknown, the partial skull described by Hunt et al. (2000) is not considered a PEFO specimen and the catalog number PEFO 5077 is disassociated with this specimen.

In addition, the specimen is indistinguishable from skull material of the Middle Triassic capitosaurid *Eocyclotosaurus* and therefore probably does not represent a lonchorhychine trematosaur as hypothesized by these authors (S. Nesbitt, pers. com., 2002).

ACKNOWLEGDMENTS

Thanks to Randall Irmis and Sterling Nesbitt for discussion. This is PEFO paleontological contribution number 8.

REFERENCES

Hunt, A. P., V. L. Santucci, and T. J. Olson. 2000. The first trematosaurid amphibian from the Middle Triassic of the United States. Mesa Southwest Museum Bulletin, 7:31-35.

Parker, W. G., Ash, S. R., and Irmis, R. B., eds., 2006.
A Century of Research at Petrified Forest National Park: Geology and Paleontology.
Museum of Northern Arizona Bulletin No. 62.

ENAMEL MICROSTRUCTURE IN *REVUELTOSAURUS CALLENDERI* (ARCHOSAURIA:CRUROTARSI) AN UNUSUAL REPTILE FROM THE TRIASSIC OF THE AMERICAN SOUTHWEST

ANDREW B. HECKERT AND JESSICA A. CAMP

Department of Geology, ASU Box 32067, Appalachian State University, Boone, NC 28608-2067 <heckertab@appstate.edu>

STUDIES OF reptilian tooth enamel microstructure are in their infancy, yet they have already yielded insight into amniote evolution ranging from functional interpretations to documenting convergent evolution at multiple levels.

Within this framework, we examined the enamel microstructure of two teeth of the unusual crurotarsan *Revueltosaurus callenderi* Hunt housed at the New Mexico Museum of Natural History and Science (NMMNH). The examined specimens include a premaxillary tooth (NMMNH P-33798) and a maxillary-dentary tooth (NMMNH P-33797), both topotypes from the Bull Canyon Formation (Revueltian, early- to mid-Norian) of east-central New Mexico. The pre-

maxillary tooth was examined in longitudinal section and the maxillary/dentary tooth in cross-section. To test the hypotheses that enamel thickness corresponds to a functional requirement and/or reflects a phylogenetic signal we analyzed *Revueltosaurus* tooth enamel at various scales, measuring enamel thickness and examining microstructural features throughout both longitudinal and cross-sectional thickness. *Revueltosaurus* teeth bore relatively thick enamel for teeth of their size; enamel thickness varies from a low of ~15 μm to as much as 130 μm. In the premaxillary tooth, this range varies from more basal enamel (~15 μm) to apical enamel (~130 μm) (Fig. 1). In the maxillary/dentary tooth, the range was not as

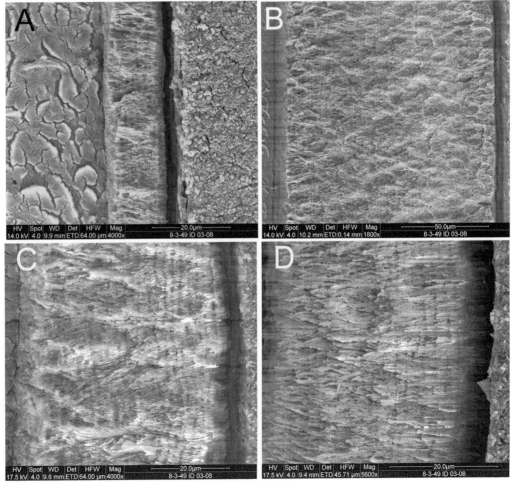

Figure *1*. Scanning electron micrographs of *Revueltosaurus callenderi* teeth, enamel dentine junction (EDJ) to left in all photos. *A.* Basal portion of labial surface of premaxillary tooth (NMMNH P-33798) in longitudinal section; enamel thickness = 15.6 μm; *B.* Apical portion of labial surface of same; enamel thickness = 125 μm; well-developed columnar enamel evident; *C.* lingual surface of maxillary tooth (NMMNH P-33797) in cross-section; enamel thickness 54 μm; note well-developed columnar enamel and incremental lines; *D.* Labial surface of same near carina; enamel thickness 43.3 μm; well-developed columnar enamel and incremental lines evident.

pronounced (~40-60 μm), which probably reflects relatively uniform thickness in cross-section, although the enamel is thicker along the denticles. At the microstructural level, both teeth exhibit columnar, as opposed to parallel, microstructure. In amniotes, parallel enamel is generally considered primitive and columnar enamel is derived, with the assumption that columnar enamel is perhaps associated with a diet requiring greater tooth strength (resistance to fracture). Existing hypotheses suggest that columnar enamel in *Revueltosaurus* reflects a diet with less emphasis on grinding. We also detected multiple incremental lines within the enamel microstructure of both teeth.

We utilized techniques similar to those described and used by Sander (1999) and Stokosa (2005). Among the many taxa Sander (1999) sampled, *Revueltosaurus* teeth are most similar to rauisuchids and tyrannosaurs in terms of enamel thickness and microstructure. Stokosa's (2005) analysis was restricted to Late Cretaceous coelurosaurian theropods, but we note that she also reported columnar enamel similar to what we report here in several dromaeosaurid and tyrannosaurid theropods. Generally, the incremental lines we report here are more pronounced than those illustrated in coelurosaurs by Stokosa (2005).

What these results demonstrate is that: (1) enamel thickness is variable within a tooth; (2) enamel thickness reports therefore must either be standardized to a specific location on a tooth (which we feel unlikely to be repeatable) or else reported as a range tied to morphological landmarks (which we consider more likely); (3) *Revueltosaurus* had columnar enamel microstructure, suggesting selection for a more durable tooth enamel; and (4) the numerous lines of incremental growth in *Revueltosaurus* suggest that it had a lengthy developmental stage.

REFERENCES

Sander, P.M. 1999. The microstructure of reptilian tooth enamel: terminology, function, and phylogeny. Müncher Geowissenschafliche Abhandlungen Reihe A, 38:1-102.

Stokosa, K. 2005. Enamel microstructure variation within the Theropoda, p. 63-178. *In* Carpenter, K. (ed.), The Carnivorous Dinosaurs: Bloomington, Indiana University Press.

Parker, W. G., Ash, S. R., and Irmis, R. B., eds., 2006.
A Century of Research at Petrified Forest National Park: Geology and Paleontology.
Museum of Northern Arizona Bulletin No. 62.

GEOGRAPHIC AND STRATIGRAPHIC DISTRIBUTION OF THE ENIGMATIC UPPER TRIASSIC (ADAMANIAN: CARNIAN) VERTEBRATE FOSSIL *COLOGNATHUS OBSCURUS* CASE

ANDREW B. HECKERT

Department of Geology, ASU Box 32067, Appalachian State University, Boone, NC 28608-2067 <heckertab@appstate.edu>

SINCE THE 1920s, paleontologists have occasionally recovered teeth and tooth-bearing skull or jaw elements of the bizarre vertebrate *Colognathus obscurus* Case from a variety of Upper Triassic localities in the American Southwest. There are now approximately 16 such specimens reposited in museums across North America. Of these, 13 have reasonable provenance and nine of these are from exposures of the Upper Triassic Tecovas Formation in Crosby County, Texas. Indeed, to date *Colognathus* localities are principally in the Tecovas Formation of Texas, but isolated occurrences are known from the Los Esteros Member of the Santa Rosa Formation in central New Mexico and the uppermost Blue Mesa Member of the Petrified Forest Formation in east-central Arizona. The holotype of *Colognathus obscurus* was recovered from the jacket bearing the holotype skull of the phytosaur *Leptosuchus*

crosbiensis Case, so its provenance is more certain than implied by some previous authors. Crosby County Texas localities thus are the type locality, including both the "upper" and "lower" Kalgary microvertebrate localities, Walker's Tank and vicinity, Brunson Ranch, Sand Creek, and Davidson Creek. Two specimens are known from the Tecovas Formation in Palo Duro Canyon, Randall County, Texas. The New Mexico locality is the "microvertebrate locality" near Lamy (NMMNH locality 1171) and the Arizona locality is "Crocodile Hill" in the Petrified Forest National Park. Almost all occurrences are single fragments, the exceptions being a partial palate and lower jaws from Davidson Creek in Crosby County (UCMP V6333/ 65767) and several specimens in the TMM collections supposedly from *Trilophosaurus* quarry 3, although their provenance and locality data are unconvincing.

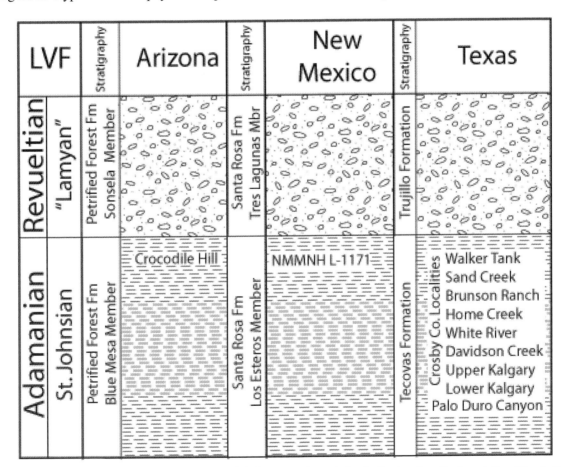

Figure *1*. Stratigraphic distribution of *Colognathus* localities and their proposed correlation in the American Southwest. Localities in Texas are not necessarily stratigraphically superposed; all are probably low in the Tecovas Formation. Lithologies are schematic of mudstone- and sandstone/conglomerate-dominated intervals.

All specimens with reasonable locality data occur in strata that have been dated as Adamanian (Carnian) in age by use of other vertebrates. The Crosby County localities are of well-established Adamanian age, based on the presence of the aetosaurs *Stagonolepis* and *Desmatosuchus haplocerus* and "*Rutiodon*-grade" phytosaurs (phytosaurs typically attributed to either *Rutiodon* or *Leptosuchus*). The occurrence at Crocodile Hill is part of the type Adamanian fauna, and so is by definition Adamanian in age. The New Mexican occurrence is less well constrained, but in general the fauna of the Los Esteros Member includes *Stagonolepis* and *D. haplocerus*. Recently workers have subdivided the Adamanian into an older, St. Johnsian fauna with the typical Adamanian fauna and a younger, Lamyan fauna with a fauna more typical of the Revueltian (early-mid Norian), including the aetosaur *Typothorax* (but as *T. antiquum*) and the phytosaur *Pseudopalatus*. Within resolution, all *Colognathus* occurrences are in the lower interval, and thus *Colognathus* is an index taxon of Adamanian (St. Johnsian) time (Fig. 1). Interestingly, correlating the lower Sonsela Member (Rainbow Forest Bed) to the Tres Laguna Member of the Santa Rosa Formation and then to the Trujillo Formation results in a "Lamyan" fauna that is comparable in composition and stratigraphic position to the "Rainbowforestan" fauna of the Revueltian, so I propose that the "Lamyan" is instead equivalent to the early Revueltian (Fig. 1).

Colognathus dentigerous fragments typically include a single, conical, anterior tooth and an elongate, molariform posterior tooth. The latter is readily recognizable when it occurs as a shed crown. Case initially considered the taxon to pertain to an osteichthyan, but later authors have generally considered it to be an aberrant procolophonid or procolophonid relative. Interestingly, there is little or no morphological evidence that indicates that the existing specimens even pertain to a marginal dentition. The possibility that known specimens of *Colognathus* are actually palatal and/or pharyngeal teeth should be explored. Evidence supporting this hypothesis includes the fact that no *Colognathus* specimens preserve evidence of skull fenestration, or even of sutures with other elements. Indeed, other than the "ankylothecodont" dentition, there is little to suggest that *Colognathus* was a tetrapod. To the extent that taphonomic data are available, most *Colognathus* specimens come from "wet" paleoenvironments—generally pond deposits with abundant osteichthyan fossils. Some osteichthyans, notably dipnoan sarcopterygians (lungfish) possess a dentition of crushing tooth plates in the palate and hyomandibular region. It is therefore possible that Case was correct in his original assessment of *Colognathus* as an osteichthyan.

Parker, W. G., Ash, S. R., and Irmis, R. B., eds., 2006.
A Century of Research at Petrified Forest National Park: Geology and Paleontology.
Museum of Northern Arizona Bulletin No. 62.

A NEW GEOLOGIC MAP OF PETRIFIED FOREST NATIONAL PARK WITH EMPHASIS ON MEMBERS AND KEY BEDS OF THE CHINLE FORMATION

JASON J. RAUCCI, RONALD C. BLAKEY, AND PAUL J. UMHOEFER

Department of Geology, Northern Arizona University, PO Box 4099, Flagstaff, AZ 86011 <jason.raucci@nau.edu>

THE NEED FOR A COMPREHENSIVE GEOLOGIC MAP

DESPITE MANY decades of geologic research on the Chinle Formation within Petrified Forest National Park (PEFO), no published geologic map of the entire park exists. There are several unpublished maps for specific localities and stratigraphic intervals (e.g., Johns, 1988; Shipman, 1999; Woody, 2003), but the U.S. Geologic Survey discontinued a comprehensive geologic mapping program in Petrified Forest National Park (PEFO) and has no plans to publish the preliminary map completed by George Billingsley, William Breed, and Sidney Ash in 1985.

We believe it is no coincidence that after 100+ years of study, there is only now an emerging consensus regarding the proper stratigraphic nomenclature of the major members of the Chinle Formation within PEFO. When a stratigraphy is constructed without comprehensive mapping, the tendency is to infer the distribution of key intervals based on correlations between stratigraphic columns, without fully confirming those correlations. The lack of a single complete map encourages a proliferation of stratigraphic interpretations and competing nomenclatures, as has been the case in PEFO.

Although the Billingsley et al. (1985) map is widely available to researchers, it remains in a preliminary condition because it is largely unchecked, contains numerous drafting errors, and it was made on a relatively small-scale topographic base. The stratigraphic relations implied by this mapping are generally simple lithologic correlations that attempt to correlate widely separated but lithologically similar sandstone beds, typically regardless of their relative stratigraphic level. Because many Chinle Formation sandstone beds are locally continuous but regionally discontinuous and several lithologically similar beds lie at different stratigraphic levels, this approach has resulted in much confusion. Woody's (2003) map was at 1:24,000 scale, but covered only the south half of the park and subdivided only the Sonsela member. Therefore, the Billingsley et al. (1985) map is still generally accepted as the standard PEFO geologic map (Heckert and Lucas, 2002).

Given that the standard reference map is preliminary and was constructed using an outdated stratigraphic model, the current state of geologic mapping in PEFO is considered unacceptable by both the NPS Geologic Resource Division and PEFO scientific personnel. The goals of our project were: 1) to work with PEFO scientific personnel to define a broadly applicable lithostratigraphic model of the Chinle Formation within PEFO; and 2) using this model, field check, update and refine the existing mapping to NPS Geologic Resource Division standards.

MAPPING PHILOSOPHY

By mapping broadly inclusive intervals and locally designated key beds, we have endeavored to accurately represent the lithologies present without implying statigraphically dubious lithologic correlations between localities. Members of the Chinle Formation were generally mapped throughout the Park, but key beds were, in general, mapped only where their continuity could be established with reasonable certainty. Key sandstone marker beds within members were identified where they mark an important horizon (e.g., Flattops 1 bed), are prominent and areally extensive (e.g., the "brown sandstone" of the Sonsela member in the north half of PEFO), and/or contain significant resources that may be the subject of research in their own right (e.g. the Black Forest Bed). In some cases, intervals were mapped rather than individual key beds. For example, the Jim Camp Wash "beds" are actually a distinctive heterolithic interval with diagnostic cut-and-fill internal architecture, and are mapped as one unit throughout PEFO. Occasionally, "key beds" were mapped in similarly inclusive manner, as with the Rainbow Forest sandstone: it is doubtful that the prominent beds at the Rainbow Forest type section continue unbroken across the whole of PEFO, but for mapping purposes we treat the nearly ubiquitous conglomeratic interval at the base of the Sonsela Member as equivalent to the Rainbow Forest Bed.

SUMMARY OF THE CHINLE FORMATION STRATIGRAPHIC MODEL

The stratigraphy utilized here is most similar to that of Heckert and Lucas (2002) and Woody (2003), although we do not raise the Chinle Formation to Group status as suggested by Heckert and Lucas (2002). Our stratigraphic model is summarized by the composite panel in Figure 1. The four members of the Chinle Formation we recognize in PEFO are from lowest to highest: Blue Mesa Member, Sonsela Member, Petrified Forest Member, and Owl Rock Member. Limited outcrops of rocks underlying the Blue Mesa Member are present

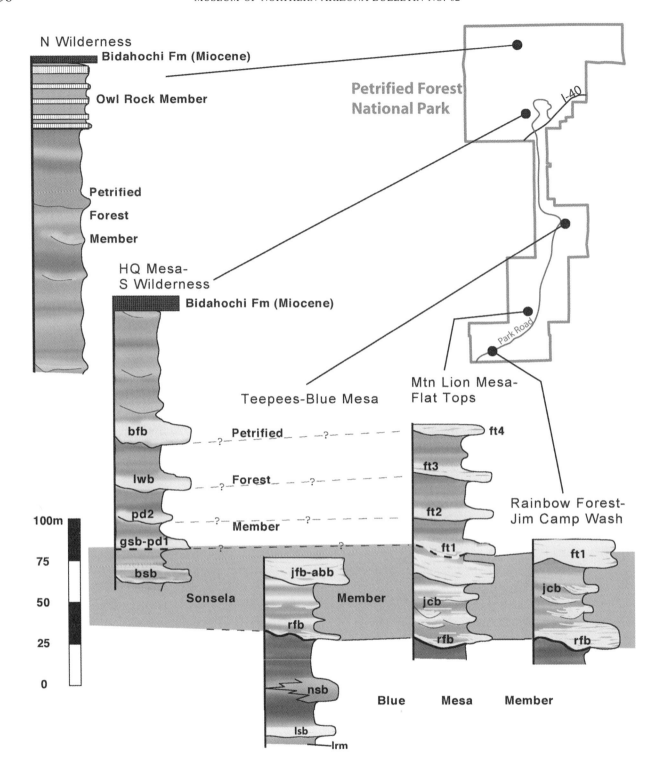

Figure *1*. Schematic columns and stratigraphic model of the Chinle Formation, Petrified Forest NP. Abbreviations of key beds are as follows: rlm = "lower red member"; lsb = lower sandstone bed; nsb = Newspaper sandstone; rfb = Rainbow Forest beds; jcb = Jim Camp Wash beds; bsb = Brown sandstone; jfb-abb = Jasper Forest/Agate Bridge bed*; ft1-4 = Flattops sandstone beds #1-4; gsb-pd1 = goblin sandstone (possibly equivalent to Painted Desert sandstone #1); pd2 = Painted Desert sandstone #2 (not mapped); lwb = Lithodendron Wash bed; bfb = Black Forest bed.

*Field relations suggest that the unit mapped as Flattops One bed by Woody (2003) and termed Agate Bridge Bed by Heckert and Lucas (2002) in the Agate Bridge/Jasper Forest area lies stratigraphically below the type section of the Flattops Bed #1 (Billingsley, 1985). We have chosen to use the new "Jasper Forest" terminology for these beds in order to reflect the possibility that this unit, which also caps Blue Mesa, may not correlate directly to the capping sandstone beds of the Sonsela Member in the Flattops and Rainbow Forest areas.

in the southern part of PEFO, but the affinity of these units is uncertain. We accept and utilize the three-part division of the Sonsela member suggested by Heckert and Lucas (2002) and Woody (2003), although we designate several additional key beds within the unit. The nomenclature of Heckert and Lucas (2002) for key beds within the Petrified Forest member is generally retained as well.

The areas north and south of I-40 have a different nomenclature, both in previous literature and as designated here, and it is not known if any of the key beds mapped in the north half of PEFO correlate directly to key beds in the south half. Particularly troublesome is the "Devil's Playground" area in the southwest corner of the north half of PEFO. We have chosen to map significant, laterally continuous, and unit-bounding sandstones using an informal nomenclature until the relationships in this area are better understood. The prominent "brown sandstone" of Billingsley et al. (1985) in the Devils Playground area is re-interpreted to lie within the Sonsela member, while the informally named "goblin sandstone" is interpreted to be equivalent to the Painted Desert sandstone #1 of Billingsley et al. (1985) and Johns (1988). The "goblin sandstone" is further interpreted to lie at or near the base of the Petrified Forest Member, or stratigraphically equivalent to the Flattops Bed #1 of southern PEFO. This is a significant change from previous schemes that placed it well within the Petrified Forest Member. We accept the designation of the Lithodendron Wash Bed (formerly Painted Desert Sandstone # 3 of Johns, 1988) proposed by Heckert and Lucas (2002).

REFERENCES

Billingsley, G. H, and Breed, W. J. assisted by S. R. Ash. 1985. Geologic map of Petrified Forest National Park, Arizona. Unpublished data, Petrified Forest Museum Association, Petrified Forest National Park, Arizona, scale 1:48.000.

Heckert, A. B. and S. G. Lucas. 2002. Revised Upper Triassic stratigraphy of the Petrified Forest National Park, Arizona (USA), p. 1-23. In A.B. Heckert, and S.G. Lucas (ed.), Upper Triassic stratigraphy and paleontology: New Mexico Museum of Natural History and Science Bulletin 21, Albuquerque.

Johns, M. E. 1988. Architectural element analysis and depositional history of the Upper Petrified Forest Member of the Chinle Formation, Petrified Forest National Park, Arizona. Unpublished M. S. thesis, Northern Arizona University, 163 p.

Shipman, T. C. 1999. Effects of volcanism on the Upper Triassic Chinle Formation, Petrified Forest National Park, Arizona. Unpublished MS thesis, Northern Arizona University, 79 p.

Woody, D. T. 2003. Revised geological assessment of the Sonsela Member, Chinle Formation, Petrified Forest National Park, Arizona. Unpublished M. S. thesis, Northern Arizona University, 206 p.

Parker, W. G., Ash, S. R., and Irmis, R. B., eds., 2006.
A Century of Research at Petrified Forest National Park: Geology and Paleontology.
Museum of Northern Arizona Bulletin No. 62.

REVIEW OF THE LATE TRIASSIC DINOSAUR RECORD FROM PETRIFIED FOREST NATIONAL PARK, ARIZONA

WILLIAM G. PARKER[1], RANDALL B. IRMIS[2], AND STERLING J. NESBITT[3,4]

[1]Division of Resource Management, Petrified Forest National Park, Box 2217, Petrified Forest, AZ. <William_Parker@nps.gov>
[2]Museum of Paleontology and Department of Integrative Biology, 1101 Valley Life Sciences Building, University of California, Berkeley, CA 94720-4780. <irmis@berkeley.edu>
[3]Division of Paleontology, American Museum of Natural History, Central Park West at 79th Street, New York City, NY 10024.
[4]Lamont-Doherty Earth Observatory, Columbia University, 61 Rt. 9W, Palisades, NY 10964. <ncsbitt@ldeo.columbia.edu>

WITH THE exception of the *Coelophysis* Quarry at Ghost Ranch, New Mexico, dinosaurs are a rare component of most Late Triassic faunas. Even taxonomically diverse quarries such as the *Placerias* Quarry near St. Johns, Arizona and the Snyder Quarry from the Chama Basin of New Mexico only contain a few dinosaur elements among hundreds of identifiable specimens (Long and Murry, 1995; Heckert et al., 2003).

Padian (1986, 1990) documented the occurrences of the theropod *Coelophysis* sp. and the purported ornithischian *Revueltosaurus callenderi* from the Dinosaur Hill locality in the Petrified Forest National Park. The fauna of this locality is dominated by pseudosuchian archosaurs such as the aetosaur *Typothorax coccinarum*, the crocodylomorph *Hesperosuchus agilis* (Parrish, 1991), phytosaurs, and "rauisuchids". Also extremely common is the small metoposaur *Apachesaurus gregorii*. By comparison, only a single associated skeleton of *Coelophysis* was recovered.

Long and Murry (1995) described a new dinosaur, *Chindesaurus bryansmalli*, from the Dinosaur Hollow locality of the park. This fragmentary skeleton was collected in 1985 and was mixed with a partial skeleton of a shuvosaurid (Long and Murry, 1995), a suchian archosaur. Long and Murry (1995) tentatively considered *Chindesaurus* to represent a herrerasaurid, a placement that was followed by Hunt et al. (1998); however, recent studies (Langer, 2004; Nesbitt et al., in review) consider *Chindesaurus* a basal saurischian outside Herrerasauridae. The Dinosaur Hill and Dinosaur Hollow localities are both in the Petrified Forest Member of the Chinle Formation.

Hunt et al. (1996), Hunt (1998), and Hunt and Wright (1999) documented purported dinosaur remains (indeterminate theropods and the "ornithischian" *Revueltosaurus callenderi*) from several other localities, including sites from the Blue Mesa Member. However, these specimens have never been described and their preliminary identifications cannot be substantiated given the remarkable convergences between theropod dinosaurs and shuvosaurids (Nesbitt and Norell, 2006). Furthermore, Parker et al. (2005) determined that *Revueltosaurus callenderi* actually represents a pseudosuchian archosaur rather than an ornithischian dinosaur, thus decreasing the number of identifiable dinosaur specimens from the park.

Stocker et al. (2004) and Parker and Irmis (2005) documented the collection of two partial skeletons of *Coelophysis*, a partial skeleton of *Chindesaurus*, and isolated elements of at least two more theropods from a site (The Giving Site) in the Petrified Forest Member. This locality is stratigraphically equivalent to the Dinosaur Hollow site and stratigraphically higher than the Dinosaur Hill site. Other taxa collected from the Giving Site include *Revueltosaurus callenderi*, *Typothorax coccinarum*, indeterminate phytosaurs and crocodylomorphs, *Apachesaurus gregorii*, *Vancleavea* sp., two partial skeletons of a shuvosaurid, and a partial skeleton of *Postosuchus* sp. This site is remarkable because dinosaurs represent a substantial portion of the fauna; it is also the first documented co-occurrence of the basal saurischian *Chindesaurus* and a true theropod, *Coelophysis*.

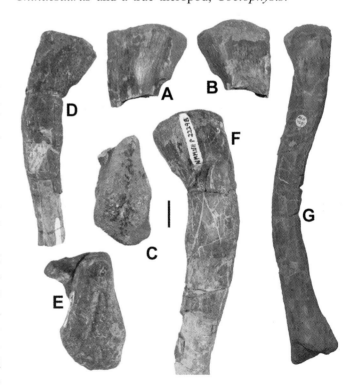

Figure 1. Femora of Late Triassic dinosauriforms. *A-C*. PEFO 34347, proximal end of left femur; *D-F*. NMMNH P-22298, *Eucoelophysis baldwini* holotype left femur; *A, D*. posterior view; *B, F*. anterior view; *C, E*. proximal view; *G. Silesaurus opolensis* holotype left femur in anterolateral view. Scale bar = 1 cm.

Sometime around 1996, an unknown individual collected the proximal end of a femur from the Dying Grounds locality in the Blue Mesa Member. We recently re-discovered this specimen and recognized that it is identical to the femora of the dinosauriforms *Silesaurus opolensis* from the Carnian of Poland (Dzik, 2003) and *Eucoelophysis baldwini* from the Norian of New Mexico (Sullivan and Lucas, 1999). Both of these taxa are thought to be basal dinosauriforms outside the Dinosauria (Nesbitt et al., in review). Because this specimen is from the Blue Mesa Member, thought to be Carnian in age on the basis of palynomorphs (Fischer and Dunay, 1984; Litwin et al., 1991), it represents the earliest dinosauriform specimen not only from the Chinle Formation, but from North America as a whole. Given the occurrence of a coelophysoid from the stratigraphically lower *Placerias* Quarry (Long and Murry, 1995; Hunt et al., 1998), this suggests the co-occurrence of basal dinosauriforms and theropod dinosaurs in the lower Chinle Formation of Arizona. This hypothesis will be supported by additional evidence if the assignment of material from the stratigraphically equivalent (and geographically adjacent) Dinosaur Ridge locality by Hunt et al. (1996) to the Theropoda is confirmed.

Confirmed Late Triassic theropod specimens from Arizona are now known from the Mesa Redondo, Sonsela, and Petrified Forest Members of the Chinle Formation, with a probable occurrence from the Blue Mesa Member. The basal saurischian *Chindesaurus* is known from the Petrified Forest Member and co-occurs with true theropods. A newly recognized indeterminate basal dinosauriform taxon occurs in the Blue Mesa Member. Thus, basal dinosauriforms and true theropods appear to occur together in the lower Chinle Formation of Arizona. If we include *Eucoelophysis* from New Mexico, basal dinosauriforms, basal saurischians, and theropods may occur together in the upper Chinle Formation as well, although no basal dinosauriform material has been found in the upper Chinle Formation of Arizona. With the removal of *Revueltosaurus* and similar forms from the Ornithischia, no unambiguous records of this group occur in the Triassic of North America (Irmis et al., in press). The same is true for the sauropodomorphs (Nesbitt et al., in review). Thus, the revised record of specimens from Petrified Forest National Park suggests that at least in the southwestern United States, the taxonomic diversity of dinosaurs and their relatives was low and relatively stable throughout the Late Triassic Period.

REFERENCES

Dzik, J. 2003. A beaked herbivorous archosaur with dinosaur affinities from the early Late Triassic of Poland. Journal of Vertebrate Paleontology, 23:556-574.

Fisher, M. K. and R. E. Dunay. 1984. Palynology of the petrified Forest Member of the Chinle Formation (Upper Triassic), Arizona. U.S.A. Pollen et Spores, 26:241-284.

Heckert, A. B., Zeigler, K. E., Lucas, S. G., and L. F. Rinehart. 2003. Coelophysoids (Dinosauria: Theropoda) from the Upper Triassic (Revueltian) Snyder Quarry. New Mexico Museum of Natural History and Science Bulletin, 24:127-132.

Hunt, A. P. 1998. Preliminary results of the Dawn of the Dinosaurs project at Petrified Forest National Park, Arizona, p. 135-137. *In* V. L. Santucci and L. McClelland (eds.), National Park Service Paleontological Research. National Park Service Technical Report NPS/NRGRD/GRDTR-98/01.

Hunt, A. P., and J. Wright. 1999. New discoveries of Late Triassic dinosaurs from Petrified Forest National Park, Arizona, p. 96-99. *In* V. L. Santucci, and L. McClellan (eds.), National Park Service Paleontological Research. National Park Service Geological Resources Division Technical Report NPS/NRGRD/GRDTR-99/03.

Hunt, A. P., Lucas, S. G., Heckert, A. B., Sullivan, R. M., and M. G. Lockley. 1998. Late Triassic dinosaurs from the western United States. Geobios, 31:511-531.

Irmis, R. B., W. G. Parker, S. J. Nesbitt, and J. Liu. In press. Early ornithischian dinosaurs: the Triassic record. Historical Biology.

Litwin, R. J., A. Traverse, and S. R. Ash 1991. Preliminary palynological zonation of the Chinle Formation, southwestern U.S.A., and its correlation to the Newark Supergroup (eastern U.S.A.). Review of Palaeobotany and Palynology, 68:269-287.

Long, R. A., and P. A. Murry. 1995. Late Triassic (Carnian and Norian) tetrapods from the southwestern United States. New Mexico Museum of Natural History and Science Bulletin, 4:1-254.

Nesbitt, S. J., and M. A. Norell. 2006. Extreme convergence in the body plans of an early suchian (Archosauria) and ornithomimid dinosaurs (Theropoda). Proceedings of the Royal Society Series B. doi:10.1098/rspb.2005.3426.

Padian, K. 1986. On the type material of *Coelophysis* Cope (Saurischia: Theropoda), and a new specimen from the Petrified Forest of Arizona (Late Triassic: Chinle Formation), p. 45-60. *In* K. Padian (ed.), The beginning of the Age of Dinosaurs: Faunal change across the Triassic-Jurassic boundary. Cambridge University Press, Cambridge.

Padian, K. 1990. The ornithischian form genus *Revueltosaurus* from the Petrified Forest of Arizona (Late Triassic; Norian; Chinle Formation). Journal of Vertebrate Paleontology, 10:268-269.

Parker, W. G., and R. B. Irmis. 2005. Advances in vertebrate paleontology based on new material from Petrified Forest National Park, Arizona. New Mexico Museum of Natural History and Science Bulletin, 29:45-58.

Parker, W. G., R. B. Irmis, S. J. Nesbitt, J. W. Martz, and L. S. Browne. 2005. The pseudosuchian *Revueltosaurus callenderi* and its implications for the diversity of early ornithischian dinosaurs. Proceedings of the Royal Society London B, 272:963-969.

Parrish, J. M. 1991. A new specimen of an early crocodylomorph (*cf. Sphenosuchus sp.*) from the Upper Triassic Chinle Formation of Petrified Forest National Park, Arizona. Journal of Vertebrate Paleontology, 11:198-212.

Stocker, M. R., W. G. Parker, R. B. Irmis, and J. M. Shuman. 2004. New discoveries from the Upper Triassic Chinle Formation as the result of the ongoing paleontological inventory of Petrified Forest National Park, Arizona. Journal of Vertebrate Paleontology, 24(3 Supplement):118A.

Sullivan, R. M. and S. G. Lucas. 1999. *Eucoelophysis baldwini*, a new theropod dinosaur from the Upper Triassic of New Mexico, and the status of the original types of *Coelophysis*. Journal of Vertebrate Paleontology, 19:81-90.

Parker, W. G., Ash, S. R., and Irmis, R. B., eds., 2006.
A Century of Research at Petrified Forest National Park: Geology and Paleontology.
Museum of Northern Arizona Bulletin No. 62.

TOWARD AN IMPROVED DEFINITION OF THE J1-CUSP: NEW PALEOMAGNETIC DATA FROM THE UPPERMOST TRIASSIC TO LOWERMOST JURASSIC, MOENAVE FORMATION, UTAH

LINDA L. DONOHOO-HURLEY[1], JOHN W. GEISSMAN[1], MOUSUMI ROY[1], AND SPENCER G. LUCAS[2]

[1]Department of Earth and Planetary Science, University of New Mexico, Albuquerque, NM 87131<ldonohoo@unm.edu>
[2]New Mexico Museum of Natural History and Science, 1801 Mountain Road NW, Albuquerque, NM 87104

THE PLATE motion history for North America during parts of the Mesozoic has been the subject of considerable debate. APW paths represent a time sequence of paleomagnetic poles that record plate motions relative to a time-averaged geomagnetic pole and, to a first order (in the absence of true polar wander), the Earth's rotation axis. Accurate APW path constructions are fundamental for understanding palegeography, plate kinematics, and terrane displacement in relation to both intraplate deformation and global tectonics. Different models of APW path construction include time averaging of paleomagnetic poles (Irving and Irving, 1982) and fitting small-circle segments that are pinned to an Euler pole of rotation through paleomagnetic poles (Gordon et al., 1984). The former model predicts variable plate motions along a smooth track. The later model defines smooth small-circle segments, representing times of constant plate velocity (tracks), and abrupt changes in plate motion, representing times of boundary reconfiguration (cusps). The paleomagnetic Euler pole model predicts a very sharp (about 160°) cusp during the very latest Triassic to earliest Jurassic (J1-cusp), which is interpreted to reflect break up of the North American, African, and South American plates. Understanding the history of North American plate motion is critical to deriving and appropriate kinematic model for the opening and early plate evolution of the central Atlantic basin.

Rocks that have provided paleomagnetic data for much of the Triassic and Jurassic segments of the North American APW path crop out either in the northeast or southwest regions of the continent. Unfortunately, the data obtained from rock in these two regions are not consistent for many parts of the Mesozoic. Sedimentary strata from northeast North America were deposited in a series of rift basins and therefore provide much thicker sequences than those exposed in the American Southwest. A new high-quality magnetostratigraphy obtained from more continuously deposited sediments in the Southwest will aid in relating coeval units between the two regions of the continent despite differences in depositional environment and dominant sedimentary rock types. We are obtaining new paleomagnetic data from previously unexamined lacustrine and fluvial facies of the uppermost Triassic to lowermost Jurassic Moenave Formation east of St. George, Utah, to prepare a more robust APW path and magnetostratigraphy for this critical time interval. To date, two independent locations, Leeds and Warner Valley, have been sampled using hand-held drilling equipment. Twenty-four sites were sampled at Leeds and twenty-eight sites were sampled at Warner Valley. Preliminary data analyzed from seven sites suggests the Dinosaur Canyon Member at both Moenave locations is dominated by normal polarity (north seeking and shallow inclination directions) remanence, which, on the basis of magnetization directions, is interpreted to have been acquired early in the diagenetic history of these rocks by both detrital and pigmentary hematite.

REFERENCES

Gordon, R. G.. 1987. Polar wandering and paleomagnetism. Annual Review of Earth and Planetary Sciences, 15:567-593.

Irving, E. and Irving, G.. A. 1982. Apparent polar wander paths Carboniferous through Cenozoic and the assembly of Gondwana. Geophysical Surveys, 5:141-148.

Parker, W. G., Ash, S. R., and Irmis, R. B., eds., 2006.
A Century of Research at Petrified Forest National Park: Geology and Paleontology.
Museum of Northern Arizona Bulletin No. 62.

REINVESTIGATION OF LATE TRIASSIC FISH SITES IN THE CHINLE GROUP, SAN JUAN COUNTY, UTAH: NEW DISCOVERIES

ANDREW R. C. MILNER[1], DEBRA L. MICKELSON[2], JAMES I. KIRKLAND[3], AND JERALD D. HARRIS[4]

[1]St. George Dinosaur Discovery Site at Johnson Farm, 2180 E. Riverside Dr., UT 84790 <amilner@sgcity.org>
[2]9151 E. 29th Ave., Denver, CO 80238
[3]Utah Geological Survey, 1594 W. North Temple, Suite 3110 P.O. Box 146100, Salt Lake City, UT 84114-6100
[4]Dixie State College, 225 S. 700 E., St. George, UT 84770.

FIELD INVESTIGATIONS of the Chinle Group, particularly the Owl Rock Formation, on Utah State Institutional Trust Lands in the area of Lisbon Valley (Figure 1.1) resulted in the collection of hundreds of specimens, consisting of fish, mollusks, tetrapod remains, plants, invertebrate traces, and tetrapod tracks, including coelophysoid theropod footprints. Exploration in the area was sparked by an interest in obtaining some of the well-preserved Late Triassic fossil fishes described by Schaeffer (1967) for the Utah Museum of Natural History in Salt Lake City.

Walter Elkington of Ogden, Utah discovered several *in situ* fish in the middle of the Owl Rock Formation. Minor

quarrying took place in 2004, followed by a week of extensive excavation at the same site in 2005. Several horizons of well-preserved fishes were quarried at this locality, now coined "Walt's Quarry" (Figure 1.2).

The facies in Walt's Quarry display a series of green, extraformational pebble conglomerate (0.1-4 cm grain sizes) commonly containing various sizes of bone fragments along with tetrapod teeth. These conglomerates are interbedded with reddish-brown, purple, gray, green, and yellow-brown sheets of mostly siltstone and fine-grained sandstone with occasional mudstone and friable shales. Many of the fish-bearing beds of fine sandstone and siltstone contain small, localized accumula

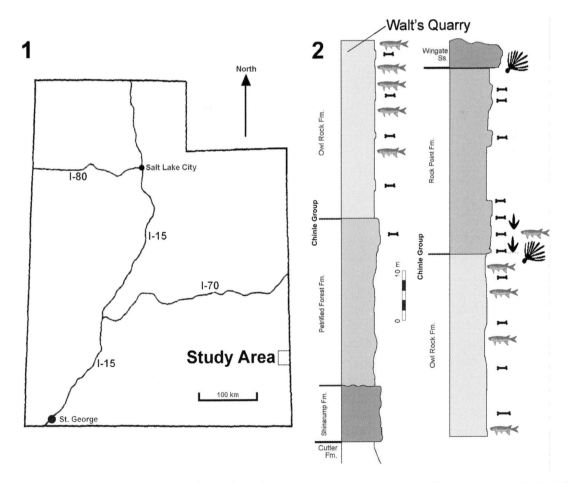

Figure 1. 1. Map of Utah showing the approximate study area (exact locality information available to qualified researchers at the Utah Geological Survey and/or the Utah Museum of Natural History); 2. Generalized stratigraphic section illustrating location of "Walt's Quarry" within the Owl Rock Formation of the Chinle Group. The approximate localities for tetrapod bones, fish plants, and vertebrate tracks are indicated. Modified after Lucas measured section (pers. com., 2006).

Figure 2. Body and trace fossils from the Upper Triassic Owl Rock and Rock Point formations, Chinle Group, San Juan County, Utah. *1*. Nearly complete specimen of a semionotid *Semionotus* n. sp.; *2*. Well-preserved redfieldiid *Cionichthys dunklei*; *3*. Conchostracan arthropod found in possible "living position"; *4*. Aetosaur scute; *5*. Phytosaur mandible fragment displaying two partial tooth sockets; *6*. Possible phytosaur tracks (*Apatopus*?); *7*. Two partial *Grallator* footprints; *8*. Very large phytosaur swim track; *9*. Cycad leaf impression, cf. *Zamites powellii*; *10*. Fern frond, cf. *Cynepteris*. Scale bars: 1, 3 and 4 = 2 cm; 2 and 5 = 1 cm; 8 = 10 cm; 6, 7, 9 and 10 = 5 cm.

tions of both extraformational pebbles with grains no bigger than 0.5 cm, and intraformational rip-up clasts of green and reddish-brown mudstone.

Within the 2.5 m thick package of Walt's Quarry, at least four very productive fish-bearing horizons have been identified, all showing excellent quality of preservation (Figures 2.1, 2.2). The following fish taxa have thus far been identified: *Synorichthys stewarti*, *Cionichthys dunklei* (Figure 2.1), *Cionichthys* sp., *Turseodus*? sp., *Lasalichthys* sp., *Semionotus* n. sp. (Figure 2.2), *Semionotus* sp., *Hemicalypterus weiri*, *Chinlea sorenseni*, and Redfieldiidae n. sp. Other fish taxa will undoubtedly be identified among the over 150 individual specimens collected in 2004-2005. Additional field work is planned for 2006 and future seasons.

The *in situ* positions of many of the articulated fossil fish were mapped and their orientation and distribution appear to be random, though this may change as additional data from future quarrying is added. Associated with the fish fossils are gastropods, and large, three-dimensional conchostracans found in possible "living position" (Figure 2.3).

Most of the tetrapod bone fragments are unidentifiable due to predepositionial weathering but several are identifiable, at least to higher taxon, including aetosaur scutes (Figure 2.4) and abundant phytosaur remains consisting of jaw fragments (Figure 2.5), a large partial ilium, vertebrae, teeth, and skull fragments. Phytosaurs from the Chinle and base of the overlying Wingate Sandstone have previously been described from the study area (Morales and Ash, 1993; Lucas et al., 1997). Other tetrapod taxa will no doubt result from further exploration and preparation.

Late Triassic tracks are known from terrestrial deposits at several dozen localities in Utah. Two track localities near the aforementioned body fossil sites are the first reported from this portion of southeastern Utah. All of the tracks recognized during this study are preserved on talus slopes in blocks originating in the Rock Point Formation of the Chinle Group (Figure 1.2). The track-producing unit is a prominent ledge that forms a rim along the upper portion of the valley below the capping Wingate Sandstone. The initial discovery site (hereafter called IDS), located very close to Walt's Quarry, reveals over a dozen isolated footprints with possible affinities to phytosaurs (*Apatopus*?) (Figure 2.6), as well as poorly preserved prints of possible *Brachychirotherium* affinities, and theropodan *Grallator* tracks (Figure 2.7). Tracks at the IDS are preserved as natural casts, actual tracks, and underprints. Poorly preserved plant fossils (Figures 2.9 and 2.10) have been found in the same talus slopes with tetrapod tracks and invertebrate burrows below the IDS; they are tentatively identifiable and add to a reconstruction of the paleoenvironment.

The second track locality produced a number of very large swim tracks (Figure 2.8) preserved as natural molds. Possible terrestrial tracks also occur at this site, but their exact relationship to the large swim tracks has not been established at this time. Most of these tracks are interpreted as having been made by large swimming phytosaurs. These proposed phytosaur swim tracks are similar in appearance to others from the Chinle Group in southwestern Utah (Lockley and Milner, in press). Fully formed, terrestrial tracks bear evidence of four and possibly five digits. Other tracks are either elongate, linear scrapes or swipe marks preserved in thick, reddish-brown sandstone. Multiple footprints preserve four and/or five ungual impressions created as the animal became more buoyant in the water. Ripple marks and mud cracks present on fallen blocks suggest periodic subaerial exposure.

REFERENCES

Lockley, M. G. and A. R. C. Milner. In press. Tetrapod tracksites from the Shinarump Formation (Chinle Group, Late Triassic) of southwestern Utah. New Mexico Museum of Natural History and Science Bulletin.

Lucas, S. G., A. B. Heckert, O. J. Anderson, and J. W. Estep 1997. Phytosaur from the Wingate Sandstone in southeastern Utah and the Triassic-Jurassic boundary on the Colorado Plateau, p. 49-59. *In* B. Anderson, D. Boaz, and R. D. McCord (eds.), Southwest Paleontological Symposium Proceedings, Volume 1. Mesa Southwest Museum and Southwest Paleontological Society, Mesa.

Morales, M. and S. R. Ash 1993. The last phytosaurs?, p. 357-358. *In* S. G. Lucas and M. Morales (eds.), The Nonmarine Triassic. New Mexico Museum of Natural History & Science Bulletin No. 3, Albuquerque.

Schaeffer, B. 1967. Late Triassic fishes from the western United States. Bulletin of the American Museum of Natural History, 135:289-342.

Parker, W. G., Ash, S. R., and Irmis, R. B., eds., 2006.
A Century of Research at Petrified Forest National Park: Geology and Paleontology.
Museum of Northern Arizona Bulletin No. 62.

NEW ADDITIONS TO THE FAUNA OF THE UPPER TRIASSIC CHINLE FORMATION OF UTAH

WILLIAM G. PARKER[1], DANIEL L. BRINKMAN[2], MARILYN FOX[2], JACQUES A. GAUTHIER[2], WALTER G. JOYCE[2], AND LYNDON K. MURRAY[3]

[1]Division of Resource Management, Petrified Forest National Park, Box 2217, Petrified Forest, AZ 86028 <William_Parker@nps.gov>
[2]Yale Peabody Museum of Natural History, Yale University, 170 Whitney Avenue, New Haven, CT 06520
[3]Department of Geological Sciences, University of Texas at Austin, 1 University Station C1100, Austin, TX 78712

THE CHINLE Formation has historically been studied extensively in Arizona and New Mexico, but less so in Utah. This could in part reflect the fact that exposures of this formation are limited in this state to seemingly endless narrow bands of outcrop that are often difficult to access. Because vertebrate fossils from elsewhere in the Chinle Formation have provided a wealth of information leading to a better understanding of Pangaean faunas during the Late Triassic (e.g., Long and Murry, 1995), Utah offers the potential for significant scientific discoveries.

The Yale Peabody Museum has been conducting fieldwork in the Chinle Formation of Utah since 2002. In the course of four field seasons, significant amounts of vertebrate fossils have been recovered, primarily from three areas, including the newly established Grand Staircase-Escalante National Monument (GSENM). These areas include the Vermillion Cliffs and Paria Canyon of GSENM (Kane County), the western rim of the Circle Cliffs in GSENM (Garfield County), and the areas surrounding Temple Butte off Red Canyon (San Juan County). Additional material was also recovered from the San Rafael Swell (Emory County) and Hurricane Mesa (Washington County; Fig. 1).

Most of this material was collected from the Monitor Butte and Petrified Forest Members of the Chinle Formation. The majority of the collected material represents crocodile-line archosaurs and metoposaurid temnospondyls; however, non-tetrapod vertebrates and unionid bivalves have also been collected. Bird-line archosaurs are represented by a single proximal end of a tibia, which is not diagnosable below the clade Dinosauriformes.

Metopotosaurid specimens tentatively referable to *Buettneria* are common in the Circle Cliffs and Paria Canyon/Vermillion Cliffs areas. This material consists mainly of interclavicle and clavicle fragments. A small metoposaurid is known from skull material and vertebrae that are diagnostic of *Apachesaurus*. These finds represent the first occurrence of

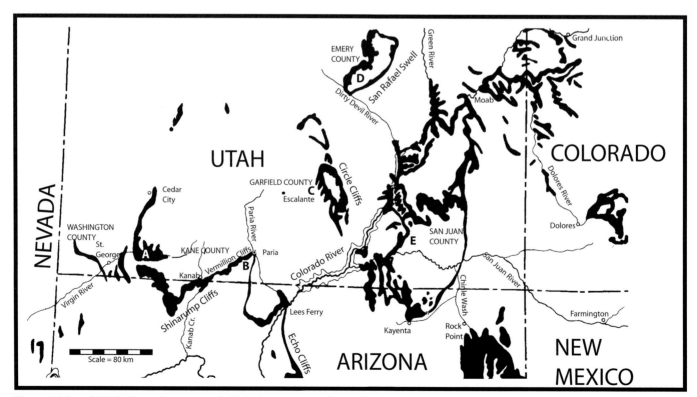

Figure *1*. Map of Chinle Formation outcrops in Utah showing areas where collections were made by the Yale Peabody Museum. *A*. Hurricane Mesa, Washington County; *B*. Vermillion Cliffs/Paria Canyon, Kane County; *C*. Circle Cliffs, Garfield County; *D*. San Rafael Swell, Emery County; *E*. Red Canyon, San Juan County. Adapted from Stewart et al. (1972).

that taxon from Utah.

Phytosaurs are represented mainly by isolated teeth, which have been collected from all areas with the exception of the San Rafael Swell. Notable specimens include two lower jaws from Wolverine Loop in the Circle Cliffs area. Unfortunately, no diagnostic skull material (e.g., squamosal) has yet been recovered. Aetosaur specimens from the Circle Cliffs include partial paramedian and lateral plates of *Stagonolepis*, *Desmatosuchus*, and a *Paratypothorax*-like species. This material represents the first Utah occurrence for the latter two taxa.

The Circle Cliffs area also provided an almost complete, articulated skeleton (missing the skull) of a poposaurid crocodile-line archosaur (Benoit and Yarborough-Fitzgerald,

2004). This specimen is currently under preparation and will be described elsewhere. A second crocodile-line archosaur from the same quarry is also being prepared for description.

Published tetrapod records from the Chinle Formation of Utah are rare. With the exception of a handful of papers (e.g., Lucas, 1898; Parrish and Good, 1987; Morales and Ash, 1993; Parrish, 1999; Heckert et al., 1999; Fraser et al., 2005), the majority of fossils from the Chinle of Utah are currently undescribed (e.g., Deblieux et al., 2003).

Although much of the material is fragmentary, it often represents the first occurrences of taxa in Utah. Furthermore, specimens such as the poposaurid demonstrate the potential for important and superbly-preserved specimens.

REFERENCES

Benoit, M., and Yarborough-Fitzgerald, V. 2004. Decay conditions of an Upper Triassic poposaur: evidence from calcium carbonate nodules. Journal of Vertebrate Paleontology 24(3 Supplement):38A.

Deblieux, D. D., Smith, J. A., McGuire, J., Santucci, V., Kirkland, J. I., and M. Butler. 2003. A paleontological inventory of Zion National Park, Utah, and the use of GIS technology to create paleontological sensitivity maps for use of resource management. Journal of Vertebrate Paleontology 23(3 Supplement):45A.

Fraser, N.C., Irmis, R.B., and Elliott, D.K. 2005. A procolophonid (Parareptilia) from the Owl Rock Member, Chinle Formation of Utah, USA. Palaeontologica Electronica, 8(1):13A:7p., 335KB.

Heckert, A.B., Lucas, S.G., and J. D. Harris. 1999. An aetosaur (Reptilia: Archosauria) from the Upper Triassic Chinle Group, Canyonlands National Park, Utah. National Park Service Paleontological Research Technical Report, 4:23-26.

Long, R.A., and P. A. Murry. 1995, Late Triassic (Carnian and Norian) tetrapods from the southwestern United States. New Mexico Museum of Natural History and Science Bulletin, 4:1-254.

Lucas, F. A. 1898. A new crocodile from the Trias of southern Utah. American Journal of Science, 6:399-400.

Morales, M., and S. R. Ash. 1993. The last phytosaurs? New Mexico Museum of Natural History and Science Bulletin, 3:357-358.

Parrish, J.M., 1999, Small fossil vertebrates from the Chinle Formation (Upper Triassic)of southern Utah, p. 45-50. *In* Gillette, D.D., (ed.), Vertebrate Paleontology in Utah, Volume 99-1, Utah Geological Survey Miscellaneous Publication, Utah Geological Survey.

Parrish, J.M., and S. C. Good. 1987. Preliminary report on vertebrate and invertebrate fossil occurrences, Chinle Formation (Upper Triassic), southeastern Utah. Four Corners Geological Society, 10:109-118.

Stewart, J. H., Poole, F. G., and R. F. Wilson. 1972. Changes in nomenclature of the Chinle Formation on the southern part of the Colorado Plateau: 1850s-1950s, pp. 75-103. *In* Breed, C. S. and W. J. Breed (eds.), Investigations in the Triassic Chinle Formation. Museum of Northern Arizona Bulletin 47, Flagstaff.

Parker, W. G., Ash, S. R., and Irmis, R. B., eds., 2006.
A Century of Research at Petrified Forest National Park: Geology and Paleontology.
Museum of Northern Arizona Bulletin No. 62.

A REFINEMENT OF MAGNETOSTRATIGRAPHY AND BIOSTRATIGRAPHY OF THE UPPER TRIASSIC CHINLE GROUP IN CENTRAL AND NORTH-CENTRAL NEW MEXICO

KATE E. ZEIGLER[1]*, JOHN W. GEISSMAN[1], AND SPENCER G. LUCAS[2]

[1]Department of Earth & Planet. Sci., Univ. of New Mexico, Albuquerque, NM 87131*<bludragon@gmail.com>
[2]New Mexico Museum of Natural History and Science, 1801 Mountain Road NW, Albuquerque, NM 87104

AS DEMONSTRATED by vertebrate biostratigraphy and palynostratigraphy, the Upper Triassic Chinle Group spans most of the Late Triassic. In New Mexico, the Zuni Mountains (central New Mexico) and the Chama Basin (north-central New Mexico) both contain excellent exposures of Chinle Group strata that are currently being examined in order to both refine Late Triassic biostratigraphy and improve the magnetic polarity chronology for the Late Triassic in the American Southwest.

Recent fossil discoveries have expanded the known fauna for both the lower Chinle Salitral Formation (= Bluewater Creek Formation and Blue Mesa Member, Petrified Forest Formation of Arizona) and the upper Chinle Mesa Montosa Member (lower Petrified Forest Formation). The addition of the metoposaurid amphibian *Buettneria* and the aetosaur *Desmatosuchus* to the fauna from the Salitral Formation confirms an Adamanian age for these strata. The discovery of material pertaining to *Buettneria*, the aetosaurs *Typothorax coccinarum* and *Paratypothorax*, the archosaur *Vancleavea*, as well as other fauna, confirms a Revueltian age for the Mesa Montosa Member.

The Chinle Group was deposited by a fluvial system and consists predominantly of red to purple mudstones with some red to orange siltstones and red to buff sandstones. In central and north-central New Mexico, both lower and upper Chinle Group strata are well-exposed and are being examined for polarity stratigraphy. Our sampling methods concentrate on hematitic mudrocks, using an intricate block sampling technique. These materials typically carry a well-defined, well-grouped, north- or south-seeking, shallow inclination magnetization dominated by pigmentary hematite that is unblocked below about 660°C. For example, a single horizon (level 39) in the Painted Desert Member of the Petrified Forest Formation yields an estimated site mean of $D=172.9°$, $I=7.0°$, $á_{95}=5.5°$ and $k=102.5$ (N = 8 independent samples). Indurated, coarser-grained deposits are sampled by more conventional methods. Sandstones and siltstones of the Poleo Formation contain both detrital and authigenic hematite and some detrital magnetite as the magnetization carriers and typically yield a well-defined magnetization at the site (single bed) level (e.g., site 11, eight independent samples, yields an estimated site mean of $D=187.4°$, $I=0.8°$, $á_{95}=3.4°$ and $k=268.1$).

A very preliminary polarity reversal stratigraphy has been developed for the Poleo and Petrified Forest formations in the Chama basin. The Petrified Forest Formation includes multiple polarity intervals, but to date a firm correlation with more complete polarity records for the Late Triassic (e.g., Newark Series) cannot be made. All accepted sites in the Poleo Formation yield data of reverse polarity. The upper part of the Bluewater Creek Formation and lower Blue Mesa Member (Petrified Forest Formation) in the Zuni Mountains, central New Mexico, appear to be entirely of reverse polarity.

Parker, W. G., Ash, S. R., and Irmis, R. B., eds., 2006.
A Century of Research at Petrified Forest National Park: Geology and Paleontology.
Museum of Northern Arizona Bulletin No. 62.

LATE TRIASSIC (NORIAN) PALAEOECOSYSTEM OF THE LOWERMOST ELLIOT FORMATION (SALPETERBERG, EASTERN CAPE, SOUTH AFRICA)

EMESE M. BORDY, ROSE PREVEC, AND CHUMANI MAKHWELO

Department of Geology, Rhodes University, Grahamstown, 6140, South Africa <e.bordy@ru.ac.za & rose.adendorff@ru.ac.za>

THIS PAPER discusses the tectonic, sedimentological and palaeontological settings of the lower Elliot Formation (Upper Triassic) in the main Karoo Basin which, together with the Parana (South-America), Beacon (Antarctica) and Bowen (Australia) basins, formed part of the extensive Late Paleozoic - Early Mesozoic pan-Gondwanan foreland system.

The Elliot Formation, together with the underlying Molteno and overlying Clarens formations, records the tectonic events which occurred during the final stages of foreland basin development in southwestern Gondwana, and therefore represent the sedimentary fill of the Late Triassic – Early Jurassic foresag (Fig. 1A). The study area exposes the basal contact of the Elliot Formation which has been reconstructed as a second order sequence boundary. On a basinal scale, this cryptic unconformity is detectable mostly through the architectural difference between the sedimentary packages below and above resulting from a fluvial style change that occurred during the Late Triassic. From a geodynamic view-point, the study area is exceptionally important because of a discontinuous layer of quartzite pebble conglomerate (Fig. 1B) which overlies the unconformity between the Molteno and Elliot formations. This <0.5 m thick, massive, poorly-sorted, matrix-supported (medium to coarse sand), coarse pebble conglomerate is detectable throughout the study area at a break in the lower part of the hill slopes, at the edge of a semi-continuous, 10-20 m wide geomorphological plateau. This quartzite pebble conglomerate further corroborates the idea that, prior to the deposition of the Elliot Formation, a minor tectonic loading event occurred south of the main Karoo Basin in the orogen (Cape Fold Belt). The formation of the conglomerate layer may be associated with the reworking of previously deposited alluvial fan and braided river units of the Molteno Formation in response to the uplift of the flexural forebulge during this minor tectonic event (Fig. 1A). Similar quartzite pebble conglomerates as well as large (cobble and boulder size), solitary quartzite pebbles are common in the underlying Molteno Formation. Solitary quartzite pebbles up to 28 cm in diameter also occur scattered throughout the Elliot Formation, but other quartzite pebble conglomerate layers have not yet been described from this stratigraphic unit. The study area provides additional evidence in support of minor, probably piggy-back thrusting-related tectonic movements in the orogen. In particular, the fact that the arenaceous units of the lower Elliot Formation show well-developed upward thickening and coarsening trends (Fig.

1C) is taken as evidence for an increasingly sagging foresag which was connected to the Cape Fold Belt via a progressively steepened foreslope during the subsequent orogenic unloading phase (Fig. 1A). These observations also suggest that previous palaeoenvironmental interpretations reconstructing the Molteno and Elliot formations as facies equivalents are debatable.

Based on sedimentological evidence, the depositional environment of the lower Elliot Formation in the study area is identical to outcrop areas of the same stratigraphic unit analyzed in the other parts of the basin. Both the internal and external geometries as well as other facies characteristics (e.g., point bar sequences), indicate that the unit was deposited in perennial meandering river systems with extensive floodplains. Features indicating channel avulsions are also particularly well-developed in the form of ripple marked surfaces at the top of the arenaceous units (Fig. 1D). Furthermore, observations of an up-sequence increase in the abundance of calcretes in the palaeosols, the deeper red colouring of the argillaceous units, as well as a distinct decrease in fossil plant remains, all support the idea that gradual aridification had already begun during the deposition of the lower Elliot Formation.

Palaeontological findings in the study area include *in situ*, but poorly preserved, postcranial elements of large dinosaurs, unidentified trace fossils and, especially in the vicinity of the basal contact, numerous megaplant fossil remains (Fig.1E). In the Molteno Formation, diverse floras are abundantly represented, and have been well documented in the literature from many localities. However, records of macroplant fossils in the uppermost Triassic, above the contact of the Molteno and Elliot formations are very rare, and mostly refer to fossil wood occurrences. Preliminary investigations indicate that impressions and casts of plants in the base of the Elliot Formation may be far more common than has been recognised in the past, and further investigations of these palaeofloras may shed some light on the floristic changes that occurred in the lead-up to the extinction associated with the Triassic-Jurassic boundary. These fossil plant remains are exclusively preserved as impressions and casts in a massive, very well cemented, very coarse grained, sandy siltstone that overlies the sequence boundary between the Molteno and Elliot formations. The material appears, in some cases, to have been preserved in growth position, and comprises moulds and impressions of large, branching woody

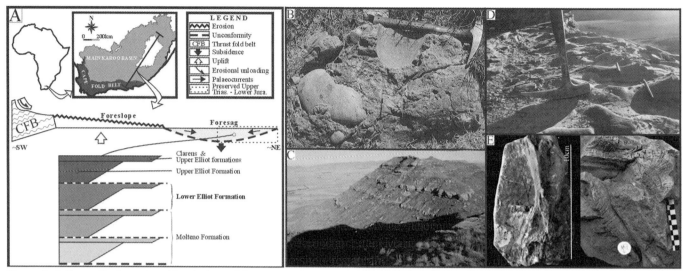

Figure *1. A.* Generalized stratigraphic relations of the Upper Triassic-Lower Jurassic Molteno, Elliot, and Clarens formations; *B.* Massive, poorly sorted, matrix-supported, coarse pebble conglomerate at the lowermost part of the Elliot Formation; *C.* Upward thickening and coarsening arenaceous units in the lower Elliot Formation; *D.* Ripple marked surfaces at the top of an upward-fining channel fill sandstone unit; *E.* Various plant imprints of woody stems and branches.

axes with peculiar rugose external ornamentation. The branches are alternate or arranged in tight whorls, as evidenced by an internal cast with robust, spirally arranged vascular traces.

Taphonomic constrains did not allow for the identification of the fossil bone material in the study area. However, based on similar findings in other parts of the basin, these large bone fossils are tentatively considered to belong to an early dinosaur group which was dominated by robust, herbivorous sauropodomorphs (associated with the basal part of the 'Euskelosaurus Range Zone').

The geological and palaeontological data collected in the study area strongly support interpretations from regional-scale investigations of the lower Elliot Formation suggesting that the perennial rivers and their fertile floodplains sustained a complex plant and animal association and included large, herbivorous dinosaurs and arborescent plant forms. The picture that also emerges from the current findings, is that during the Norian, the main Karoo Basin experienced gradual aridification, perhaps escalating into a serious environmental stress towards the end of Triassic and leading to the gradual decrease in biotic diversity as well as significant differences in faunal composition between the Upper Triassic and Lower Jurassic units of the Elliot Formation.

Parker, W. G., Ash, S. R., and Irmis, R. B., eds., 2006.
A Century of Research at Petrified Forest National Park: Geology and Paleontology.
Museum of Northern Arizona Bulletin No. 62.

THE REGIONAL TETRAPOD FAUNA OF THE CENTRAL EUROPEAN TYPE IN THE LOWER TRIASSIC OF EASTERN EUROPE

IGOR V. NOVIKOV AND ANDREY G. SENNIKOV

Paleontological Institute of RAS, 123 Profsoyuznaya St., Moscow, 117647 <inovik@paleo.ru>

A STUDY of the spatial differentiation of the tetrapod faunas of Eastern Europe during the Early Triassic has resulted in the recognition of three biogeographical areals. These include (1) the central and northern areas of the East European platform (including the Timan-North Urals region), (2) the South Cis-Urals, (3) the southern area of the platform. Among the reasons for the differentiation are the biogeographical peculiarities connected with the influence of the regional biotas beyond Eastern Europe, and the belonging to the specific biotopes are the most well-defined.

The main localities of the southern biogeographic unit are situated in the Don River Basin (Volgograd region), known as "Donskaya Luka locality" in the literature. The bone-bearing deposits there are conglomerates and sandstones pertaining to the Lipovskaya Formation, which lies unconformably on the Carboniferous limestones. The locality is unique for its abundance and faunal composition. The vertebrate community known from there includes fishes (dipnoans, actinopterygians, elasmobranchs and coelacanths), temnospondyl amphibians, thecodonts, prolacertiforms, procolophonids, trilophosaurids, therapsids, sauropterygians and, probably ichthyopterygians.

The bulk of the tetrapod materials from the Donskaya Luka locality belong to temnospondyls that are represented by three families, Capitosauridae (*Parotosuchus panteleevi*), Trematosauridae (*Trematosaurus* sp. nov.) and Brachyopidae (*Batrachosuchoides lacer*). The thecodonts are known to include the rauisuchids (*Tsylmosuchus donensis*, *Scythosuchus basileus*) and the erythrosuchid *Garjainia* (?) sp. The prolacertiforms are represented by a new genus and species (unpublished) reminiscent of the *Tanystropheus antiquus* from the

Triassic of Germanic Basin in morphology of cervical vertebrae. The procolophonid, trilophosaurid and therapsid materials are extremely rare and consist of lower jaw fragments. The procolophonids *Orenburgia* (*O. enigmatica*) and *Kapes* (?) sp. are known by just four finds. The first recorded trilophosaurids include *Coelodontognathus* (*C. donensis* and *C. ricovi*) and *Vitalia* (*V. grata*). A poorly known *Doniceps* (*D. lipovensis*) is thought to be assignable to the trilophosaurids also. The only known therapsid find is a new genus and species of a kannemeyerid dicynodont (*Putillosaurus sennikovi*). This is the only evidence of a dicynodont of Olenekian age in Eastern Europe. The sauropterygian materials include the isolated bones, both cranial and postcranial, of the cymatosaurid *Tanaisosaurus kalandadzei*. This form probably is the earliest known Triassic eosauropterygian. The ichthyopterygians are represented by a single tooth presumably assignable to ichthyosaurs.

As a whole, the tetrapod assemblage of the Donskaya Luka locality pertains to the late grouping of the *Parotosuchus* fauna, specific to the Gamskian horizon (Upper Olenekian) in the Lower Triassic of the East European platform. The presence of a number of marine forms (especially sauropterygians, ichthyopterygians and coelacanths) caused by the formation of the locality on the northern coast of Tethys is one of the main peculiarities of the assemblage that distinguishes it from those of South Cis-Urals and northern areas of the East European platform. On the other, the temnospondyl *Trematosaurus*, trilophosaurids, cymatosaurids, and tanystropheids as well as the prevalence of the rauisuchids clearly indicate relations with the Central European and Euroamerican tetrapod communities.

Parker, W. G., Ash, S. R., and Irmis, R. B., eds., 2006.
A Century of Research at Petrified Forest National Park: Geology and Paleontology.
Museum of Northern Arizona Bulletin No. 62.

THE WESTERN TETHYS FAUNA: THE SALTED SIDE OF THE NORIAN

ANDREA TINTORI

Dipartimento di Scienze della Terra 'A. Desio', Via Mangiagalli 34, I-20133 Milano <andrea.tintori@unimi.it>

AT THE beginning of the 1970s, the first fossil locality in the upper Calcare di Zorzino (Zorzino Limestone = ZZ) was discovered near Cene (Bergamo). Several hundred fishes, crustaceans, and a few reptiles, including the oldest known pterosaurs, were recovered from a 6 cm bed. Within few years it was clear that the Cene site was not an exception in the Norian and many other localities were discovered in the Bergamo and Brescia Prealps. More or less coeval localities (Seefeld and Hallein in Austria, Giffoni near Salerno in southern Italy) have been known since the beginning of the last century. They yield only a few taxa, usually common to the ZZ fauna: the latter appears much richer, but possibly only because of twenty years of regular collection. Also less diverse are faunas from the 'Rhaetian' Bone Beds of Central Europe and England, where erosion and transportation preserved only some of the hardest elements such as teeth of durophagous or large predatory fishes.

The ZZ was deposited in several, small (width up to several kilometers) semigraben basins inside a huge carbonate platform (Dolomia Principale= Haupdolomite) extending from Spain to Greece. Being surrounded by very shallow environments, they had a restricted water circulation which led anoxic conditions developing in their deepest part especially in correspondence to the Middle/Late Norian transgression that is represented by the passage from the ZZ to the Agillite di Riva di Solto. The only connections with open sea was throughout long tidal channels which acted as ecological barriers for large nectonic organisms such as ichthyosaurs, which have been never found in this area. The carbonate platform, owing to warmer and more salted waters, was probably poorly inhabited. The organic mounds surrounding the basins could emerge, giving rise to ephemeral islands colonized by the cheirolepidiacean conifer *Brachyphillum*, which can survive at least in brackish waters. Thus, all fossils from the ZZ must be considered alloctonous, yet they are intrabasinal like marine organisms. Mainly nectonic, but also benthic and terrestrial organisms are represented in the ZZ fauna, allowing the restoration of the shallow marine environments and of the nearby emerged land. The high number of specimens and taxa together with the excellent preservation of almost all the material induce us to consider these Norian localities as Konservative Fossil- Lagerstaeten though soft tissue preservation is very rare.

THE FISH FAUNA

The fish fauna from the ZZ is the richest of the Triassic if we consider a single fossiliferous level: at least 30 genera have been already described or are under description, while several others have been simply recorded in the collections, waiting for more specimens to be prepared. Thus, probably more than 50 genera are represented, ranging from about 2 cm in standard length up to the 180 cm of the longest *Saurichthys* so far known. A few species are represented by hundreds or thousands of specimens, like pholidophorids, several others by dozens and many others by few or single specimens.

Apart from the numbers, this fauna is important because it records the first important radiation of neopterygians at a time when paleopterygians were still important, especially at the top of the trophic hierarchy. In fact, all the large predators are basal actinopterygians: *Saurichthys*, *Birgeria* and the peltopleuriform *Gabanellia* can be considered as the high-level predators, together with a couple of coelacanth genera. A peculiar chondrostean is *Thoracopterus*, a flying (gliding) fish also known from the Carnian sites of Raibl (Italy) and Lunz (Austria). Regarding neopterygians, the several pholidophorid species were by far the commonest fishes, reaching about 70% of the collected specimens, but durophagous fishes also bloomed. Macrosemiids (*Legnonotus* and a new genus), pycnodonts (*Brembodus*, *Eomesodon*, *Gibbodon* and a new genus from Early Norian of the Brescia area), and semionotiforms (*Paralepidotus*, *Sargodon*, *Dapedium*, *Dandya*, *Semionotus* and other undescribed genera) are very well represented. *Paralepidotus* was probably the most common and is now very well known also in its ontogeny, collected specimens range from 7 cm up to 50 cm in standard length. Durophagy seems to be the 'new deal' for neopterygians: the changes in the suspensorium rendered the closing of their jaws much more powerful so that many new groups entered a large trophic niche till then underexploited. Each of these species shows a peculiar dentition: prehensile teeth are present or absent and variously shaped molariform teeth are arranged in more or less regular rows. Body shape and size also vary a lot; from fusiform macrosemiids to discoidal, laterally compressed pycnodonts; from a few centimeters (*Dandya*, *Eomesodon*) up to one meter (*Sargodon*). The result of these variations is that different species exploited similar niches without interferring with one-another. Ejecta, coprolites and coquinas made of shell fragments, witness the great feeding activity on benthic molluscs. On the other hand, there are very few hybodont remains, usually common in the 'Rhaetian' Bone Beds of Central Europe. Here, the only widespread 'shark' is *Pseudodalatias barnstonensis*: its remains are made of tooth-rows with 11 teeth symmetrically arranged and are found by the hundreds.

THE REPTILE FAUNA

Though numerically speaking it is the poorest section of the ZZ fauna, reptiles are very important for the presence of endemic genera and the oldest pterosaurs so far known. Curiously enough for the preservation environment, most reptiles are terrestrial with land, arboreal or flying specializations. Only the thalattosaur *Endennasaurus* and the armoured placodont *Psephoderma* could spend part of their life in water, especially for feeding.

R. Wild started working on these reptiles, carefully describing the beautifully preserved pterosaurs from Cene, while the completion of reptile work has been recently undertaken by S. Renesto. His work indicates the presence of arboreal forms such as *Megalancosaurus, Vallesaurus* and *Drepanosaurus*. The ephemeral islands with *Brachyphillum* could well have supported flying and arboreal reptiles, feeding on insects. Land reptiles include *Langobardisaurus* and the sphenodontid *Diphydontosaurus*, as well as *Aetosaurus* and *Mystriosuchus*. The former two could have lived on the small islands, while the life site of the latter two is more problematic, because they only are common to the Norian terrestrial deposits (Stubensandstein) of Germany. Taphonomically speaking, *Aetosaurus* is different from the other reptiles: only one small fragment has been recorded, while all the others include more or less complete, articulated specimens. This is also true for *Mystriosuchus*, known also by a complete individual, the most complete example of the genus. The endemic reptiles are usually small sized, very lightly built, and often have hollow bones. They could not have survived a long post mortem transport in superficial oxic and warm waters, while *Aetosaurus*, possibly from a larger landmass, floated for a long time, loosing body fragments along the way.

THE INVERTEBRATE FAUNA

Among invertebrates the most common fossils are crustaceans and bivalves, but also corals, brachiopods, echinoderms, gastropods can be found. Bivalves are almost all bissate epibenthic forms such as *Modiolus, Isognomon, 'Macrodus',* and *Gervillia*. Small specimens reached the anoxic waters often still articulated, transported by superficial currents or waves. Bivalves fragments are present in ejecta and coprolites from durophagous fishes and placodonts. They thrived all along the basins margins, together with calcareous algae, Porostromata, and many encrousting forams and problematics.

FIELD TRIP GUIDE

Parker, W. G., Ash, S. R., and Irmis, R. B., eds., 2006.
A Century of Research at Petrified Forest National Park: Geology and Paleontology.
Museum of Northern Arizona Bulletin No. 62.

ROADLOG THROUGH PETRIFIED FOREST NATIONAL PARK

WILLIAM G. PARKER[1], SIDNEY R. ASH[2], AND DAVID D. GILLETTE[3]

[1]Division of Resource Management, Petrified Forest National Park, Box 2217, Petrified Forest, AZ. <William_Parker@nps.gov>
[2]Department of Earth and Planetary Sciences, University of New Mexico, Albuquerque, NM 87120 <sidash@aol.com>
[3]Museum of Northern Arizona, 3101 N. Fort Valley Road, Flagstaff, AZ 86001.

This roadlog begins at the north entrance of the park and is adapted from Ash (1974), Gillette et al. (1986), and Parker (2005). Distances are in miles. For map see Appendix A.

0.0 Turn right off of Interstate 40 and follow signs to the park entrance.

0.2 Enter Petrified Forest National Park.

0.3 Painted Desert Visitor Center and Park Headquarters to the right. Go straight ahead to the entrance station. Completed in 1962, this complex was placed on the National Register of Historic Places in 2005. It is one of the only remaining examples of NPS "Mission 66" architecture designed by noted architect Richard Neutra. These buildings house the museum collections and a fossil preparation facility, as well as park administrative offices and personal residences. A bookshop and restrooms are in the headquarters building. A souvenir shop, lunchroom and gas station, managed by the Fred Harvey (Xanterra) organization, are also situated here.

0.4 Entrance Station. Eight viewpoints are scattered along the highway for the next few miles where the Painted Desert, Black Forest, and other features may be observed. Each viewpoint has something different to offer in the way of scenery. If visitors have the time, they should stop at each point for rewarding and slightly different views of the Painted Desert, Black Forest and other features.

For several miles, the road lies on a thin veneer of Cenozoic sediments and basalts which overly the colorful Upper Triassic Chinle Formation.

0.8 Tiponi Point. This is the first of several view points overlooking the "Painted Desert." The majority of reddish rocks visible from here and all along this escarpment belong to the Petrified Forest Member of the Chinle Formation. The brownish strata above the Chinle Formation are assigned to the Tertiary Bidahochi Formation.

1.7 Tawa Point.

2.0 Kachina Point. Excellent views of the Painted Desert and the large deposit of black-colored petrified wood called the Black Forest are visible from this viewpoint. The dry wash on the floor of the broad valley is appropriately named Lithodendron Wash because so many petrified logs are found in it and on the adjacent floodplain and hillsides. Chinde Mesa is on the skyline directly north of this point.

The prominent white band visible (Fig. 1A) on the sides or tops of many hills adjacent to Lithodendron Wash is a reworked volcaniclastic unit known as the Black Forest Bed (Ash, 1992). This distinctive unit was named for the Black Forest that occurs within it. Stratigraphically the Black Forest Bed lies a little below the middle of the Petrified Forest Member of the Chinle Formation (Ash and Creber, 1992). Although the Black Forest Bed is relatively thin and has a limited distribution in just the northern part of the park it is quite significant. Riggs et al. (2003) obtained a radiometric date of 213 ± 1.7 ma for this unit using detrital zircons. This date is important because it is the only absolute date for the Chinle Formation. The unit is of considerable interest to paleobotanists because it contains a small and rather unique flora and was the source of the holotype of the common Late Triassic wood *Araucarioxylon arizonicum* Knowlton (1888). In addition to *A. arizonicum* the flora includes the peculiar woods *Woodworthia arizonica* Jeffrey (1910) and *Schilderia adamanica* Daugherty (1934), as well as a small amount of mostly unidentifiable comminuted leaf matter.

Historical evidence indicates that the first non-Native Americans who explored a part of the area now included in Petrified Forest National Park and saw the petrified wood it contains arrived in the broad valley north of this viewpoint on December 2, 1853. They were members of the U.S. Army exploring expedition led by Lieutenant A. W. Whipple and entered the park area through the broad valley ahead of us. Whipple was so impressed by all the wood that was scattered about that he named the wash draining the area Lithodendron Creek, now more appropriately called Lithodendron Wash because it rarely has water in it. Fragments of the wood were collected and turned over to the American geologist W. P. Blake who reported (1856) that the cells in the wood "…are distinctly and beautifully preserved, and can be clearly seen by the naked eye." A German traveler by the name of Mollhausen who was accompanying the Whipple expedition also collected some small fragments of petrified wood and gave them to the famous German paleobotanst H. R. Goeppert for study. After examining them, Goeppert reported (in Mollhausen, 1858) that the wood was araucarian and suggested that it should be called

Figure 1. A, the Painted Desert looking north from Kachina Point. The whitish bed capping the hills in the front-center of the photo is the Black Forest Bed; B, the Painted Desert Inn in March 2006 after major renovations.

Araucarites mollhausianus but he neglected to properly describe it so the name is considered a "nomen nudum."

In May 1879, a small detail of soldiers under the command of Lieutenant J. F. C. Hegewald was sent to Lithodendron Wash from Fort Wingate, New Mexico to obtain two petrified logs for the Smithsonian Institution. The detail camped near Bear Spring, a few miles northeast of here, where they collected two sections of a large black log from the Black Forest Bed and transported them to Fort Wingate on special stone wagons. In a report, Hegewald (in Swaine and Hegewald, 1882) noted that the Navajos who lived in the area of Lithodendron Wash "thought it strange the Great Father in Washington" should want the logs. That may be so, but the soldiers who did the actual digging and lifting of the logs probably had much saltier comments to make about the project and General of the Army William T. Sherman who had proposed it. The sections were eventually shipped to the Smithsonian together with another log from the Fort Wingate area where they are now on display. There, Frank Knowlton studied them in thin section, and reported (1888) that they represented a new species which he called *Araucarioxylon arizonicum*.

He admitted that the name might be a synonym of *Araucarites mollhausianus*, the name Goeppert had applied to the wood Mollhausen had collected from Lithodendron Wash. Since that name is a *nomen nudum*, Knowlton could not verify his suspicion. It may never be possible to determine the identity of that wood because recent efforts by one of us (SRA) to locate the material studied by Goeppert indicate that it probably was destroyed during World War II.

The Spanish Pueblo Revival style buildings at the point include the famed Painted Desert Inn (Fig. 1B), which was originally constructed in the 1920s and remodeled in the 1930's by the CCC, after the structure and surrounding land was purchased by the National Park Service. The interior design work was directed by famed architect Mary Jane Colter. For many years a souvenir shop, restaurant, bar and gas station operated at the Inn but eventually the building became unstable because of foundation problems and was closed. In 2005, the Painted Desert Inn was stabilized and meticulously restored to its 1947 appearance when it was run by the Fred Harvey Company.

2.3 Road to Chinde Point picnic area. Picnic tables, shelters, and rest rooms are available at the picnic area. An excellent view of Chinde Mesa, a south-facing escarpment several miles north of the Park, is visible from Chinde Point. Chinde is a Navajo term meaning devil or ghost. Some of the logs in the Black Forest Bed can also be seen from this point.

In 1985, the partial skeleton of a small early dinosaur *Chindesaurus bryansmalli* (known to some affectionately as "Gertie") was collected below this point. At the time it was featured as the 'world's earliest dinosaur' and its collection received widespread media attention. While technically not the world's 'earliest dinosaur'; it is probably a basal member of the Saurischia and still of significance. The remains and a reconstruction of "Gertie" are on display in the Rainbow Forest Museum near the south entrance to the park.

2.9 Pintado Point. Pintado is the Spanish word for painted and refers to the Painted Desert which is so widely visible from this view point. This is the easternmost part of the Painted Desert which stretches northwest from here to the Colorado River and thence northward along the Echo Cliffs. Although Spanish explorers have been credited in popular publications with naming the Painted Desert, there is absolutely no primary documentary evidence to support this claim. In fact, the best evidence indicates that the name was coined by members of the exploring expedition led by Lieutenant Joseph P. Ives which passed north of here on its way to the Colorado River. The authorship of the name Painted Desert is attributed to the Ives Expedition in the most recent edition of "Arizona Place Names."

4.0 Nizhoni Point. Nizhoni is the Navajo term for beautiful.

Figure 2. The Painted Desert from Whipple Point looking northeast. The mesa to the right consists of deposits of the Petrified Forest Member of the Chinle Formation (note the white band that represents the Black Forest Bed) capped by lacustrine and volcanic deposits of the Miocene/Pliocene Bidahochi Formation.

This site offers views of the Devil's Playground to the west and the Dinosaur Hill area to the southwest. The Devil's Playground area was prospected heavily by Charles Camp in the 1920s, Ned Colbert in 1946, and the UCMP in the 1980s. Phytosaur skulls are common in the area, including the holotype of *Machaeroprosopus lithodendrorum* (*Leptosuchus crosbiensis*) and specimens of *Pseudopalatus*. In 2002, another complete skull of *Leptosuchus* sp. was collected from the area by National Park Service personnel, the first complete phytosaur skull collected from the park in 16 years. A second skull of *Leptosuchus sp.* was collected in 2005. The lighter colored outcrops in the Devil's Playground area belong to the Sonsela Member of the Chinle Formation. They are exposed due to structural folding between those outcrops and Nizhoni Point.

To the southwest the Petrified Forest Member is exposed along a north facing escarpment. This area includes famous fossil localities such as Lacey Point, Dinosaur Hill, and the Giving Site, which was discovered in 2004. The Giving Site has produced more dinosaur material than any other site in the southwest except for Ghost Ranch and possibly the Snyder Quarry (Heckert et al., 2003). To date, three partial coelophysoid skeletons, isolated coelophysoid elements, and a partial *Chindesaurus* skeleton have been recovered. In addition, the Giving Site has provided numerous skeletons of the pseudosuchian *Revueltosaurus callenderi*, which was originally believed to represent an ornithischian dinosaur (Parker et al., 2005).

Dinosaur Hill (PFV 40) and Lacey Point (PFV 27) are both quarries discovered in the 1980s by crews from the University of California, Berkeley. Lacey Point is a productive microsite (Murry, 1989), while Dinosaur Hill produced a partial theropod skeleton (Padian, 1986), a partial skeleton of

Figure 3. Looking west along old Route 66 (marked by the telephone poles). This 1922 Studebaker is part of an interpretive exhibit on Route 66.

the crocodylomorph *Hesperosuchus* (Parrish, 1991; Sereno and Wild, 1992), numerous *Revueltosaurus* teeth (Padian, 1990), as well as a large amount of amphibian material referable to *Apachesaurus gregorii* (Hunt, 1993). Just north of Dinosaur Hill is the "Billingsley Hill" Locality (PFV 34) where the tooth of an enigmatic amniote was collected in 1984. This specimen was previously believed to represent a traversodontid synapsid (Long and Murry, 1995) but its true affinities are still unclear (Irmis and Parker, 2005).

4.2 Whipple Point. This point is named after Lieutenant A. W. Whipple, who discovered the Black Forest section of the Petrified Forest on December 2, 1853 as described above. It offers views the Painted Desert (Fig. 2).

4.7 Lacey Point. This point is named in honor of Congressman John F. Lacey of Iowa, an ardent supporter of American antiquities in the early 20th century who introduced bills in Congress in 1902, 1904, and 1905 to establish Petrified Forest National Park. For various reasons, the bills always failed to pass both houses of Congress and it was not until December 1906 that President Theodore Roosevelt, using the powers granted him by the newly authorized Antiquities Act, established Petrified Forest National Monument.

4.9 Route 66. The line of telephone poles on either side of the park road follows the route of the original Route 66, which was the main highway through this area until I-40 was completed in the early 1960s. These poles carried wires used for long distance telephone services until they were transferred to relay stations a few years after Route 66 was abandoned and then to satellites.

5.0 Overpass over Interstate 40. The surface of the road slopes southward at a low angle to the Puerco River a distance of almost 4 miles.

8.9 On the left, there is a small exposure of the upper part of

Figure *4.* Looking south along the main park road towards a mesa capped by the sandstone facies of the Newspaper Rock bed in the Puerco River Valley.

the Chinle Formation in a hill that rises above the general topography of the area. At one time, the material in the hill was quarried for road material. The hill is informally known as "Rattlesnake Hill."

Nearly all of the rocks that we can see south of here are assigned to the Chinle Formation. The sloping surface of the mesa across the river is held up by the dip slope of the northward dipping (3°) Newspaper Rock bed (Fig. 4). The bed was deposited in a shallow meandering northeastern flowing stream. The name of this bed is derived from Newspaper Rock, a large talus block of this bed which is covered with many petroglyphs. At Newspaper Rock, the bed is about 30 feet thick and forms a distinct massive cliff. It thins toward the southeast and within a few miles of Newspaper Rock it divides into several thin tongues. Eventually they grade into mudstone deposits. The Newspaper Rock bed is of interest because it provides an excellent marker bed in the otherwise more or less homogeneous Blue Mesa Member of the Chinle. Also, most of the leaf localities in the Petrified Forest are closely associated with the bed.

The trees on the left are all that is left of a homestead that was bought out by the federal government.

10.2 Burlington Northern-Santa Fe Railroad Overpass.

10.3 Adamana. Road to the right (west) leads to the village of Adamana (Fig. 5). The town was established in 1890 by the Santa Fe Railroad Company as a stop where trains could take on water and passengers could eat. Tours of the Petrified Forest also originated here. Installation of a mill to grind petrified wood into abrasives in Adamana convinced some of the residents of northern Arizona that the petrified forests would totally disappear if they were not protected by the federal government. Through their action, the largest deposits of petrified wood in Arizona were preserved. Some say that the town was named after one of the residents, Adam Hanna. According to the paleobotanist, Lyman Daugherty, Adam Hanna and his girl friend, Anna, had a hotel there which was named "Adam and Anna." Later the name was shortened to Adamana. Adam Hanna made a living by running the hotel and by taking tourists on tours into the Petrified Forest. Lyman Daugherty, who first described the Chinle flora, tells of an incident that occurred when Adam Hanna was still running the hotel. It

seems that one night, a group of tourists from New York arrived at the hotel at a time when there was no food available. Adam butchered a calf at 3 o'clock in the morning so the guests would have meat for breakfast. The guests, however, refused to eat it because as they explained, they were vegetarians. On hearing this Adam said, "I don't give a..... about your religion, you will either eat veal or go hungry."

John Muir, the famous nineteenth century naturalist lived here briefly in 1905-1906 while he explored the 'fossil forests', and the town was also the base of operations for paleontologist Charles Camp in 1921 and 1923. The advent of a bridge over the Puerco River and the decline in railroad travel after Route 66 was completed reduced the viability of the town. Finally, a fire in the 1970s destroyed the Forest Hotel essentially marking the end of Adamana. Today, all that is left of the town consists of three structures and two inhabitants. This is private property and visitors are not welcome without permission. A natural gas storage plant sits north across the tracks from the town site.

10.6 Bridge over the Puerco River. The Puerco, or muddy, river originates northwest of Grants, New Mexico and flows southwestward into east-central Arizona, where it unites with the Little Colorado River a few miles east of Holbrook. During the spring and early summer, the Puerco often contains water, but most other times it is dry. When the bridge that preceded

Figure 5. Robert R. Alton and his general store in Adamana, Arizona circa 1923. Photo by Charles L. Camp (courtesy of the UCMP).

this structure was completed in 1930 and an access road was built to it from Route 66, tourists no longer patronized the facilities at Adamana and the little town soon withered and died.

10.9   Puerco Indian Ruins to left. Archaeological investigations indicate that this small village or pueblo was occupied about 600 years ago. The pueblo is built on the top or dip slope of the northward dipping Newspaper Sandstone bed. A significant fossil leaf locality (Axsmith and Ash, this volume) which has been investigated in the past decade is on the north east side of the pueblo and has yielded several species not known from other localities in the park.

Continue south on the park road traveling on the top of the Newspaper Rock bed in the Blue Mesa Member of the Chinle Formation.

11.7   Turn off to Newspaper Rock. As we slowly turn to the left after passing the turnoff, we see exposures of the Blue Mesa Member that are above the Newspaper Rock bed. On the eastern horizon, Blue Mesa, a large mesa capped by the Flattops One Bed of the Sonsela Member is visible. It is underlain by about 100 feet of blue-gray mudstone assigned to the Jim Camp Wash beds (Woody, this volume).

13.1 The highway begins to swing to the right (south). As it does, we see that the sandstone facies of the Newspaper Rock bed have thinned considerably and in this area are represented by several thin tongues which disappear to the east, just beyond the highway. Note the candy-striped redbeds just above the thin beds of sandstone on the left. The candy striped beds are thought to be splay deposits associated with the sandstones (Demko, 1994).

13.5 The road cut we are now passing through was constructed during the early 1930s by members of the CCC. During its construction, fossil leaves were noted in the greenish mudstone directly beneath one of the tongues of sandstone of the Newspaper Rock bed that is exposed here. Many of the fossils collected here at that time were turned over to Lyman Daugherty for study, who described them in 1941. See the article on the biostratigraphy of the park by Parker in this volume for more details. The large conical hills on the right are termed the Tepees.

13.8 Pull into parking area on the right and park. Blue Mesa is to the left. The turnout here leads to the old Blue Mesa Road. This road originally led to a turnout, picnic area, and trailhead, and was closed in the 1950s. This is not possible today and more conventional methods (e.g., walking) must be used. The prominent reddish band in the Tepees buttes is a pedogenic horizon associated with the Newspaper Rock bed. This sequence of sandstones and mudstones is incised into

Figure 6. Stake #17 from Colbert's (1956, 1966) study of erosional rates in the Chinle Formation. This stake had washed out at some point during the study and Colbert (1966) noted it as missing.

lower Blue Mesa Member deposits and contains a wealth of plant and trace fossils. Interestingly, no vertebrate fossils have ever been recovered from within or below this sequence.

In 1956, Edwin Colbert placed wooden stakes in the mudstones of this area to determine erosional rates in the badlands (Fig. 6). Colbert (1956; 1966) determined that approximately 2.5 to 5.7 mm of erosion occurred on these surfaces each year. Many of these stakes are still in place today.

Several stumps that appear to be in the position of growth have been found in the badlands at the western base of Blue Mesa. See Gottesfeld (1972), Ash and Creber (1992), and Jones and Ash (this volume) for details.

Detour. Short hike into badlands to examine fossiliferous sites in the Blue Mesa Member, many of which are of historical significance (Fig. 7). Here the group will split to examine either sites pertaining to vertebrate paleontology or sites pertaining to paleobotany. Sites to be visited for the vertebrate paleontology portion include: the Alexander/Camp 1921 campsite (Fig. 7A); the type locality of the phytosaur *Machaeroprosopus* (=*Leptosuchus*) *adamananesis*, excavated by Charles Camp in 1921; the Crocodile Hill Quarry, excavated by Camp in 1923 (Fig. 7C); the Dying Grounds fossil locality; and the Phytosaur Basin locality (Fig. 7D). Sites to be visited by the paleobotany group include the Blue Mesa Stump field (Fig. 7B), the original fossil plant locality discovered in 1932; and several more of Daugherty's and Ash's localities in the Tepees area.

After returning to vehicles continue southward.

15.5 Junction. Turn left on Blue Mesa road, heading east, to drive up onto Blue Mesa. Blue Mesa is capped by the Flattops One bed (the traditional Sonsela Sandstone Bed), while the flanks are the Jim Camp Wash beds, with the Blue Mesa

Figure 7. Historic paleontological localities in the Blue Forest area. *A*, 1921 campsite of Annie Alexander and Charles Camp (courtesy of the UCMP); *B*, Blue Mesa stump field; *C*, using a plow and scraper to uncover the bone bed at Crocodile Hill, 1923 (courtesy of the UCMP); *D*. collecting fossils at Phytosaur Basin, 1921 (courtesy of the UCMP).

Member at the base. Blue Mesa is the type section of the Blue Mesa Member (Lucas, 1993); however, this earlier designation included much of what is now considered to be the Sonsela Member (Heckert and Lucas, 2002; Woody, 2003).

17.6 Overlook. Pedestal logs (*Araucarioxylon arizonicum*) in the Flattops One bed. This spot also allows for a distant view of the Dry Creek Tank area where the type specimens of the phytosaurs *Pseudopalatus mccauleyi* (Ballew, 1989) and "*Machaeroprosopus*" *tenuis* (Camp, 1930b) were collected. These sites are on private property originally outside of the park; however, both sites fall within the new administrative boundary of 2004.

17.9 Overlook. This spot offers an excellent view of Blue Mesa Member exposures to the north and northwest of Blue Mesa. The "Camp Butte sandstone" (=Rainbow Forest Bed) is well exposed at the base of the cliff and in isolated patches above the Blue Mesa Member mudstones. The "sinking ship" butte to the north consists mainly of the Sonsela Member with a thin capping remnant of Petrified Forest Member. The trough

of a broad northwest-southeast trending syncline is preserved in this hill. A bank of fresh water clam shell is present in the rocks here.

Lunch.

Retrace route to main park road.

20.1 Junction. After stopping, turn left on main park road. Continue southward. For the next mile or so, we will be passing over a relatively flat area developed on the Blue Mesa Member of the Chinle. Just after we pass an irregular erosional remnant of the Chinle which stands above the general topography of the area on the right, the road starts a slow ascent of a mesa that is capped by the Flattops One Bed of the Sonsela Member (see Parker, this volume).

21.2 Lots Wife/King's Throne. The landform to the right of the road is called Lots Wife. A sandstone pinnacle at the top of the mudstone hills was a local landmark for decades (Fig. 8); however, after an abnormally wet spring and a period

Figure 8. The landform known as "Lots Wife" as it appeared before the sandstone pinnacle collapsed in April of 2005.

of high winds in April 2005, the sandstone pinnacle collapsed. The landform to the left of the road is called "King's Throne". The base of both of these features are the Rainbow Forest beds. Woody (2003) traced this bed into the Blue Mesa area to the north where it was informally called the "Camp Butte sandstone" (Murry, 1990).

Ascend Agate Bridge Mesa.

22.3 Roadcut in Flattops One bed at top of mesa. Just past Agate Bridge turn off on the left the park road cuts through the Flattops One bed. Note the channel structures preserved in this sandstone in cross-section. Paleocurrents in this unit, and the entire Sonsela Member, are mainly north and northeast in contrast to the rest of the Chinle Formation, which mainly have northwesterly paleocurrents (Woody, this volume). This strongly suggests a different possible source area and depositional regime for this unit.

22.4 Agate Mesa. Junction. The road to the left leads to a parking area near Agate Bridge. Agate Bridge is a partially exhumed petrified log that spans a 40 foot wide ravine.

Figure 9. Logs along the trail in Crystal Forest weathering out of the Jim Camp Wash beds.

23.6 Junction. The road to the right leads to Jasper Forest Overlook. Formerly visitors could drive into Jasper Forest, but the road had to be removed to protect the petrified wood deposit from thieves. The petrified wood in the Jasper Forest is derived from the Flattops One bed of the Sonsela Member, which caps the mesa to the right.

25.2 The turnout to the left is for Crystal Forest. The irregular hill to the right is called the Battleship. Cavities in some of the logs in this area contain quartz crystals. Many of the logs were blasted apart by people searching for crystals during the late 1800's. The wood in this "Forest" came from the Rainbow Forest beds or from the rocks above (Jim Camp Wash beds) (Fig. 9). Savidge and Ash (this volume) described a new genus and species of conifer from this locality.

26.1 Walker's Stump. In 1935, park naturalist Myrl V. Walker excavated a standing "stump" in a low gray hill next to the prominent "Martha's Butte" about a half mile west of the highway (Fig. 10). Leaf material was also recovered during this excavation (Walker, 1936).

26.4 Dry Wash. The road now precedes down section passing back through exposures of the Sonsela Member. Dry Wash is floored by a sandstone bed in the Jim Camp Wash beds. Jones and Ash (this volume) describe fossilized charcoal from this horizon and discuss its paleoecological implications. Well-developed paleosol horizons can be observed beneath an intraformational conglomerate of the Jim Camp Wash beds in the butte across the road.

27.5 Flattops. Ahead of us are a series of buttes called "the Flattops". Exposures of the Petrified Forest Member are capped with a bed of hard sandstone (Flattops Sandstone Four) which has protected the underlying rocks from erosion. These exposures of the Petrified Forest Member are characterized by the presence of several ribbon sandstones that Billingsley (1985) termed Flattops Sandstones Two through Four (from

Figure 10. Walker's Stump (see inset). (Courtesy of the AMNH).

Figure *11*. "Ridge and swale" topography in the Flattops One bed north of the parkroad and south of the Flattops area.

bottom to top). The road is situated on the second Flattops Sandstone Bed, whereas Flattops Sandstone Four caps the buttes in the vicinity. Fossil mollusc beds are common in the mudstones between these sandstones, as are the remains of vertebrates. The phytosaur *Pseudopalatus* and the aetosaur *Typothorax* are the most commonly recovered vertebrates from this unit.

28.0 Ridge and Swale Topography. To the left and below the road bed can be seen excellent exposures of "ridge and swale" topography in the Flattops One bed (Fig. 11). These have been interpreted as representing preserved scroll bars. The strata overlying the Flattops One bed contains a small quantity of scattered petrified logs.

28.3 Turnout. This turnout offers excellent views of the Sonsela and Petrified Forest Members of the Chinle Formation. The Flattops (to the northeast) and Red Butte (to the west) consist of reddish mudstone and thin intermittent sandstone ribbons of the Petrified Forest Member.

28.7 Flattops One bed. The road drives up onto the Flattops One bed (=Flattops Sandstone #1 of Billingsley, 1985) at this point.

29.0   Siliceous layer. The reddish material capping the small hills to the left of the road comes from a thin, strongly silicified bed which has been erroneously termed a silcrete (Woody, 2003) (Fig. 12). Creber and Ash (1990) observed

Figure *13*. Agate House.

this distinctive layer in the late 1980s and attributed it to the petrification (silicification) of tree trunks that had been subject to fungal attack after dying. Strictly speaking the layer is not a silcrete because it does not contain sand and gravel and is organic in origin, and merely consists of plant matter, primarily wood that has been silicified. Indeed, examination of this layer demonstrates that it mainly consists of flattened pieces of fossil wood, and at several localities flattened tree trunks are clearly discernable in this layer.   Whatever it is called, Ash and Creber (1990) and Woody (2003) state that this unit is always found within 7-9 meters above the main Rainbow Forest Bed and forms a useful stratigraphic marker because it is widespread throughout the region. Creber and Ash (1990) reported a similar siliceous layer at about the same stratigraphic level in New Mexico and Texas, while Woody (2003) observed it in southern Utah near Paria. Thus, there is strong evidence of a widespread coniferous forest that once existed in this region and now has all but disappeared!

30.3 The vast deposits of petrified wood on both sides of the road to which we are coming are collectively known as Rainbow Forest.

30.8 Entrance to trail to the Long Logs section of the Rainbow

Figure *12*. Siliceous layer capping and eroding from low hills in the foreground near Jim Camp Wash.

Figure *14*. Dick Grigsby in Rainbow Forest. Date unknown.

Figure *15*. Old Faithful log at Giant Logs (Rainbow Forest). *A*, in a 1923 (courtesy of the UCMP); *B*, 2006. Concrete supports were added after log was struck by lightning in 1962.

Forest and Agate House. This section of the Forest contains many exceptionally long logs. Some of them appear to be meshed together in a "fossil" log jam. Agate House (Fig. 13) is a partially reconstructed Native American pueblo built of blocks of petrified wood. One of the early guides in this area is reputed to have told tourists that the pueblo was so old that the blocks in its walls had petrified after it was built.

30.81 Bridge over Jim Camp Wash. Rainbow Forest Museum and Historical District. The area was the original park headquarters from the 1920s until the Painted Desert Visitor Center was built to the north along Interstate 40 in the early 1960s. The stone buildings were built by the Civilian Conservation Corps (CCC) in the 1930s. This area was the main contact station for park visitors and where information regarding the park was presented.

The original headquarters building is now a museum, which contains displays on Late Triassic paleontology. The other stone buildings serve as offices and residences for park staff. The Fred Harvey building (originally the Rainbow Forest Lodge) was built in the 1920s by local cowboy and entrepreneur Homer "Uncle Dick" Grigsby (Fig. 14). Grigsby was interested in the local fossil fauna and flora and often "donated" interesting fossils to vertebrate paleontologist Charles Camp and paleobotanist Lyman Daugherty, resulting in at least one plant being named in his honor, *Lyssoxylon grigsbyi* Daugherty (1941). Camp visited Grigsby regularly during his field seasons in Arizona and New Mexico. During the 1940s and 1950s a campground and picnic area was situated here.

Behind the Rainbow Forest Museum is a trail through the petrified wood deposit known as Giant Logs. The centerpiece of Giant Logs is a large specimen, with a basal circumference of almost 3 meters (Ash and Creber, 2000), christened by the wife of the first superintendent as "Old Faithful". The Old Faithful log has been the subject of countless photographs and at 2:05 pm on June 29, 1962 was struck by a bolt of lightning causing heavy damage (NPS naturalist reports, 1962). Park staff decided to reconstruct the log and added concrete and a base for support. All of the logs in the southern end of the park have been assigned to a single taxon, *Araucarioxylon arizonicum* (However, see Savidge and Ash [this volume] for discussion of this taxon).

33.7 Rainbow Forest Entrance Station.

33.8 Park boundary. Just outside of the park entrance are two commercial businesses that sell souvenirs, petrified wood, and offer information about the park. These facilities are not associated with the National Park Service and are not part of Petrified Forest National Park. The petrified wood they sell was obtained outside the boundaries of Petrified Forest National Park.

Turn right at intersection on U.S. Highway 180 and return to Holbrook.

REFERENCES

Ash, S. R. 1974. Guidebook to Devonian, Permian, and Triassic plant localities of east-central Arizona. Paleobotany section of the Botanical Society of America, 63 p.

Ash, S. R. 1992. The Black Forest Bed, a distinctive unit in the Upper Triassic Chinle Formation, northeastern Arizona. Journal of the Arizona-Nevada Academy of Science, 24/25:59-73.

Ash, S. R., and G. Creber. 1992. Paleoclimatic interpretation of the wood structures of the trees in the Chinle Formation (Upper Triassic) in the area of Petrified Forest National Park, Arizona, U.S.A. Palaeogeography, Palaeoclimatology, Palaeoecology, 96:299-317.

Ballew, K. L. 1989. A phylogenetic analysis of Phytosauria (Reptilia: Archosauria) from the late Triassic of the western United States, p. 309-339. *In* S. G. Lucas and A. P. Hunt (eds.), Dawn of the age of dinosaurs in the American Southwest. New Mexico Museum of Natural History, Albuquerque.

Billingsley, G. H. 1985. General stratigraphy of the Petrified Forest National Park, Arizona. Museum of Northern Arizona Bulletin, 54:3-8.

Camp, C. L. 1921. Unpublished field notes: Triassic Chinle of northeastern Arizona, University of California Museum of Paleontology archives.

Camp, C. L. 1923. Unpublished field notes: Triassic Chinle of northeastern Arizona, University of California Museum of Paleontology archives.

Camp, C. L. 1930a. Stratigraphic distribution of Arizona phytosaurs. Geological Society of America Bulletin, 41:213.

Camp, C. L. 1930b. A study of the phytosaurs with description of new material from western North America. Memoirs of the University of California, 10:1-174.

Colbert, E. H. 1946. Paleontological field work of the American Museum of Natural History in the Petrified Forest National Monument area, 1946. Unpublished report, Petrified Forest National Park archives.

Colbert, E. H. 1956. Rates of erosion in the Chinle Formation. Plateau, 28:73-76.

Colbert, E. H. 1966. Rates of erosion in the Chinle Formation – ten years later. Plateau, 38:68-74.

Creber, G. and S. R. Ash. 1990. A widespread fungal epidemic on Upper Triassic trees in the southwestern United States. Review of Palaeobotany and Palynology, 63:189-195.

Daugherty, L. H. 1934. *Schilderia adamanica* - A new fossil wood from the petrified forests of Arizona. Botany Gazette, 96:363-366.

Daugherty, L. H. 1941. The Upper Triassic flora of Arizona. Carnegie Institution of Washington Publication 526, 108 p.

Daugherty, L.H. 1960, *Itopsidema,* a new genus of the Osmundaceae from the Triassic of Arizona. American Journal of Botany, 47:771-777.

Demko, T. M. 1994. Candy striped Tepees: sedimentology and plant taphonomy of a Triassic channel-levee-crevasse complex, Petrified Forest, Arizona. Geological Society of America Abstracts with Programs, 26(6):10-11.

Gillette, D. D., S. R. Ash, and R. A. Long. 1986. Paleontology of the Petrified Forest National Park, AZ, p. 59-70. *In* Nations, J. D., Conway, C. M., and G. A. Swann (eds.), Geology of Central and Northern Arizona: Field trip guidebook for Geological Society of America, Rocky Mountain Section Meeting, Flagstaff, Arizona. Northern Arizona University, Flagstaff, AZ, 176p.

Goeppert, H. R. 1858. Uber die von Mollhausen mitgebrachten Fragments des Hlzes aus dem versteinerten Walde *in* Mollhausen, H. B. Tagebuch einer Reise vom Mississippi, nach K u s t e n der Sudsee. Leipzig, p. 492. Also on p. 31 of v. 2 of the English translation of Mollhausen's book.

Gottesfeld, A. S. 1972. Paleoecology of the lower part of the Chinle Formation in the Petrified Forest, p. 59-73. *In* Breed, C.S. and W.J. Breed (eds.), Investigations in the Triassic Chinle Formation. Museum Northern Arizona Bulletin, 47.

Heckert, A., 2004. Late Triassic microvertebrates from the lower Chinle Group (Otischalkian-Adamanian: Carnian) southwestern U.S.A.. New Mexico Museum of Natural History Bulletin, 27:1-170.

Heckert, A. B., and S. G. Lucas. 2002. Revised Upper Triassic stratigraphy of the Petrified Forest National Park. New Mexico Museum of Natural History and Science Bulletin 21:1-36.

Heckert, A. B., Zeigler, K. E., Lucas, S. G., and L. F. Rinehart. 2003. Coelophysids (Dinosauria: Theropoda) from the Upper Triassic (Revueltian) Snyder Quarry. New Mexico Museum of Natural History and Science Bulletin, 24:.

Hunt, A.P. 1993. A revision of the Metoposauridae (Amphibia: Temnospondyli) of the Late Triassic with a description of a new genus from western North America. Museum of Northern Arizona Bulletin, 59:67-97.

Irmis, R. B., and W. G. Parker. 2005. Unusual tetrapod teeth from the Upper Triassic Chinle Formation, Arizona. Canadian Journal of Earth Sciences, 42:1339-1345.

Knowlton, F. H. 1888. New species of fossil wood (*Araucarioxylon arizonicum*) from Arizona and New Mexico. U.S. National Museum Proceedings, 11:1-4.

Long, R. A., and P. A. Murry. 1995. Late Triassic (Carnian and Norian) tetrapods from the southwestern United States. New Mexico Museum of Natural History and Science Bulletin, 4, 254p.

Lucas, S. G. 1993. The Chinle Group: revised stratigraphy and chronology of Upper Triassic non-marine strata in the western United States. Museum of Northern Arizona Bulletin, 59:27-50.

Murry, P. A. 1989. Microvertebrate fossils from the Petrified Forest and Owl Rock Members (Chinle Formation) in Petrified Forest National Park and vicinity, Arizona; p. 249-277. *In* S. G. Lucas and A. P. Hunt (eds.), Dawn of the age of dinosaurs in the American Southwest. New Mexico Museum of Natural History, Albuquerque.

Murry, P. A. 1990. Stratigraphy of the Upper Triassic Petrified Forest Member (Chinle Formation) in Petrified Forest National Park, Arizona, USA. Journal of Geology, 98:780-789.

Murry, P. A., and R. A. Long. 1989. Geology and paleontology of the Chinle Formation, Petrified Forest National Park and vicinity, Arizona and a discussion of vertebrate fossils of the southwestern Upper Triassic, p. 29-64. *In* S. G. Lucas and A. P. Hunt (eds.), Dawn of the age of dinosaurs in the American Southwest. New Mexico Museum of Natural History, Albuquerque.

Padian, K. 1986. On the type material of *Coelophysis* Cope (Saurischia: Theropoda), and a new specimen from the Petrified Forest of Arizona (Late Triassic: Chinle Formation), p. 45-60. *In* Padian, K. (ed.), The beginning of the Age of Dinosaurs: Faunal change across the Triassic-Jurassic boundary. Cambridge University Press, Cambridge.

Padian, K. 1990. The ornithischian form genus *Revueltosaurus* from the Petrified Forest of Arizona (Late Triassic; Norian; Chinle Formation). Journal of Vertebrate Paleontology, 10:268-269.

Parker, W. G. 2005. Petrified Forest National Park. A roadlog, p. 37-59. *In* Nesbitt, S. J., Parker, W. G., and R. B. Irmis (eds.), Guidebook to the Triassic Formations of the Colorado Plateau in northern Arizona: Geology, Paleontology, and History. Mesa Southwest Museum Bulletin, 9.

Parker, W. G., Irmis, R. B., Nesbitt, S. N., Martz, J. W., and L. S. Browne. 2005. The pseudosuchian *Revueltosaurus callenderi* and its implications for the diversity of early ornithischian dinosaurs. Proceedings of the Royal Society of London B 272:963-969.

Parrish, J. M. 1991. A new specimen of an early crocodylomorph (cf. *Sphenosuchus* sp.) from the Upper Triassic Chinle Formation of Petrified Forest National Park, Arizona. Journal of Vertebrate Paleontology, 11:198-212.

Riggs, N. R., Ash, S. R., Barth, A. P., Gehrels, G. E., and J. L. Wooden. 2003. Isotopic age of the Black Forest Bed, Petrified Forest Member, Chinle Formation, Arizona: an example of dating a continental sandstone. Geological Society of America Bulletin, 115:1315-1323.

Sereno, P. C., and R. Wild. 1992. *Procompsognathus*: theropod, "thecodont" or both?. Journal of Vertebrate Paleontology, 12:435-458.

Stein, B. R. 2001. On her own terms: Annie Montague Alexander and the Rise of Science in the American West. University of California Press, Berkeley, 380 p.

Swaine, P. T., and J. F. C. Hegewald. 1882. Information concerning